GW00775771

LESS STRESS MORE SUCCESS

Maths Revision
Higher Level
Paper 1

Brendan Guildea & Louise Boylan

g GILL EDUCATION

Gill Education

Hume Avenue

Park West

Dublin 12

www.gilleducation.ie

Gill Education is an imprint of M.H. Gill & Co.

© Brendan Guildea and Louise Boylan 2019

ISBN 978 07171 8624 2

Design by Liz White Designs Artwork and print origination by MPS Limited

At the time of going to press, all web addresses were active and contained information
relevant to the topics in this book. Gill Education does not, however, accept
responsibility for the content or views contained on these websites. Content, views and
addresses may change beyond the publisher or authors' control. Students should always
be supervised when reviewing websites.

For permission to reproduce photographs, the authors and publisher gratefully
acknowledge the following:

© Shutterstock: 39, 136, 143, 176.

The authors and publisher have made every effort to trace all copyright holders, but if
any have been inadvertently overlooked we would be pleased to make the necessary
arrangement at the first opportunity.

The paper used in this book is made from the wood pulp of managed forests. For every
tree felled, at least one tree is planted, thereby renewing natural resources.

Acknowledgements

The authors would like to thank Carol Guildea and Joe Heron who helped with the
proofreading, checked the answers and made many valuable suggestions that are
included in the final text.

CONTENTS

Please note:
- The philosophy of your mathematics course is that topics can overlap, so you may encounter Paper 1 material on Paper 2 and vice versa.
- The exam questions marked by the symbol (exam Q) in this book are selected from the following:
  1. SEC exam papers (relevant year indicated)
  2. Sample exam papers
  3. Original and sourced exam-type questions

Introduction

□ To learn how to revise most effectively
□ To familiarise yourself with the structure of the exam paper
□ To learn to allocate the correct time for each question
□ To know and understand the words which appear often on the exam paper
□ To familiarise yourself with the syllabus

The aim of this revision book is to help you enhance your grade in your Leaving Certificate. This book is designed to be exam focused. To do this, the book is based not just on the syllabus, but also on the examination paper. As a result, this revision book can be used in conjunction with **any** textbook.

Throughout this book, **examples and exam-type questions are graded by level of difficulty**.

The level of difficulty is indicated by calculator symbols, as follows:

The number of calculators shown beside a question indicates how difficult the question is. One calculator indicates a question which is relatively basic. As the questions get harder, the symbol will have more calculators. Three calculators indicates an average-level question, whereas five calculators indicates that it is a very challenging question. These questions may be beyond some students, but give them a go! **Students hoping to achieve a high grade should aim to complete all of the 'five calculator' questions**. The calculator symbol given for each question relates to the most difficult part of that question. **Do not be discouraged by a challenging question**. As in the Leaving Certificate exam, difficult questions can sometimes begin with one or two simple parts. You should attempt as much as you can.

It is very important to realise that **you are your own best teacher**. Revision is when you begin to teach yourself. Thus, it is very important for you to start your revision as soon as possible. Make notes while you are revising. If you are having difficulty with a particular question, seek help from your teacher, a friend or a member of your family. As with all subjects, the best examination preparation is to work through past examination or sample papers so that you are familiar with the layout and style of questions.

So let's start at the beginning. If you want to do well in your Leaving Certificate, then two things are essential:

- Revise effectively.
- Be familiar with the exam paper and so be prepared on the day of the exam.

These may seem obvious, but it's worth taking a moment to think about what these tips mean.

How to revise most effectively

If you are going to do well in the Leaving Certificate, you are going to spend quite a bit of time revising. Spending a little time learning how to revise effectively will help you get more from your time and help you absorb and understand more of the material on the course. Here are some tips to help you revise for maths.

- Find a quiet place where you can work. This place should be dedicated to study and free of potential distractions. Turn off music, the TV, computer and mobile phone.
- Write a study plan. Don't be afraid to ask your parents/teachers/guidance counsellor for help at this stage.
- Do the more challenging revision first, when you are fresh. Trying to focus on difficult problems when you are tired can be counter-productive.

Study in small chunks lasting 25 to 35 minutes. Your memory and concentration will work better if you study in short, frequent bursts.

- Maths is based on understanding, so while you can 'learn' some elements of the course, it is important that you develop an understanding of the material.
- Drill and practice are essential ingredients for success in maths.
- Try to link any new material to things you know already. This is learning through association and helps long-term retention.

Don't get hung up on more difficult material. Concentrate on understanding the fundamental concepts and being able to answer all of the straightforward questions. Then, with time, you can build up to the more challenging problems.

Leaving Certificate examination

Exam focus is critical to exam success. It is important to prepare yourself for the challenge you will face. By learning about the structure of the exam, you will learn how to maximise your points, allocate your time effectively and manage the paper without panic.

The order of the questions is not set and some questions may include cross-syllabus topics. The examination paper will be presented in two sections, as follows:

Section A – 150 marks
Concepts and Skills

Read the exam paper right through at the start in order to determine which question is the easiest one to start with. Your mind may also be subconsciously processing some of the other problems.

Section B – 150 marks
Contexts and Applications

Start with your best question, then your next best and so on. This way, if you are short of time, at least your best questions will be done.

Time yourself as follows

- Reading the paper at the start:
  5 minutes
- Section A : 70 minutes
- Section B : 70 minutes
- Reviewing your answers at the end:
  5 minutes
- Try to stick closely to these times.
  If you run out of time on a question,
  leave it and come back at the end.

Rule of thumb for timing yourself during the exam:

Time spent on question = ½ (marks for question)

That is, a 25-mark question should take no more than 12·5 minutes.

Further exam tips

- There is no such thing as rough work in maths –
  all work is relevant. If the examiner doesn't
  know how you reached an answer, even a
  correct answer, then full marks will not usually
  be awarded. Thus, **show all your work**.
- Attempt marks will be awarded for any step in
  the right direction. Therefore, **make an attempt
  at each part of the question**. Even if you do not

Attempt marks (partial credit) are valuable, so it is vital that you attempt all questions. Leave **NO** blanks.

get the correct answer, you can still pick up most of the marks on offer if you show how you worked it out. Also, **draw a diagram where possible**, because this can help in seeing the solution.

- If you cannot finish part of a question, leave a space and come back to it later. **Never scribble out any work or use Tipp-Ex**. Put a single line through it so that the examiner can still read it. In many cases, work that had a line through it received more marks. **Avoid using pencil** because the writing can be very faint and difficult to read.

- It is a good idea to show each stage of a calculation when using a calculator (in case you press a wrong key). Familiarise yourself with your calculator. Know your *booklet of formulae and tables* well and write down any formula that you use.

Your calculator and *booklet of formulae and tables* are two extremely valuable resources to have in the exam. Make sure that you are very familiar with how your calculator works and that you know how to perform all functions on it. Familiarise yourself with the *booklet of formulae and tables* so that you don't waste any time in the exam trying to find formulae.

Glossary of words used on the examination paper

Write down, state

You can write down your answer without showing any work. However, if you want you can show some workings.

Calculate, find, show that, determine, prove

Obtain your answers by showing all relevant work. Marks are available for showing the steps leading to your final answer or conclusion.

Solve

Find the solution, or root, of an equation. The solution is the value of the variable that makes the left-hand side balance with the right-hand side.

Evaluate

Usually to work out, or find, a numerical value by putting in numbers for letters.

Comment on

After studying the given information or your answers, give your opinion on their significance.

Plot

Indicate the position of points on a graph, usually on the x- and y-planes.

Construct

Draw an accurate diagram, usually labelled, using a pencil, ruler, set square, compass and protractor. Leave all constructions on your diagram.

Sketch

Make a rough diagram or graph, labelled if needed.

Hence

You *must* use the answer or result from the previous part of the question.

Hence or otherwise

It is recommended that you use the answer or result from the previous part of the question, but other methods are acceptable.

Syllabus and checklist for Leaving Certificate Higher Level Maths Paper 1 exam

The philosophy of your mathematics course is that topics can overlap, so you may encounter Paper 2 material on Paper 1 and vice versa.

Throughout your course you will be asked to apply your knowledge and skills to solve problems in familiar and unfamiliar contexts. In problem solving, you should use some of the following strategies:

- Trial and improvement
- Draw a diagram
- Look for a pattern
- Act it out
- Draw a table

- Simplify the problem
- Use an equation
- Work backwards
- Eliminate possibilities

The syllabus stresses that in all aspects of the Leaving Certificate Maths course, students should be able to:

☐ Explore patterns and formulate conjectures

☐ Explain findings

☐ Justify conclusions

☐ Communicate mathematics verbally and in written form

☐ Apply their knowledge and skills to solve problems in familiar and unfamiliar contexts

☐ Analyse information presented verbally and translate it into mathematical form

☐ Devise, select and use appropriate mathematical models, formulae or techniques to process information and to draw relevant conclusions

Number systems

- ☐ Recognise irrational numbers and appreciate that $\mathbb{R} \neq \mathbb{Q}$
- ☐ Revisit the operations of addition, multiplication, subtraction and division in the following domains:
  - ○ $\mathbb{N}$ of natural numbers
  - ○ $\mathbb{Z}$ of integers
  - ○ $\mathbb{Q}$ of rational numbers
  - ○ $\mathbb{R}$ of real numbers

  and represent these numbers on a number line
- ☐ Develop decimals as special equivalent fractions strengthening the connection between these numbers and fraction and place value understanding
- ☐ Consolidate your understanding of factors, multiples and prime numbers in $\mathbb{N}$
- ☐ Express numbers in terms of their prime factors
- ☐ Appreciate the order of operations, including brackets
- ☐ Work with irrational numbers
- ☐ Express non-zero positive rational numbers in the form $a \times 10^n$, where $n \in \mathbb{Z}$ and $1 \leq a < 10$ and perform arithmetic operations on numbers in this form
- ☐ Geometrically construct $\sqrt{2}$ and $\sqrt{3}$ (covered in the book for Paper 2)
- ☐ Prove that $\sqrt{2}$ is not rational
- ☐ Apply the rules for sums, products and quotients of limits

Expressions

- ☐ Evaluate expressions given the value of the variables
- ☐ Expand and simplify expressions
- ☐ Factorise expressions of order 2
- ☐ Add and subtract expressions of the form:
  - ○ $(ax + by + c) \pm \cdots \pm (dx + ey + f)$
  - ○ $(ax^2 + bx + c) \pm \cdots \pm (dx^2 + ex + f)$ where $a, b, c, d, e, f \in \mathbb{Z}$.
  - ○ $\dfrac{a}{bx + c} \pm \dfrac{q}{px + r}$ where $a, b, c, p, q, r \in \mathbb{Z}$.
- ☐ Use the associative and distributive properties to simplify expressions of the form:
  - ○ $(bx + cy + d) + \cdots + e(fx + gy + h)$
  - ○ $(x \pm y)(w \pm z)$
- ☐ Rearrange formulae

☐ Perform the arithmetic operations of addition, subtraction, multiplication and division on polynomials and rational algebraic expressions, paying attention to the use of brackets and surds

☐ Apply the binomial theorem

Solving equations

☐ Select and use suitable strategies (graphic, numeric, algebraic, mental) for finding solutions to equations of the form:

○ $f(x) = g(x)$

with $f(x) = \dfrac{ax + b}{ex + f} \pm \dfrac{cx + b}{px + q};\ \ g(x) = k$ where $a, b, c, d, e, f, p, q \in \mathbb{Z}$

○ $f(x) = k$ with $f(x) = ax^2 + bx + c$ (and not necessarily factorisable) where $a, b, c \in \mathbb{Q}$

and interpret the results

☐ Use the *factor theorem* for polynomials

☐ Select and use suitable strategies (graphic, numeric, algebraic, mental) for finding solutions to:

○ cubic equations with at least one integer root and interpret the results

○ simultaneous linear equations with two unknowns and interpret the results

○ simultaneous linear equations with three unknowns and interpret the results

○ one linear equation and one equation of order 2 with two unknowns and interpret the results

☐ Form quadratic equations given whole number roots

Inequalities

☐ Select and use suitable strategies (graphic, numeric, algebraic, mental) for finding solutions to inequalities of the form:

○ $g(x) \le k, g(x) \ge k$, where $g(x) = ax + b$, $g(x) = ax^2 + bx + c$ or

$g(x) = \dfrac{ax + b}{cx + d}$ and $a, b, c, d, k \in \mathbb{Q}, x \in \mathbb{R}$

☐ Use notation $|x|$

☐ Select and use suitable strategies (graphic, numeric, algebraic, mental) for finding solutions to inequalities of the form:

$|x - a| < b, |x - a| > b$ and combinations of these, where $a, b \in \mathbb{Q}, x \in \mathbb{R}$

Indices and logarithms

☐ Solve problems using the rules for indices

☐ Solve problems using the rules for logarithms

Arithmetic (financial maths)

☐ Check a result by considering whether it is of the right order of magnitude and by working the problem backwards. Round off a result

☐ Make and justify estimates and approximations of calculations; calculate percentage error and tolerance

☐ Calculate average rates of change (with respect to time)

☐ Make estimates of measures in the physical world around you

☐ Accumulate error (by addition or subtraction only)

☐ Solve problems that involve:

  ○ costing: materials, labour and wastage

  ○ metric system; change of units; everyday imperial units (conversion factors provided for imperial units)

  ○ cost price

  ○ selling price

  ○ loss

  ○ discount

  ○ mark-up (profit as a % of cost price)

  ○ margin (profit as a % of selling price)

  ○ compound interest

  ○ depreciation (reducing balance method)

  ○ income tax and net pay (including other deductions)

☐ Use *present value* when solving problems involving loan repayments and investments

Complex numbers

☐ Investigate the operations of addition, multiplication, subtraction and division with complex numbers $\mathbb{C}$ in rectangular form $a + ib$

☐ Illustrate complex numbers on an Argand diagram

☐ Interpret the modulus as distance from the origin on an Argand diagram and calculate the complex conjugate

☐ Calculate conjugates of sums and products of complex numbers

☐ Use the *conjugate root theorem* to find the roots of polynomials

☐ Work with complex numbers in rectangular and polar form to solve quadratic and other equations, including those in the form $z^n = a$, where $n \in \mathbb{Z}$ and $z = r(\cos\theta + i\sin\theta)$

☐ Use De Moivre's theorem

☐ Prove De Moivre's theorem by induction for $n \in \mathbb{N}$

☐ Use applications such as n^{th} roots of unity, $n \in \mathbb{N}$ and identities such as $\cos 3\theta = 4\cos 3\theta - 3\cos\theta$

Patterns, sequences and series

- ☐ Appreciate that processes can generate sequences of numbers or objects
- ☐ Investigate patterns among these sequences
- ☐ Use patterns to continue the sequence
- ☐ Generate rules and formulae from those patterns
- ☐ Generalise and explain patterns and relationships in algebraic form
- ☐ Recognise whether a sequence is arithmetic, geometric or neither
- ☐ Find the sum to n terms of an arithmetic series
- ☐ Verify and justify formulae from number patterns
- ☐ Investigate geometric sequences and series
- ☐ Solve problems involving finite and infinite geometric series, including applications such as recurring decimals and financial applications, e.g. deriving the formula for a mortgage repayment (covered in Chapter 12 Financial Maths II)
- ☐ Derive the formula for the sum to infinity of geometric series by considering the limit of a sequence of partial sums
- ☐ Find by inspection the limits of sequences such as

$$\lim_{n \to \infty} \frac{n}{n+1}; \qquad \lim_{n \to \infty} r^n \qquad |r| < 1$$

Prove by induction

- ☐ Simple identities such as the sum of the first n natural numbers and the sum of a finite geometric series
- ☐ Simple inequalities such as:
  - ○ $n! > 2^n$
  - ○ $2^n > n^2 \ (n \ge 4)$
  - ○ $(1 + x)^n \ge 1 + nx \ (x > -1)$
- ☐ Factorisation results such as 3 is a factor of $4^n - 1$

Functions

- ☐ Recognise that a function assigns a unique output to a given input
- ☐ Graph functions of the form:
  - ○ ax where $a \in \mathbb{Q}, x \in \mathbb{R}$
  - ○ $ax + b$ where $a, b \in \mathbb{Q}, x \in \mathbb{R}$
  - ○ $ax^2 + bx + c$ where $a, b, c \in \mathbb{Q}, x \in \mathbb{R}$
  - ○ $ax^3 + bx^2 + cx + d$ where $a, b, c, d \in \mathbb{Z}, x \in \mathbb{R}$

- ○ ab^x where $a, b \in \mathbb{R}$
- ○ logarithmic
- ○ exponential
- ○ trigonometric
- ☐ Interpret equations of the form $f(x) = g(x)$ as a comparison of the above functions
- ☐ Form composite functions
- ☐ Use graphical methods to find approximate solutions to:
  - ○ $f(x) = 0$
  - ○ $f(x) = k$
  - ○ $f(x) = g(x)$

  where $f(x)$ and $g(x)$ are of the above form, or where graphs of $f(x)$ and $g(x)$ are provided
- ☐ Recognise surjective, injective and bijective functions
- ☐ Find the inverse of a bijective function
- ☐ Given a graph of a function, sketch the graph of its inverse
- ☐ Express quadratic functions in complete square form
- ☐ Use the complete square form of a quadratic function to:
  - ○ find the roots and turning points
  - ○ sketch the function
- ☐ Informally explore limits and continuity of functions

Calculus

- ☐ Associate derivatives with slopes and tangent lines
- ☐ Differentiate linear and quadratic functions from first principles
- ☐ Find first and second derivatives of linear, quadratic and cubic functions by rule
- ☐ Differentiate the following functions:
  - ○ polynomial
  - ○ exponential
  - ○ trigonometric
  - ○ rational powers
  - ○ inverse functions
  - ○ logarithms
- ☐ Find the derivatives of sums, differences, products, quotients and compositions of functions of the above form
- ☐ Apply the differentiation of above functions to solve problems

- ☐ Apply differentiation to:
  - ○ rates of change
  - ○ maxima and minima
  - ○ curve sketching
- ☐ Recognise integration as the reverse process of differentiation
- ☐ Use integration to find the average value of a function over an interval
- ☐ Integrate sums, differences and constant multiples of functions of the form
  - ○ x^a, where $a \in \mathbb{Q}$
  - ○ a^x, where $a \in \mathbb{R}$
  - ○ $\sin ax$, where $a \in \mathbb{R}$
  - ○ $\cos ax$, where $a \in \mathbb{R}$
- ☐ Determine areas of plane regions bounded by polynomial and exponential curves

1 Algebra

Factorising and simplifying expressions

You must be able to factorise expressions using the following methods:

Take out common terms	Factorise by grouping
$ab + ad = a(b + d)$	$ab + ad + cb + cd = (a + c)(b + d)$
Factorise a trinomial	**Difference of two squares**
$a^2 - 2ab + b^2 = (a - b)(a - b)$	$a^2 - b^2 = (a + b)(a - b)$
Difference of two cubes	**Sum of two cubes**
$a^3 - b^3 = (a - b)(a^2 + ab + b^2)$	$a^3 + b^3 = (a + b)(a^2 - ab + b^2)$

exam focus

Factorising is a basic and vital skill for you to have throughout your maths course. You must be able to factorise expressions quickly and easily. This will take practice, but it is worthwhile spending time on.

Example
Factorise the following:

(i) $3p^2 + 6pq$ (ii) $6ab + 12bc - 8ac - 9b^2$ (iii) $3x^2 - 12y^2$

Solution

(i) $3p^2 + 6pq$
$3p(p + 2q)$

(ii) $6ab + 12bc - 8ac - 9b^2$
$6ab - 9b^2 - 8ac + 12bc$
$3b(2a - 3b) - 4c(2a - 3b)$
$(2a - 3b)(3b - 4c)$

(iii) $3x^2 - 12y^2$
$3(x^2 - 4y^2)$
$3(x + 2y)(x - 2y)$

Example

Factorise the following:

(i) $2x^2 - 7x - 15$ (ii) $64 - 27x^3$ (iii) $4a^3 + 32b^3$

Solution

(i) $2x^2 - 7x - 15$
$(2x + 3)(x - 5)$

(ii) $64 - 27x^3$
$(4)^3 - (3x)^3$
$(4 - 3x)(4^2 + (4)(3x) + (3x)^2)$
$(4 - 3x)(16 + 12x + 9x^2)$

(iii) $4a^3 + 32b^3$
$4(a^3 + 8b^3)$
$4((a)^3 + (2b)^3)$
$4(a + 2b)(a^2 - (a)(2b) + (2b)^2)$
$4(a + 2b)(a^2 - 2ab + 4b^2)$

Example

Simplify $\dfrac{x^3 + 7x^2 + 12x}{x^2 + 2x - 3}$.

A question asking you to simplify often involves factorising.

Solution

Factorise the top and bottom:

$\dfrac{x(x^2 + 7x + 12)}{x^2 + 2x - 3}$

$\dfrac{x(x + 3)(x + 4)}{(x + 3)(x - 1)}$ (divide top and bottom by $(x + 3)$)

$\dfrac{x(x + 4)}{x - 1}$ (in simplest form)

Example

Simplify $\dfrac{5}{2x - 3} - \dfrac{3}{2x^2 - 3x} - \dfrac{1}{x}$.

Solution

$\dfrac{5}{2x - 3} - \dfrac{3}{x(2x - 3)} - \dfrac{1}{x}$ (factorise the denominator)

$$\frac{5(x) - 3(1) - 1(2x - 3)}{x(2x - 3)}$$ (common denominator $x(2x - 3)$)

$$\frac{5x - 3 - 2x + 3}{x(2x - 3)}$$

$$\frac{3x}{x(2x - 3)}$$ (divide top and bottom by x)

$$\frac{3}{2x - 3}$$

Example

Simplify $\dfrac{a + b}{\dfrac{1}{a} + \dfrac{1}{b}}$.

Solution

$$\frac{a + b}{\dfrac{1}{a} + \dfrac{1}{b}}$$

$$\frac{a + b}{\dfrac{1}{a} + \dfrac{1}{b}} \times \frac{ab}{ab}$$ (multiply top and bottom by ab)

$$\frac{ab(a + b)}{ab\left(\dfrac{1}{a}\right) + ab\left(\dfrac{1}{b}\right)}$$

$$\frac{ab(a + b)}{b + a}$$ (divide top and bottom by $(a + b)$)

$$ab$$

exam
Q

Let $f(x) = \dfrac{x^3 - 1}{x^2 - 1}$, $x \neq \pm 1$, and $g(x) = \dfrac{x^2 + x + 1}{x^2 - x - 2}$, $x \neq -1, 2$.

If $f(x) \div g(x) = ax + b$, find the value of a and b.

Solution

$$f(x) \div g(x) = \frac{x^3 - 1}{x^2 - 1} \div \frac{x^2 + x + 1}{x^2 - x - 2}$$

$$= \frac{x^3 - 1}{x^2 - 1} \times \frac{x^2 - x - 2}{x^2 + x + 1} \qquad \text{(invert the second fraction and multiply)}$$

$$= \frac{(x - 1)(x^2 + x + 1)}{(x + 1)(x - 1)} \times \frac{(x - 2)(x + 1)}{x^2 + x + 1} \qquad \text{(factorise each part)}$$

$$= \frac{1}{1} \times \frac{(x - 2)}{1} \qquad \begin{array}{l}\text{(divide top and bottom by} \\ (x - 1)(x^2 + x + 1)(x + 1))\end{array}$$

$$= x - 2, \quad \text{which is in the form } ax + b$$

Therefore $a = 1$, $b = -2$.

Changing the subject of a formula

When we rearrange a formula so that one of the variables is given in terms of the others, we are said to be **changing the subject of the formula or manipulating the formula**. The rules in changing the subject of a formula are the same as when solving an equation. That is, we can:

1. **Add** or **subtract** the same quantity to both sides.
2. **Multiply** or **divide** both sides by the same quantity.
3. **Square** both sides, **cube** both sides, etc.
4. Take the **square root** of both sides, take the **cube root** of both sides, etc.

Note: Whatever letter comes after the word 'express' is to be on its own.

Changing the subject of a formula (manipulating a formula) is an essential skill, which arises in many sections of the course. These include area and volume, trigonometry and coordinate geometry.

Three common errors made when manipulating formulae are:

1. $\dfrac{1}{a} + \dfrac{1}{b} \neq \dfrac{1}{a + b}$ 2. $\dfrac{a}{b + c} \neq \dfrac{a}{b} + \dfrac{a}{c}$ 3. $a\left(\dfrac{b}{c}\right) \neq \dfrac{ab}{ac}$

Example

If $c = \dfrac{b^2 - ac}{b + a}$, express a in terms of the other variables.

Solution

$$c = \frac{b^2 - ac}{b + a}$$

$$(b + a)c = (b + a)\left(\frac{b^2 - ac}{b + a}\right) \qquad \text{(multiply both sides by } (b + a))$$

$$(b + a)c = (b^2 - ac)$$

$$bc + ac = b^2 - ac \qquad \text{(multiply out brackets)}$$

$$ac = b^2 - ac - bc \qquad \text{(subtract } bc \text{ from both sides)}$$

$$ac + ac = b^2 - bc \qquad \text{(add } ac \text{ to both sides)}$$

$$2ac = b^2 - bc$$

$$\frac{2ac}{2c} = \frac{b^2 - bc}{2c} \qquad \text{(divide both sides by } 2c)$$

$$a = \frac{b^2 - bc}{2c}$$

Example

(i) If $\dfrac{1}{f} = \dfrac{1}{u} + \dfrac{1}{v}$, express v in terms of the other variables.

(ii) Hence, determine the value of v when $f = 15$ and $u = 20$.

Solution

(i) $$\frac{1}{f} = \frac{1}{u} + \frac{1}{v}$$

$$fuv\left(\frac{1}{f}\right) = fuv\left(\frac{1}{u}\right) + fuv\left(\frac{1}{v}\right) \qquad \text{(multiply all parts by } fuv)$$

$$uv = fv + fu$$

$$uv - fv = fv + fu - fv \qquad \text{(subtract } fv \text{ from both sides)}$$

$$uv - fv = fu$$

$$v(u - f) = fu \qquad \text{(factorise out } v)$$

$$\frac{v(u - f)}{(u - f)} = \frac{fu}{(u - f)} \qquad \text{(divide both sides by } (u - f))$$

$$v = \frac{fu}{u - f}$$

(ii) $f = 15$ and $u = 20$: $v = \dfrac{fu}{u - f}$

$$v = \frac{(15)(20)}{20 - 15} = \frac{300}{5} = 60$$

exam Q

The time taken, in seconds, for a satellite to complete an orbit of the Earth is given by the formula:

$$T = \sqrt{\frac{4\pi^2 r^3}{GM}}$$

where r = radius of rotation from the centre of the Earth

G = universal gravitational constant

M = mass of the Earth.

 (i) Express the radius of rotation, r, in terms of the other variables.

(ii) The International Space Station (ISS) orbits the Earth once every 91 minutes. Given that the value for $G = 6{\cdot}67 \times 10^{-11}$ and the mass of the Earth is $6{\cdot}4 \times 10^{24}$, find the radius of rotation of the ISS, correct to the nearest metre.

(iii) Find the height the ISS is above the surface of the Earth, given that the radius of the Earth is 6,371 km. Give your answer to the nearest kilometre.

Solution

(i) $\qquad T = \sqrt{\dfrac{4\pi^2 r^3}{GM}}$

$\qquad T^2 = \left(\sqrt{\dfrac{4\pi^2 r^3}{GM}}\right)^2$ $\qquad$ (square both sides)

$\qquad T^2 = \dfrac{4\pi^2 r^3}{GM}$

$\qquad GM(T^2) = GM\left(\dfrac{4\pi^2 r^3}{GM}\right)$ $\qquad$ (multiply both sides by GM)

$\qquad GMT^2 = 4\pi^2 r^3$

$\qquad \dfrac{GMT^2}{4\pi^2} = r^3$ $\qquad$ (divide both sides by $4\pi^2$)

$\qquad \sqrt[3]{\dfrac{GMT^2}{4\pi^2}} = r$ $\qquad$ (take cube root of both sides)

(ii) $G = 6.67 \times 10^{-11}$, $M = 6.4 \times 10^{24}$, $T = 91$ minutes $= 5{,}460$ seconds

Index notation
When dealing with very large or very small numbers, it can be easier to perform calculations if the numbers are expressed in the form $a \times 10^n$, where $0 < a < 10$.

$$\sqrt[3]{\frac{GMT^2}{4\pi^2}} = r$$

$$\sqrt[3]{\frac{(6.67 \times 10^{-11})(6.4 \times 10^{24})(5{,}460)^2}{4\pi^2}} = r$$

$$\sqrt[3]{3.224 \times 10^{20}} = r$$

$$6{,}856{,}625.858 = r$$

Thus, the radius of rotation $= 6{,}856{,}626$ m.

(iii)   Radius of rotation $=$ radius of Earth $+$ height above Earth

$$6{,}856{,}626 = 6{,}371{,}000 + \text{height above Earth}$$

$$6{,}856{,}626 - 6{,}371{,}000 = \text{height above Earth}$$

$$485{,}626 = \text{height above Earth}$$

Thus, the ISS is at a height of $485{,}626$ m $= 486$ km above the surface of the Earth.

Undetermined coefficients

When two expressions in x (or any other variable) are equal to one another for all values of x, we can equate the coefficients of the same powers of x in the two expressions. This is known as the **principle of undetermined coefficients**.

Method:

1. Remove all fractions and brackets.
2. Form equations by equating coefficients of like terms.
3. Solve the equations to find the coefficients.

It may help to highlight, colour or underline the like terms.
For example:

$$x^2 + 15x + kx - c = x^2 + 3kx + k^3$$

Example

$x^2 - 6x + t = (x + k)^2$, where t and k are constants. Find the value of k and the value of t.

Solution

$x^2 - 6x + t = (x + k)^2$

$x^2 - 6x + t = x^2 + 2xk + k^2$ (multiply out the brackets)

$x^2 - 6x + t = x^2 + 2xk + k^2$ (colour like terms)

Equate like terms:

Terms containing x:	Terms independent of x:
$-6x = 2xk$	$t = k^2$
$-6 = 2k$	$t = (-3)^2$
$-3 = k$	$t = 9$

Thus, $k = -3, t = 9$.

Example

The following equation is true for all y.

$$ay^2 + by(y - 4) + c(y - 4) = y^2 + 13y - 20$$

Find the values of the constants a, b and c.

Solution

$ay^2 + by(y - 4) + c(y - 4) = y^2 + 13y - 20$

$ay^2 + by^2 - 4by + cy - 4c = y^2 + 13y - 20$ (multiply out brackets)

$ay^2 + by^2 - 4by + cy - 4c = y^2 + 13y - 20$ (colour like terms)

Equate like terms:

Terms containing y^2:	Terms containing y:	Terms independent of y:
$ay^2 + by^2 = y^2$	$-4by + cy = 13y$	$-4c = -20$
$a + b = 1$ ①	$-4b + c = 13$ ②	$c = 5$ ③

Substitute $c = 5$ into ②: Substitute $b = -2$ into ①:

$-4b + c = 13$ $a + b = 1$

$-4b + (5) = 13$ $a + (-2) = 1$

$-4b = 8$ $a = 1 + 2$

$b = -2$ $a = 3$

Therefore, $a = 3$, $b = -2$ and $c = 5$.

Surds

Properties of surds:

1. $\sqrt{ab} = \sqrt{a}\sqrt{b}$ **2.** $\sqrt{\dfrac{a}{b}} = \dfrac{\sqrt{a}}{\sqrt{b}}$ **3.** $\sqrt{a}\sqrt{a} = a$

key point

Simplification of surds

Find the largest possible perfect square number greater than 1 that will divide evenly into the number under the square root. Then use the property $\sqrt{ab} = \sqrt{a}\sqrt{b}$.

Example

Express each of the following in its simplest surd form:

(i) $\sqrt{99}$ (ii) $\dfrac{1}{2}\sqrt{112}$ (iii) $\sqrt{2\dfrac{1}{4}}$

Solution

(i) $\sqrt{99}$

$\sqrt{9 \times 11}$

$\sqrt{9}\sqrt{11}$

$3\sqrt{11}$

(ii) $\dfrac{1}{2}\sqrt{112}$

$\dfrac{1}{2}\sqrt{16 \times 7}$

$\dfrac{1}{2}\sqrt{16}\sqrt{7}$

$\dfrac{1}{2}(4)\sqrt{7} = 2\sqrt{7}$

(iii) $\sqrt{2\dfrac{1}{4}}$

$\sqrt{\dfrac{9}{4}}$

$\dfrac{\sqrt{9}}{\sqrt{4}}$

$\dfrac{3}{2}$

exam focus

The natural display calculators can be very useful when verifying answers to questions on surds.

Example

Express each of the following in its simplest surd form:

$$\sqrt{180} + \sqrt{20} - \sqrt{125}$$

Solution

$$\sqrt{180} + \sqrt{20} - \sqrt{125}$$

$$\sqrt{36 \times 5} + \sqrt{4 \times 5} - \sqrt{25 \times 5}$$

$$\sqrt{36}\sqrt{5} + \sqrt{4}\sqrt{5} - \sqrt{25}\sqrt{5}$$

$$6\sqrt{5} + 2\sqrt{5} - 5\sqrt{5}$$

$$8\sqrt{5} - 5\sqrt{5}$$

$$3\sqrt{5}$$

Addition and subtraction

Only like surds can be added or subtracted. Express each surd in its simplest form and add or subtract like surds.

Rationalising the denominator

It is poor practice to have surds on the bottom of a fraction. The process of removing a surd from the denominator is called **rationalising the denominator**. To rationalise the denominator, multiply the top and bottom of the fraction by the surd.

If the denominator is a compound surd, such as $a + \sqrt{b}$, you rationalise the denominator by multiplying the top and bottom by the conjugate of the denominator, which is the same as the compound surd, but with one of the signs changed.

$$\frac{x}{a + \sqrt{b}} \times \frac{a - \sqrt{b}}{a - \sqrt{b}}$$

Example

Express $\dfrac{1}{3\sqrt{5}} - \dfrac{1}{2\sqrt{20}}$ in the form $k\sqrt{5}$, where $k \in \mathbb{Q}$.

Solution

$$\frac{1}{3\sqrt{5}} - \frac{1}{2\sqrt{20}}$$

$$\frac{1}{3\sqrt{5}} - \frac{1}{2\sqrt{4}\sqrt{5}} \quad \text{(break down the } \sqrt{20})$$

$$\frac{1}{3\sqrt{5}} - \frac{1}{2(2)\sqrt{5}}$$

$$\frac{1}{3\sqrt{5}} - \frac{1}{4\sqrt{5}}$$

$$\frac{4-3}{12\sqrt{5}} \qquad \text{(add the fractions)}$$

$$\frac{1}{12\sqrt{5}} \times \frac{\sqrt{5}}{\sqrt{5}} \qquad \text{(multiply the top and bottom by the surd)}$$

$$\frac{\sqrt{5}}{12(5)}$$

$$\frac{\sqrt{5}}{60} = \frac{1}{60}\sqrt{5}$$

key point

To rationalise the denominator, you multiply the top and bottom by the surd.

exam Q

Express $\dfrac{1-\sqrt{3}}{1+\sqrt{3}}$ in the form $a\sqrt{3} - b$, where a and $b \in \mathbb{N}$.

Solution

$$\frac{1-\sqrt{3}}{1+\sqrt{3}}$$

$$\frac{1-\sqrt{3}}{1+\sqrt{3}} \times \frac{1-\sqrt{3}}{1-\sqrt{3}} \qquad \text{(multiply the top and bottom by the conjugate of the bottom } (1-\sqrt{3}))$$

$$\frac{1-\sqrt{3}-\sqrt{3}+3}{1+\sqrt{3}-\sqrt{3}-3} \qquad \text{(multiply out)}$$

$$\frac{1-2\sqrt{3}+3}{1-3} \qquad \text{(simplify)}$$

$$\frac{4-2\sqrt{3}}{-2}$$

$$\frac{-2(-2+\sqrt{3})}{-2}$$

$$-2+\sqrt{3}$$

Therefore, $\dfrac{1-\sqrt{3}}{1+\sqrt{3}}$ can be written in the form $\sqrt{3} - 2$.

key point

Multiply the top and bottom by the conjugate of the bottom.

2 Quadratic and Cubic Equations

Quadratic equations

Any equation of the form $ax^2 + bx + c = 0$, $a \neq 0$, is called a quadratic equation. Solving a quadratic equation gives us the roots of the equation. These are the two values which satisfy the equation. To solve a quadratic equation, we either:

> **1.** Factorise and let each factor = 0
>
> or
>
> **2.** Use the formula $x = \dfrac{-b \pm \sqrt{b^2 - 4ac}}{2a}$

Example

Solve the following quadratic equations

(i) $3x^2 - 5x - 12 = 0$

(ii) $2x^2 - 7x + 4 = 0$, leaving your answer in surd form.

Solution

(i) $3x^2 - 5x - 12 = 0$

$(3x + 4)(x - 3) = 0$ (factorise the left-hand side)

$3x + 4 = 0$ or $x - 3 = 0$ (let each factor = 0)

$3x = -4$ or $x = 3$

$x = -\dfrac{4}{3}$ or $x = 3$ (solve each simple equation)

(ii) $2x^2 - 7x + 4 = 0$

We cannot factorise the quadratic, so we must use the formula:

$$x = \frac{-b \pm \sqrt{b^2 - 4ac}}{2a} \qquad a = 2, b = -7, c = 4$$

$$x = \frac{-(-7) \pm \sqrt{(-7)^2 - 4(2)(4)}}{2(2)} = \frac{7 \pm \sqrt{49 - 32}}{4} = \frac{7 \pm \sqrt{17}}{4}$$

So, $x = \dfrac{7 + \sqrt{17}}{4}$ or $x = \dfrac{7 - \sqrt{17}}{4}$

(2016 Q.5 (a))

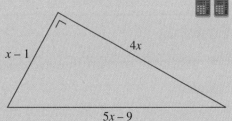

(i) The lengths of the sides of a right-angled triangle are given by the expressions:

$x - 1$, $4x$ and $5x - 9$
as shown in the diagram.

Find the value of x.

(ii) Verify, with this value of x, that the lengths of the sides of the triangle above form a Pythagorean triple.

Solution

(i) Apply Pythagoras's theorem:
$$c^2 = a^2 + b^2$$
$$(5x - 9)^2 = (4x)^2 + (x - 1)^2$$
$$25x^2 - 90x + 81 = 16x^2 + x^2 - 2x + 1$$
$$8x^2 - 88x + 80 = 0$$
$$x^2 - 11x + 10 = 0$$
$$(x - 10)(x - 1) = 0$$
$$x - 10 = 0 \quad \text{or} \quad x - 1 = 0$$
$$x = 10 \quad \text{or} \quad x = 1$$

x cannot be equal to 1, as the side $(x - 1)$ would equal to 0 and the side $(5x - 9)$ would be a negative value. Therefore, $x = 10$.

(ii) Let $x = 10$:

Sides are: $x - 1 \Rightarrow 10 - 1 \quad = 9$

$\qquad\qquad 4x \Rightarrow 4(10) \quad\quad = 40$

$\qquad 5x - 9 \Rightarrow 5(10) - 9 = 41$

Apply Pythagoras's Theorem:

$\qquad c^2 = a^2 + b^2$

$(41)^2 = (40)^2 + (9)^2$

$1681 = 1600 + 81$

$1681 = 1681$

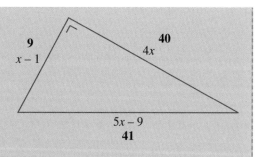

Thus, the length of the sides form a Pythagorean triple.

To form a quadratic equation when given its roots:

$x^2 -$ (sum of the roots)$x +$ (product of the roots) $= 0$

Example

Form the quadratic equation whose roots are $\frac{1}{2}$ and 3.

Solution

Firstly, we need to find the sum and the product of the roots:

Sum of the root $= \frac{1}{2} + 3 = \frac{7}{2}$ $\qquad$ Product of the roots $= \left(\frac{1}{2}\right)(3) = \frac{3}{2}$

To form the quadratic equation:

$x^2 -$ (sum of the roots)$x +$ (product of the roots) $= 0$

$$x^2 - \left(\frac{7}{2}\right)x + \left(\frac{3}{2}\right) = 0 \qquad (\times 2)$$

$$2x^2 - 7x + 3 = 0$$

Nature of the roots of a quadratic equation

The nature of the roots of a quadratic equation is determined by the value for the $b^2 - 4ac$ part in the formula.

$b^2 - 4ac$ **is known as the discriminant**

If $b^2 - 4ac > 0$, the equation has two real distinct roots.

If $b^2 - 4ac = 0$, the equation has two equal real roots.

If $b^2 - 4ac < 0$, the equation has no real roots.

Example

Verify that the equation $2x^2 - x + 3 = 0$ has no real roots.

Solution

Determine the value of the discriminant $b^2 - 4ac$, where $a = 2, b = -1, c = 3$.

$$(-1)^2 - 4(2)(3)$$
$$1 - 24 = -23$$

Since $b^2 - 4ac < 0$, the quadratic equation has no real roots.

Equations involving fractions

Use the common denominator to rewrite the equation by multiplying all parts by the common denominator. Then factorise and solve the resulting quadratic equation.

Example

Solve $\dfrac{1}{x+1} + \dfrac{4}{2x-1} = \dfrac{5}{3}$.

Solution

Multiply each part by the common denominator: $(x + 1)(2x - 1)(3)$.

$$(x+1)(2x-1)(3)\left(\frac{1}{x+1}\right) + (x+1)(2x-1)(3)\left(\frac{4}{2x-1}\right) = (x+1)(2x-1)(3)\left(\frac{5}{3}\right)$$

$$(2x-1)(3)(1) + (x+1)(3)(4) = (x+1)(2x-1)(5)$$
$$(2x-1)(3) + (x+1)(12) = (x+1)(10x-5)$$
$$6x - 3 + 12x + 12 = 10x^2 + 5x - 5$$
$$18x + 9 = 10x^2 + 5x - 5$$
$$10x^2 - 13x - 14 = 0$$
$$(10x+7)(x-2) = 0$$
$$10x + 7 = 0 \qquad x - 2 = 0$$
$$x = -\frac{7}{10} \qquad x = 2$$

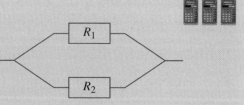

A resistor is an electrical component which reduces the current flowing through a circuit. The resistance of these resistors is measured in units called ohms and resistance is always a positive value. Two resistors are placed in parallel, as in the diagram. One resistor is 3 ohm greater than the other resistor. Their total effective resistance (R_T) is found to be 2 ohm.

Calculate the value of each resistor, given that the formula for calculating the total resistance is:

$$\frac{1}{R_T} = \frac{1}{R_1} + \frac{1}{R_2}$$

Solution

Let resistor one (R_1) = R,   resistor two (R_2) = R + 3,   total resistance (R_T) = 2.

$$\frac{1}{R_T} = \frac{1}{R_1} + \frac{1}{R_2}$$

$$\frac{1}{2} = \frac{1}{R} + \frac{1}{R + 3} \qquad \text{(multiply all parts by } 2(R)(R + 3)\text{)}$$

$$(2)(R)(R + 3)\left(\frac{1}{2}\right) = (2)(R)(R + 3)\left(\frac{1}{R}\right) + (2)(R)(R + 3)\left(\frac{1}{R + 3}\right)$$

$$(R)(R + 3)(1) = (2)(R + 3)(1) + (2)(R)(1)$$

$$R^2 + 3R = 2R + 6 + 2R$$

$$R^2 - R - 6 = 0$$

$$(R - 3)(R + 2) = 0$$

$$R = 3 \text{ or } R = -2$$

Reject R = −2, as you can't have a negative resistance.
Therefore, the resistance of R_1 = 3 ohm and the resistance of R_2 = 6 ohm.

To solve problems which involve real-life situations, draw a diagram if possible. Write the problem in the form of an algebraic equation. Manipulate the equation and solve.

Modulus equations

The modulus of x, written $|x|$, is defined as its positive or absolute value.
For example, $|5| = 5$ and $|-2| = 2$.

A modulus equation is one where the variable is contained within a modulus.
For example, $|x - 1| = 4$ is a modulus equation.

Note: If $|x| = 3$, then x = 3 or x = −3.

Solving a modulus equation is a vital skill to have in topics like coordinate geometry and trigonometry.

Example

Solve $|3x - 2| = 4$.

Solution

Method 1: Remove the modulus and allow the inside part to equal $+4$ or -4. Then solve each equation.

$$3x - 2 = 4 \qquad\qquad 3x - 2 = -4$$
$$3x = 4 + 2 \qquad\qquad 3x = -4 + 2$$
$$3x = 6 \qquad\qquad 3x = -2$$
$$x = 2 \qquad\qquad x = \frac{-2}{3}$$

Method 2: Square both sides of the given equation (this removes the modulus bars) and solve the resulting quadratic equation.

$$|3x - 2|^2 = 4^2$$
$$9x^2 - 12x + 4 = 16$$
$$9x^2 - 12x - 12 = 0$$
$$3x^2 - 4x - 4 = 0$$
$$(3x + 2)(x - 2) = 0$$

$$x = \frac{-2}{3} \quad \text{or} \quad x = 2$$

Solve $2|x + 1| - |x + 3| = 0$.

Solution

$$2|x + 1| - |x + 3| = 0$$
$$2|x + 1| = |x + 3|$$
$$(2|x + 1|)^2 = |x + 3|^2$$
$$4(x^2 + 2x + 1) = x^2 + 6x + 9$$
$$4x^2 + 8x + 4 = x^2 + 6x + 9$$
$$3x^2 + 2x - 5 = 0$$
$$(3x + 5)(x - 1) = 0$$
$$x = \frac{-5}{3} \text{ or } x = 1$$

key point

If there are two modulus parts, arrange to have one modulus part on each side. Then square both sides and solve the resulting quadratic equation.

Irrational equations

An irrational equation is one where the variable is contained under a square root.

For example, $\sqrt{x + 2} = x - 4$ is an irrational equation.

Irrational equations are solved with the following steps.

1. Arrange to have the surd (root) part on its own on one side.
2. Square both sides (removes square root symbol).
3. Solve the resultant equation.
4. Test every solution in the **original** equation.

Example

Solve $x = \sqrt{3x + 7} - 1$.

Solution

$$x = \sqrt{3x + 7} - 1$$
$$x + 1 = \sqrt{3x + 7}$$
$$(x + 1)^2 = (\sqrt{3x + 7})^2$$
$$x^2 + 2x + 1 = 3x + 7$$
$$x^2 - x - 6 = 0$$
$$(x - 3)(x + 2) = 0$$
$$x = 3 \text{ or } x = -2$$

Test the two solutions in the original equation.

Let $x = 3$:
$$3 = \sqrt{3(3) + 7} - 1$$
$$3 = \sqrt{9 + 7} - 1$$
$$3 = \sqrt{16} - 1$$
$$3 = 4 - 1 \qquad \text{(true)}$$

Let $x = -2$:
$$-2 = \sqrt{3(-2) + 7} - 1$$
$$-2 = \sqrt{-6 + 7} - 1$$
$$-2 = \sqrt{1} - 1$$
$$-2 = 1 - 1 \qquad \text{(false)}$$

$\therefore x = 3$ is the only solution.

Squaring both sides may introduce a new root, called an **extraneous** root.
This root does not satisfy the original equation and hence it is rejected. This is why it is vital to test your solutions in the original equation.

Completing the square

Completing the square means taking any quadratic polynomial in the form $px^2 + qx + r$ and expressing it in the form $p(x + a)^2 + b$ for some a and b.

To complete the square:
1. Halve the coefficient of the x term, when the coefficient of x^2 equals one.
2. Square this value and then add and subtract this value to the expression.
3. Factorise the portion which is a perfect square and tidy up the constants.

Completing the square can be used:
1. To solve an equation instead of using the '$-b$ formula'.
2. To find the maximum or minimum points on a quadratic graph, which will be covered in Chapter 6: Functions and Graphing Functions.

Example

(i) Express $x^2 - 6x - 12 = 0$ in the form $(x - p)^2 + q = 0$.

(ii) Hence, solve for x.

Solution

(i) Half of the x term is -3. Add and subtract $(-3)^2 = 9$ to the equation:
$$x^2 - 6x + 9 - 9 - 12 = 0$$
$$x^2 - 6x + 9 - 21 = 0$$
$$(x - 3)(x - 3) - 21 = 0$$
$$(x - 3)^2 - 21 = 0$$

(ii) To solve for x, rearrange $(x - 3)^2 - 21 = 0$ to get x on its own:
$$(x - 3)^2 - 21 = 0$$
$$(x - 3)^2 = 21$$
$$x - 3 = \pm\sqrt{21} \qquad \text{(square root both sides)}$$
$$x = 3 \pm \sqrt{21}$$

(i) Express $-x^2 + 11x + 15 = 0$ in the form $q - (x - p)^2 = 0$.

(ii) Hence, solve for x.

Solution

(i) Start by factorising out -1: $-1(x^2 - 11x - 15) = 0$.

Now complete the square on the part inside the bracket by adding and subtracting $(-5·5)^2 = 30·25$:

$$-1(x^2 - 11x + 30·25 - 30·25 - 15) = 0$$

$$-1(x^2 - 11x + 30·25 - 45·25) = 0$$

$$-1((x - 5·5)(x - 5·5) - 45·25) = 0$$

$$-1((x - 5·5)^2 - 45·25) = 0$$

$$-1(x - 5·5)^2 + 45·25 = 0$$

$$45·25 - (x - 5·5)^2 = 0$$

We could also have done part (i) by letting: $-x^2 + 11x + 15 = q - (x - p)^2$ and use the method of undetermined coefficients to find the values of p and q.

(ii) To solve for x, rearrange $45·25 - (x - 5·5)^2 = 0$ to get x on its own:

$$45·25 - (x - 5·5)^2 = 0$$

$$45·25 = (x - 5·5)^2$$

$$\pm\sqrt{45·25} = x - 5·5$$

$$5·5 \pm \sqrt{45·25} = x$$

Factor theorem

If an algebraic expression is divided by one of its factors, then the remainder is zero. The expression $(x - k)$ is a factor of a polynomial $f(x)$ if the remainder when we divide $f(x)$ by $(x - k)$ is zero.

Generalising this:

> **1.** If $f(k) = 0$, then $(x - k)$ is a factor of $f(x)$.
>
> **2.** If $(x - k)$ is a factor of $f(x)$, then $f(k) = 0$.

Example

$f(x) = 3x^3 + mx^2 - 17x + n$, where m and n are constants.
Given that $x - 3$ and $x + 2$ are factors of $f(x)$, find the value of m and the value of n.

Solution

Since $x - 3$ is a factor, $x = 3$ is a root.	Since $x + 2$ is a factor, $x = -2$ is a root.
$\therefore f(3) = 0$	$\therefore f(-2) = 0$
$3(3)^3 + m(3)^2 - 17(3) + n = 0$	$3(-2)^3 + m(-2)^2 - 17(-2) + n = 0$
$81 + 9m - 51 + n = 0$	$-24 + 4m + 34 + n = 0$
$9m + n = -30$	$4m + n = -10$

Solve these equations simultaneously:

$9m + n = -30$	Let $m = -4$:
$4m + n = -10 \quad (\times -1)$	$4m + n = -10$
$9m + n = -30$	$4(-4) + n = -10$
$-4m - n = \quad 10$	$-16 + n = -10$
$5m \quad\quad = -20$	$n = 6$
$m = -4$	

Cubic equations

Any equation of the form $ax^3 + bx^2 + cx + d = 0$, $a \neq 0$, is called a cubic equation.

A cubic equation is solved with the following steps.

1. Find the first root, k, by trial and error, i.e. try $f(1)$, $f(-1)$, $f(2)$, $f(-2)$, etc. (Only try numbers that divide evenly into the constant in the equation.)
2. If $x = k$ is a root, then $(x - k)$ is a factor.
3. Divide $f(x)$ by $(x - k)$, which always gives a quadratic expression.
4. Let the (given cubic) = (linear factor)(quadratic factor).
   Then let (linear factor)(quadratic factor) = 0 and solve by factors or formula.

Note: Each cubic equation we are asked to solve must have at least one integer root.

exam Q

(2015 Q.2)

Solve the equation $x^3 - 3x^2 - 9x + 11 = 0$.

Write any irrational solution in the form $a + b\sqrt{c}$, where $a, b, c \in \mathbb{Z}$.

Solution

Use trial and improvement to find the first root:

$f(1) = (1)^3 - 3(1)^2 - 9(1) + 11$

$f(1) = 1 - 3 - 9 + 11$

$f(1) = 0$

Therefore, $x = 1$ is a root and so $(x - 1)$ is a factor of $f(x)$.

Use long division to find the other two factors of $f(x)$:

$$
\begin{array}{r}
x^2 - 2x - 11 \\
x - 1 \overline{\smash{\big)}\, x^3 - 3x^2 - 9x + 11} \\
\underline{x^3 - x^2} \\
-2x^2 - 9x \\
\underline{-2x^2 + 2x} \\
-11x + 11 \\
\underline{-11x + 11} \\
0
\end{array}
$$

(change signs and add rows)

(change signs and add rows)

(change signs and add rows)

Therefore, $(x^3 - 3x^2 - 9x + 11) \div (x - 1) = x^2 - 2x - 11$

Solve: $x^2 - 2x - 11 = 0$ $a = 1,\ \ b = -2,\ \ c = -11$

$$x = \frac{-b \pm \sqrt{b^2 - 4ac}}{2a}$$

$$x = \frac{-(-2) \pm \sqrt{(-2)^2 - 4(1)(-11)}}{2(1)}$$

$$x = \frac{2 \pm \sqrt{4 + 44}}{2} = \frac{2 \pm \sqrt{48}}{2} = \frac{2 \pm 4\sqrt{3}}{2} = 1 \pm 2\sqrt{3}$$

Therefore, $x = 1,\quad 1 + 2\sqrt{3},\quad 1 - 2\sqrt{3}$

 exam focus

This question was worth 25 marks. 10 marks were awarded for finding a correct root, 15 for attempting the division and 20 marks for finding the correct quadratic.

3 Inequalities

□ To learn how to solve linear and quadratic inequalities
□ To learn how to solve rational and modulus inequalities
□ To learn how to graph a solution set on a number line
□ To learn how to solve abstract inequalities

Introduction

The four inequality symbols are:

> 1. $>$ means 'greater than'   2. $\geq$ means 'greater than or equal to'
> 3. $<$ means 'less than'   4. $\leq$ means 'less than or equal to'

Algebraic expressions that are linked by one of the four inequality symbols are called **inequalities**. For example, $3x - 1 > 11$ and $-3 < 2x - 1 \leq 7$ are inequalities.

Solving inequalities is exactly the same as solving equations, with the following exception:

> Multiplying or dividing both sides of an inequality by a
> **negative** number **reverses** the direction of the inequality symbol.

Solving an inequality means finding the values of x that make the inequality true.

The following rules apply to graphing inequalities on a number line:

> Number line for $x \in \mathbb{N}$ or $x \in \mathbb{Z}$, use **dots**.
> Number line for $x \in \mathbb{R}$, use a **full heavy line**.

Note: Inequalities can be turned around. For example:

$$5 \leq x \text{ means the same as } x \geq 5.$$
$$8 \geq x \geq 3 \text{ means the same as } 3 \leq x \leq 8.$$

Linear inequalities

Example

Find the solution set of $11 - 3x \geq 2$, $x \in \mathbb{N}$ and graph your solution on the number line.

Solution

$11 - 3x \geq 2$

$\quad -3x \geq -9 \qquad$ (subtract 11 from both sides)

$\quad\ \ 3x \leq 9 \qquad$ (multiply both sides by -1 and reverse the direction of the inequality)

$\quad\ \ \ x \leq 3 \qquad$ (divide both sides by 3)

As $x \in \mathbb{N}$, this is the set of natural numbers less than or equal to 3.

Thus, the values of x are 1, 2 and 3.

Number line:

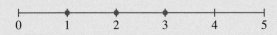

As $x \in \mathbb{N}$, dots are used on the number line.

Example

(i) Find the solution set A of $2x + 7 \leq 11$, $x \in \mathbb{R}$.

(ii) Find the solution set B of $4 - 2x < 10$, $x \in \mathbb{R}$.

(iii) Find $A \cap B$ and graph your solution on the number line.

> Remember: $A \cap B$ means A intersection B.

Solution

We solve each inequality separately and then combine the solutions.

(i) A: $2x + 7 \leq 11$ (ii) B: $4 - 2x < 10$

            $2x \leq 4$ $-2x < 6$

               $x \leq 2$ $2x > -6$

                                                        $x > -3$

(iii) Combining the two inequalities gives:

$$A \cap B: \ -3 < x \leq 2, \qquad x \in \mathbb{R}$$

This is the set of positive and negative real numbers between -3 and 2, including 2 but not including -3.

Number line:

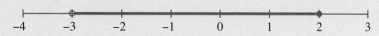

key point

1. As $x \in \mathbb{R}$, we use full heavy shading on the number line.
2. A hollow circle is put around -3 to indicate that it is **not** included in the solution.
3. A dot is put on 2 to indicate that it is included in the solution.

Quadratic inequalities

Quadratic inequalities are solved with the following steps.

1. Replace the $\geq$, $\leq$, $>$ or $<$ with an $=$ (make the inequality into an equation) and, if necessary, rearrange the equation into the form $ax^2 + bx + c = 0$, where $a > 0$.
2. Solve the quadratic equation to find the two roots of the equation.
3. Draw a sketch of the graph. (Remember: if $a > 0$, your graph will be U-shaped.)
4. From the given question, determine if you are looking for the region where the graph is greater than zero (above the x-axis) or less than zero (below the x-axis).

Example

Find the solution set of the following inequality: $15 + 2x \geq x^2, x \in \mathbb{R}$.

Solution

$15 + 2x \geq x^2$

$15 + 2x = x^2$ (change $\geq$ to $=$)

$\quad 0 = x^2 - 2x - 15$ (rearrange)

$\quad 0 = (x + 3)(x - 5)$ (factorise)

$\quad x = -3 \quad$ and $\quad x = 5 \quad$ (solve)

Marks may be lost for not changing the inequality sign to an equal sign at this point.

Draw a sketch of the quadratic graph:

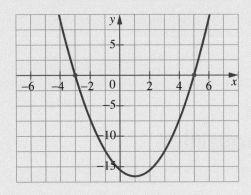

$0 \geq x^2 - 2x - 15$ means that $0 \geq$ graph or graph ≤ 0.

So we are looking for the set of values of x for which the graph is equal to or below the x-axis.

$$-3 \leq x \leq 5$$

(2013 Q.2 (a))

Find the set of all real values of x for which $2x^2 + x - 15 \geq 0$.

Solution

$2x^2 + x - 15 \geq 0$

$2x^2 + x - 15 = 0$

$(2x - 5)(x + 3) = 0$

$2x - 5 = 0 \quad$ or $\quad x + 3 = 0$

$2x = 5 \quad$ or $\quad x = -3$

$x = \dfrac{5}{2} \quad$ or $\quad x = -3$

Sketch a graph of the quadratic:

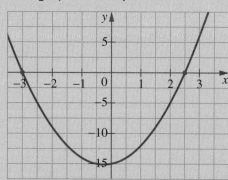

$2x^2 + x - 15 \geq 0$ means the region where the graph is above or equal to the x-axis.

$x \leq -3 \quad$ and $\quad x \geq \dfrac{5}{2}$

Students often have difficulty determining the correct region for the final answer. Spend some time practising this.

A boy throws a ball from the top of a building. The ball leaves his hands 2 m above the building. The height, h m, reached by the ball above the ground after t seconds is given by $h = 9 + 8t - t^2$.

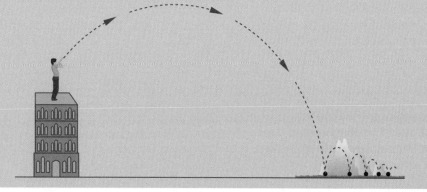

(i) Find the height of the building.

(ii) Find the time taken for the ball to hit the ground for the first time.

(iii) Find the range of values of t for which the ball is more than 21 m above the ground.

Solution

(i) $h = 9 + 8t - t^2$ represents the height of the ball, where t is the time, in seconds, for which the ball has been thrown. At the instant the ball is released, $t = 0$ seconds.

$h = 9 + 8(0) - (0)^2$

$h = 9$

Thus, the ball is 9 m above the ground when it is released. However, it is released 2 m above the building, so the height of the building is 7 m.

(ii) When the ball hits the ground, its height off the ground is 0 m, so let $h = 0$ and solve for t:

$0 = 9 + 8t - t^2$

$0 = t^2 - 8t - 9$ (multiply both sides by -1)

$0 = (t - 9)(t + 1)$

$t = 9$ or $t = -1$

Can't have a negative time, $\therefore t = 9$ sec when the ball hits the ground.

(iii) Find t for when $h > 21$ m

$h = 9 + 8t - t^2$

$9 + 8t - t^2 > 21$

$-12 + 8t - t^2 > 0$

$12 - 8t + t^2 < 0$ (multiply all parts by -1 and change the direction of the inequality)

$t^2 - 8t + 12 = 0$ (change to an equation)

$(t - 2)(t - 6) = 0$ (factorise)

$t = 2$ or $t = 6$ (solve)

Sketch a graph of the quadratic:

$12 - 8t + t^2 < 0$ means the region where the graph < 0

So, we are looking for the set of values of x for which the graph is equal to or below the x-axis.

$2 < t < 6$

Therefore, the height is above 21 m for the time being between 2 and 6 seconds.

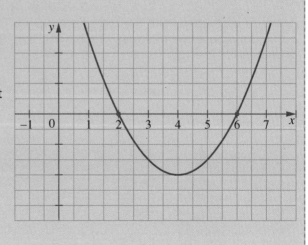

Rational inequalities

> Multiply both sides of the inequality by the square of the denominator.

This will remove the denominator, leaving us with a quadratic inequality. Since a perfect square can't be negative, this does not affect the direction of the inequality.

(2018 Q.1 (b))

Solve the inequality $\dfrac{2x - 3}{x + 2} \geq 3$, where $x \in \mathbb{R}$ and $x \neq -2$.

Solution

$$\frac{2x - 3}{x + 2} \geq 3$$

$$(x + 2)^2\left(\frac{2x - 3}{x + 2}\right) \geq 3(x + 2)^2$$

$$(x + 2)(2x - 3) \geq 3(x^2 + 4x + 4)$$

$$2x^2 + x - 6 \geq 3x^2 + 12x + 12$$

$$0 \geq x^2 + 11x + 18$$

Solve:

$x^2 + 11x + 18 = 0$

$(x + 9)(x + 2) = 0$

$x = -9, x = -2$

Graph the quadratic:

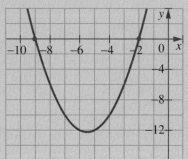

$x^2 + 11x + 18 \leq 0$ means the region where the graph is below or equal to the x-axis. This occurs when:

$$-9 \leq x \leq -2$$

But, we are told that $x \neq -2$, so

$$-9 \leq x < -2$$

Let $f(x) = x^2 - 7x + 12$.

(i) Show that if $f(x + 1) \neq 0$, then $\frac{f(x)}{f(x + 1)}$ simplifies to $\frac{x - 4}{x - 2}$.

(ii) Find the range of values of x for which $\frac{f(x)}{f(x + 1)} > 3$.

Solution

(i) $f(x) = x^2 - 7x + 12$

$f(x + 1) = (x + 1)^2 - 7(x + 1) + 12$

$f(x + 1) = x^2 + 2x + 1 - 7x - 7 + 12$

$f(x + 1) = x^2 - 5x + 6$

$\dfrac{f(x)}{f(x + 1)} = \dfrac{x^2 - 7x + 12}{x^2 - 5x + 6}$

$\dfrac{f(x)}{f(x + 1)} = \dfrac{(x - 3)(x - 4)}{(x - 3)(x - 2)}$

$\dfrac{f(x)}{f(x + 1)} = \dfrac{x - 4}{x - 2}$

> You can do part **(ii)** of this question without being able to do part **(i)**. You should attempt all sections of every question.

(ii) $\dfrac{f(x)}{f(x + 1)} > 3$

$\dfrac{x - 4}{x - 2} > 3$ (multiply both sides by $(x - 2)^2$)

$(x - 2)^2 \left(\dfrac{x - 4}{x - 2} \right) > 3(x - 2)^2$

$(x - 2)(x - 4) > 3(x^2 - 4x + 4)$

$x^2 - 6x + 8 > 3x^2 - 12x + 12$

$0 > 2x^2 - 6x + 4$

$0 > x^2 - 3x + 2$

$0 = x^2 - 3x + 2$

$0 = (x - 2)(x - 1)$

$x = 2$ and $x = 1$

Sketch a graph of the quadratic:

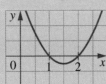

$0 > x^2 - 3x + 2$ means the region where the $0 >$ graph or the graph < 0.

So, we are looking for the set of values of x for which the graph is below the x-axis.

$1 < x < 2$

Modulus inequalities

The modulus of a number is its positive value.

If $|x| = 2$, then x could be 2 or -2.

Modulus inequality

If $\quad |x| \leq a,\quad$ then $\quad -a \leq x \leq a \quad$ for $\quad a \in \mathbb{R} \quad$ and $\quad a > 0$.

If $\quad |x| \geq a,\quad$ then $\quad x \leq -a$ or $x \geq a \quad$ for $\quad a \in \mathbb{R} \quad$ and $\quad a > 0$.

If $<$ or $>$ is used, then the critical values, $\pm a$, are not included.

Example

Solve the following inequality: $|5 - 2x| \leq 3$.

Solution

Since the modulus is on the 'less than' side of the inequality, place the modulus between -3 and $+3$:

$$-3 \leq 5 - 2x \leq 3$$
$$-8 \leq -2x \leq -2 \qquad \text{(subtract 5 from all parts)}$$
$$8 \geq 2x \geq 2 \qquad \text{(multiply all parts by } -1 \text{ and change the direction of the inequality)}$$
$$4 \geq x \geq 1 \qquad \text{(divide all parts by 2)}$$

key point

A modulus inequality can also be solved by squaring both sides and solving the resulting quadratic inequality.

exam Q

(2016 Q.2 (a))

Find the range of values of x for which $|x - 4| \geq 2$, where $x \in \mathbb{R}$.

Solution

Since the modulus is on the 'greater than' side of the inequality:

$x - 4 \geq 2$	or	$x - 4 \leq -2$
$x \geq 2 + 4$	or	$x \leq -2 + 4$
$x \geq 6$	or	$x \leq 2$

key point

The modulus function changes any negative values, for y, into positive values.

Therefore, the graph of a modulus function has a V-shape. The point at the bottom of the V is known as the vertex of the graph.

For a function $f(x) = |ax + b|$, the vertex is at the point where $f(x) = 0$.

The diagram shows the graph of the function $f(x) = |x - 2|$. The vertex is at the point (2, 0).

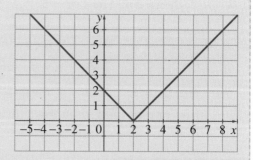

Abstract inequalities

An example of an **abstractly inequality** is $a^2 + b^2 \geq 2ab$.

Many of the abstract inequalities in this section are establised using the fact that:

$$\text{(any real number)}^2 \geq 0 \quad \text{or} \quad -\text{(any real number)}^2 \leq 0$$

Abstract inequalities are usually solved with the following steps.

1. Write down the given inequality to be proved.
2. Using **reversible** steps for inequalities, arrive at an algebraic inequality that is true.
3. Therefore, the given inequality is true.

Note: We can only square both sides of an inequality when we are sure that both sides are positive (non-negative). For example, $-3 < 2$; squaring both sides gives $9 < 4$, which is not true.

exam focus

Abstract inequalities usually appear on the exam paper in the form of proofs.

Example

Prove that for all $a, b \in \mathbb{R}$, $a^2 + 4b^2 \geq 4ab$.

Solution

$$a^2 + 4b^2 \geq 4ab$$

$$a^2 - 4ab + 4b^2 \geq 0 \qquad \text{(subtract } 4ab \text{ from both sides)}$$

$$(a - 2b)(a - 2b) \geq 0 \qquad \text{(factorise)}$$

$$(a - 2b)^2 \geq 0$$

This is true, since $(\text{any} \in \mathbb{R})^2 \geq 0$. $\quad \therefore a^2 + 4b^2 \geq 4ab$

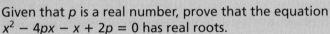

Given that p is a real number, prove that the equation
$x^2 - 4px - x + 2p = 0$ has real roots.

Solution

If the roots of a quadratic equation are real, $b^2 - 4ac \geq 0$.

$$x^2 - 4px - x + 2p = 0$$

$$x^2 - (4p + 1)x + 2p = 0 \qquad a = 1, \qquad b = -(4p + 1), \quad c = 2p$$

$$b^2 - 4ac \geq 0$$

$$[-(4p + 1)]^2 - 4(1)(2p) \geq 0$$

$$(4p + 1)^2 - 8p \geq 0$$

$$16p^2 + 8p + 1 - 8p \geq 0$$

$$16p^2 + 1 \geq 0$$

This is true, since $(\text{any} \in \mathbb{R})^2 \geq 0$. $\quad \therefore b^2 - 4ac \geq 0$

$\therefore$ The roots are real.

4 Simultaneous Equations

☐ To learn how to use suitable strategies for finding solutions to:
  ○ Simultaneous linear equations with two unknowns
  ○ Simultaneous linear equations with three unknowns
  ○ One linear equation and one quadratic equation with two unknowns
☐ To learn how to interpret the results from solving two equations simultaneously

Simultaneous linear equations with two unknowns

Simultaneous linear equations in two variables are solved with the following steps.

1. Write both equations in the form $ax + by = k$ and label the equations ① and ②.
2. Multiply one or both of the equations by a number in order to make the coefficients of x or y the same, but of opposite sign.
3. Add to remove the variable with equal coefficients but of opposite sign.
4. Solve the resultant equation to find the value of the remaining unknown (x or y).
5. Substitute this value in equation ① or ② to find the value of the other unknown.

key point

Solution containing fractions: If the answer at step 4 is a fraction, the substitution might be difficult. In such cases, you can repeat steps 1 to 4 for the other variable.

Example

Solve the equations for x and y:

$$\frac{2x - 5}{3} + \frac{y}{5} = 6; \quad \frac{3x}{10} + 2 = \frac{3y - 5}{2}$$

Solution

Equation 1: $\quad \dfrac{2x - 5}{3} + \dfrac{y}{5} = 6$ $\qquad (\times 15)$

$$5(2x - 5) + 3(y) = 15(6)$$

$$10x - 25 + 3y = 90$$

$$10x + 3y = 115 \quad ①$$

Equation 2: $\quad \dfrac{3x}{10} + 2 = \dfrac{3y - 5}{2}$ $\qquad (\times 10)$

$$1(3x) + 10(2) = 5(3y - 5)$$

$$3x + 20 = 15y - 25$$

$$3x - 15y = -45 \qquad ②$$

Now solve ① and ②: $10x + 3y = 115$ $\qquad (\times 5)$

$$\underline{3x - 15y = -45}$$

$$50x + 15y = 575$$

$$\underline{3x - 15y = -45}$$

$$53x = 530 \qquad (\div 53)$$

$$x = 10$$

Sub $x = 10$ into ①: $10(10) + 3y = 115$

$$100 + 3y = 115$$

$$3y = 15 \qquad (\div 5)$$

$$y = 5$$

Answers: $x = 10 \quad$ and $\quad y = 5$

exam Q

The image shows two lines, *l* and *k*, graphed on the coordinated plane.

(i) Use the graph to estimate the point of intersection of the two lines.

(ii) By observation or otherwise, write down the equation of each of the lines in the form $y = mx + c$.

(iii) Solve these equations simultaneously to find the point of intersection. Give your answer to two significant figures.

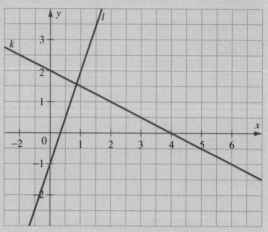

Solution

(i) Estimated point of intersection: (0·8, 1·6).

(ii) To express equations in the form of $y = mx + c$, we need to find the slope of the line and the point where it crosses the y-axis (y-intercept).

Line *l*: Slope, $m = \frac{3}{1} = 3$ y-intercept, $c = -1$

$$\therefore l : y = 3x - 1$$

Line *k*: Slope, $m = \frac{-2}{4} = -\frac{1}{2}$ y-intercept, $c = 2$

$$\therefore k : y = -\frac{1}{2}x + 2$$

 key point

slope = $\dfrac{\text{rise}}{\text{run}}$

(iii) Equation 1: $y = 3x - 1$

Equation 2: $y = -\dfrac{1}{2}x + 2$

Let $y = y$:

$$3x - 1 = -\frac{1}{2}x + 2$$
$$6x - 2 = -x + 4$$
$$6x + x = 4 + 2$$
$$7x = 6$$
$$x = \frac{6}{7} \Rightarrow x = 0·857$$

Substitute $x = \frac{6}{7}$ into equation 1:

$$y = 3x - 1$$
$$y = 3\left(\frac{6}{7}\right) - 1 \qquad (\times 7)$$
$$7y = 18 - 7$$
$$7y = 11$$
$$y = \frac{11}{7} \qquad \Rightarrow \qquad y = 1·571$$

 exam focus

It is very important when solving simultaneous equations to maintain total concentration. If you make a mistake near the start of the solution, you will have difficulty and waste valuable exam time.

Thus, the point of intersection to two significant figures = (0·86, 1·6).

Simultaneous linear equations with three unknowns

Simultaneous linear equations in three variables are solved with the following steps.

1. Write all three equations in the form $ax + by + cz = k$ and label the equations ①, ② and ③.
2. Select one pair of equations and eliminate one of the variables; call this equation ④.
3. Select another pair of equations and eliminate the same variable; call this equation ⑤.
4. Solve the equations ④ and ⑤.
5. Put the answers from step 4 into ① or ② or ③ to find the value of the third variable.

(2018 Q.1 (a))

Solve the simultaneous equations:
$$2x + 3y - z = -4$$
$$3x + 2y + 2z = 14$$
$$x - 3z = -13$$

Solution

The third equation only contains the letters x and z, so we will use the first and second equations to eliminate the ys:

$2x + 3y - z = -4$ ①   (multiply by −2)
$3x + 2y + 2z = 14$ ②   (multiply by 3)
$$\begin{array}{l} -4x - 6y + 2z = 8 \\ \underline{9x + 6y + 6z = 42} \\ 5x \quad\quad + 8z = 50 \quad ④ \end{array}$$

Use equations ③ and ④ to eliminate the xs:

$$\begin{array}{l} x - 3z = -13 \quad (x - 5) \\ \underline{5x + 8z = 50} \\ -5x + 15z = 65 \\ \underline{5x + 8z = 50} \\ \quad\quad 23z = 115 \\ \quad\quad\quad z = 5 \end{array}$$

Substitute $z = 5$ into ④:

$$5x + 8z = 50$$
$$5x + 8(5) = 50$$
$$5x + 40 = 50$$
$$5x = 10$$
$$x = 2$$

Substitute $x = 2$ and $z = 5$ into ①:
$$2x + 3y - z = -4$$
$$2(2) + 3y - 5 = -4$$
$$4 + 3y - 5 = -4$$
$$3y = -3$$
$$y = -1$$

Answers: $x = 2$, $y = -1$, $z = 5$

(2013 Q.2 (b))

Solve the simultaneous equations: $x + y + z = 16$

$$\frac{5}{2}x + y + 10z = 40$$

$$2x + \frac{1}{2}y + 4z = 21$$

Solution

$$x + y + z = 16$$

$$\frac{5}{2}x + y + 10z = 40 \qquad \text{(multiply by 2)}$$

$$2x + \frac{1}{2}y + 4z = 21 \qquad \text{(multiply by 2)}$$

$$\underline{}$$

$$x + y + z = 16 \quad ①$$

$$5x + 2y + 20z = 80 \quad ②$$

$$\underline{4x + y + 8z = 42} \quad ③$$

The first thing to do is to get rid of all fractions within the equations.

③ − ①: $4x + y + 8z = 42$

$$\underline{-x - y - z = -16}$$

$$3x + 7z = 26 \quad ④$$

② −2①: $5x + 2y + 20z = 80$

$$\underline{-2x - 2y - 2z = -32}$$

$$3x + 18z = 48 \quad ⑤$$

⑤ − ④: $3x + 18z = 48$

$$\underline{-3x - 7z = -26}$$

$$11z = 22 \quad (\div 11)$$

$$z = 2$$

Substitute $z = 2$ into ④:

$$3x + 7z = 26$$

$$3x + 7(2) = 26$$

$$3x + 14 = 26$$

$$3x = 12$$

$$x = 4$$

Substitute $x = 4$ and $z = 2$ into ①:

$$x + y + z = 16$$

$$(4) + y + (2) = 16$$

$$y + 6 = 16$$

$$y = 10$$

Answers: $x = 4$, $y = 10$, $z = 2$

Craig invested a total of €50,000 in three funds paying 6%, 8% and 10% interest per annum. The total interest earned on these funds in the first year of investment was €3,700. Twice as much money was invested at 6% as was invested at 10%.

How much was invested in each of the funds?

Solution

Use x, y and z to represent the amount invested in each of the funds.

Let: x = amount invested at 6%.

y = amount invested at 8%.

z = amount invested at 10%

key point

There are three unknowns, so we must form three equations from the given information.

1. Total of all three funds is €50,000.

2. Total interest earned is €3,700.
   (Note: 6% = 0·06, etc.)

3. Amount invested at 6% (x) was twice as much as the amount invested at 10% (z).

$$x + y + z = 50000 \qquad ①$$

$$0·06x + 0·08y + 0·1z = 3700 \qquad (\times 50)$$

$$3x + 4y + 5z = 185000 \qquad ②$$

$$x = 2z$$

$$x - 2z = 0 \qquad ③$$

Equation ③ only contains the letters x and z, so we should eliminate the letter y from ① and ②:

$$x + y + z = 50000 \qquad ① \qquad (\times - 4)$$

$$3x + 4y + 5z = 185000 \qquad ②$$

$$-4x - 4y - 4z = -200000$$

$$\underline{3x + 4y + 5z = 185000}$$

$$-x \qquad\quad + z = -15000$$

$$-x + z = -15000 \qquad ④$$

Now solve between equations ③ and ④ to find the values of x and z:

Substitute $z = 15000$ into ③ or ④.

$$x - 2z = 0 \qquad ③$$

$$\underline{-x + z = -15000} \qquad ④$$

$$-z = -15000$$

$$z = 15000$$

$$x - 2z = 0$$

$$x - 2(15000) = 0$$

$$x - 30000 = 0$$

$$x = 30000$$

Substitute $x = 30000$ and $z = 15000$ into ① and ②:

$$x + y + z = 50000 \qquad ①$$
$$(30000) + y + (15000) = 50000$$
$$y = 5000$$

€30,000 is invested at 6%, €5,000 is invested at 8% and €15,000 is invested at 10%.

The previous exam question is a good example of where there can be links between different topics.

One linear equation and one quadratic equation with two unknowns

Linear equation
The highest exponent of each term is 1,
e.g. $2x + y - 8 = 0$.

Quadratic equation
The highest exponent, or the sum of the exponents, of any term is 2,
e.g. $x^2 + xy + y^2 = 5$.

To solve one linear equation and one quadratic equation with two unknowns, use the following steps.

1. From the linear equation, express one variable in terms of the other.
2. Substitute this into the quadratic equation and solve.
3. Substitute separately the value(s) obtained in step 2 into the linear equation in step 1 to find the corresponding value(s) of the other variable.

Solve the simultaneous equations: $x^2 + xy + 2y^2 = 4$

$$2x + 3y = -1$$

Solution

Rearrange the linear equation: $2x + 3y = -1$

$$2x = -1 - 3y$$

$$x = \frac{-1 - 3y}{2}$$

Substitute this value for x into the quadratic equation:

$$x^2 + xy + 2y^2 = 4$$

$$\left(\frac{-1 - 3y}{2}\right)^2 + \left(\frac{-1 - 3y}{2}\right)y + 2y^2 = 4$$

$$\left(\frac{-1 - 3y}{2}\right)\left(\frac{-1 - 3y}{2}\right) + \left(\frac{-y - 3y^2}{2}\right) + 2y^2 = 4$$

$$\left(\frac{1 + 6y + 9y^2}{4}\right) + \left(\frac{-y - 3y^2}{2}\right) + 2y^2 = 4$$

$$4\left(\frac{1 + 6y + 9y^2}{4}\right) + 4\left(\frac{-y - 3y^2}{2}\right) + 4(2y^2) = 4(4)$$

$$(1 + 6y + 9y^2) + 2(-y - 3y^2) + 8y^2 = 16$$

$$1 + 6y + 9y^2 - 2y - 6y^2 + 8y^2 = 16$$

$$1 + 4y + 11y^2 = 16$$

$$11y^2 + 4y - 15 = 0$$

$$(11y + 15)(y - 1) = 0$$

$$11y + 15 = 0 \text{ or } y - 1 = 0$$

$$11y = -15 \text{ or } y = 1$$

$$y = -\frac{15}{11} \text{ or } y = 1$$

Find the *x* values:

$y = -\dfrac{15}{11}$:

$$x = \dfrac{-1 - 3y}{2}$$

$$x = \dfrac{-1 - 3\left(-\dfrac{15}{11}\right)}{2}$$

$$x = \dfrac{-1 + \dfrac{45}{11}}{2}\left(\times \dfrac{11}{11}\right)$$

$$x = \dfrac{-11 + 45}{22}$$

$$x = \dfrac{34}{22} = \dfrac{17}{11}$$

$y = 1$:

$$x = \dfrac{-1 - 3y}{2}$$

$$x = \dfrac{-1 - 3(1)}{2}$$

$$x = \dfrac{-1 - 3}{2}$$

$$x = \dfrac{-4}{2}$$

$$x = -2$$

Therefore, the solutions are:

$$x = \dfrac{17}{11}, \ y = -\dfrac{15}{11} \quad \text{and} \quad x = -2, \ y = 1$$

An asteroid belt follows a pattern, which is modelled by the equation

$3x^2 + y^2 - 13x - 7y = -12$.

A rocket is on a linear path, which can be modelled by the equation

$4x + 3y = 12$.

typical asteroid orbit

(i) Find the two points where the rocket enters and leaves the asteroid belt.

(ii) One unit is equivalent to 75,000 km, and the rocket is travelling at a speed of 58,000 km/h. Find the time taken from when the rocket enters the asteroid belt until it leaves on the far side.

Solution

(i) Rearrange the linear equation to get *y* on its own: $4x + 3y = 12$

$$3y = 12 - 4x$$

$$y = \dfrac{12 - 4x}{3}$$

Substitute $y = \dfrac{12 - 4x}{3}$ into the quadratic equation:

$$3x^2 + y^2 - 13x - 7y = -12$$

$$3x^2 + \left(\frac{12 - 4x}{3}\right)^2 - 13x - 7\left(\frac{12 - 4x}{3}\right) = -12$$

$$3x^2 + \frac{144 - 96x + 16x^2}{9} - 13x - 7\left(\frac{12 - 4x}{3}\right) = -12 \qquad (\times 9)$$

$$9(3x^2) + 9\left(\frac{144 - 96x + 16x^2}{9}\right) - 9(13x) - 9\left(7\left(\frac{12 - 4x}{3}\right)\right) = 9(-12)$$

$$27x^2 + 144 - 96x + 16x^2 - 117x - 21(12 - 4x) = -108$$

$$43x^2 + 144 - 213x - 252 + 84x = -108$$

$$43x^2 - 129x = 0$$

$$x^2 - 3x = 0$$

$$x(x - 3) = 0$$

$$x = 0 \text{ and } x = 3$$

Substitute the values for x into the linear equation to find values for y:

Let $x = 0$: $y = \dfrac{12 - 4(0)}{3}$

$y = \dfrac{12 - 0}{3}$

$y = \dfrac{12}{3} = 4$

$(0, 4)$

Let $x = 3$: $y = \dfrac{12 - 4(3)}{3}$

$y = \dfrac{12 - 12}{3}$

$y = \dfrac{0}{3} = 0$

$(3, 0)$

Therefore, the rocket enters and leaves the asteroid belt at the points $(0, 4)$ and $(3, 0)$.

(ii) Find the distance between the points when the rocket enters and leaves the asteroid belt.

$(0, 4) = (x_1, y_1)$

$(3, 0) = (x_2, y_2)$

Distance $= \sqrt{(x_2 - x_1)^2 + (y_2 - y_1)^2}$

$= \sqrt{(3 - 0)^2 + (0 - 4)^2}$

$= \sqrt{9 + 16}$

$= 5$ units

Distance through the asteroid belt $= 5 \times 75{,}000 \text{ km} = 375{,}000 \text{ km}$

$$\text{Time} = \frac{\text{Distance}}{\text{Speed}} = \frac{375{,}000}{58{,}000} = 6{\cdot}4655$$

Therefore, it takes the rocket 6·47 hours to pass through the asteroid belt.

5 Indices and Logarithms

Indices

In the expression a^m, a is the base and m is the index or exponent.

key point

a^m is read as 'a to the power of m'.

Rules of indices

(See the booklet of formulae and tables, indices and logarithms, page 21.)

Where $a, b \in \mathbb{R}$; $p, q \in \mathbb{Q}$; $a^p, a^q \in \mathbb{Q}$; $a, b \neq 0$:

- $a^p a^q = a^{p+q}$
- $\dfrac{a^p}{a^q} = a^{p-q}$
- $(a^p)^q = a^{pq}$
- $a^0 = 1$
- $a^{-p} = \dfrac{1}{a^p}$

- $a^{\frac{1}{q}} = \sqrt[q]{a} \quad q \in \mathbb{Z}, q \neq 0, a > 0$
- $a^{\frac{p}{q}} = \sqrt[q]{a^p} = (\sqrt[q]{a})^p \quad p, q \in \mathbb{Z}, q \neq 0, a > 0$
- $(ab)^p = a^p b^p$
- $\left(\dfrac{a}{b}\right)^p = \dfrac{a^p}{b^p}$

exam focus

The ability to work with negative and rational indices is an essential skill to have for differential calculus.

Example

Simplify each of the following.

(i) $125^{\frac{2}{3}}$

(ii) $32^{\frac{2}{5}} - 81^{\frac{1}{4}}$

(iii) $\dfrac{4^{-\frac{1}{2}}}{64^{\frac{2}{3}}}$

Solution

(i) $125^{\frac{2}{3}}$

$\sqrt[3]{125^2}$

$(\sqrt[3]{125})^2$

5^2

25

(ii) $32^{\frac{2}{5}} - 81^{\frac{1}{4}}$

$\sqrt[5]{32^2} - \sqrt[4]{81^1}$

$(\sqrt[5]{32})^2 - \sqrt[4]{81}$

$2^2 - 3$

$4 - 3$

1

(iii) $\dfrac{4^{-\frac{1}{2}}}{64^{\frac{2}{3}}}$

$4^{-\frac{1}{2}} \times 64^{-\frac{2}{3}}$

$\sqrt[2]{4^{-1}} \times \sqrt[3]{64^{-2}}$

$(\sqrt[2]{4})^{-1} \times (\sqrt[3]{64})^{-2}$

$2^{-1} \times 4^{-2}$

$2^{-1} \times (2^2)^{-2}$

$2^{-1} \times 2^{-4}$

2^{-5}

$\dfrac{1}{2^5}$

$\dfrac{1}{32}$

You could use your natural display calculator to verify these expressions. Make sure you are familiar with all the functions on your calculator.

Exponential equations

An equation involving the variable in the power is called an **exponential equation**. Exponential equations are solved with the following steps.

1. Write all the numbers as powers of the same number (usually a prime number).
2. Write both sides as one power of the same number, using the laws of indices.
3. Equate these powers and solve the equation.

Solve for x in each of the following equations.

(i) $27^{4+3x} = 243^{1+2x}$

(ii) $2^{x^2} = 8^{2x+9}$

Solution

(i) $27^{4+3x} = 243^{1+2x}$

$(3^3)^{4+3x} = (3^5)^{1+2x}$

$3^{12+9x} = 3^{5+10x}$

$12 + 9x = 5 + 10x$ (equate powers)

$7 = x$

(ii) $2^{x^2} = 8^{2x+9}$

$2^{x^2} = (2^3)^{2x+9}$

$2^{x^2} = 2^{6x+27}$

$x^2 = 6x + 27$ (equate powers)

$x^2 - 6x - 27 = 0$

$(x - 9)(x + 3) = 0$

$x = 9, \quad x = -3$

Solve for x and y: $2^x = 8^{y+1}$

$3^{x-9} = 9^y$

Solution

$2^x = 8^{y+1}$	$3^{x-9} = 9^y$
$2^x = (2^3)^{y+1}$	$3^{x-9} = (3^2)^y$
$2^x = 2^{3y+3}$	$3^{x-9} = 3^{2y}$
$x = 3y + 3$	$x - 9 = 2y$
$x - 3y = 3$ ①	$x - 2y = 9$ ②

Use simultaneous equations to solve:

$x - 3y = 3$ ① $(\times -1)$	Substitute $y = 6$ into ①.
$\underline{x - 2y = 9}$ ②	$x - 3y = 3$
$-x + 3y = -3$	$x - 3(6) = 3$
$\underline{x - 2y = 9}$	$x - 18 = 3$
$y = 6$	$x = 21$

$x = 21$ and $y = 6$

Solving by substitution

Often a substitution of the form $y = a^x$ is required to obtain an equation in y.

Example

Solve the equation $2^{2x+1} - 5(2^x) + 2 = 0$.

Solution

Let $y = 2^x$.

Write 2^{2x+1} in terms of y: 2^{2x+1}

$(2^{2x})(2^1)$

$(2^x)^2(2)$

$2y^2$

> It can be difficult to recognise when to use the method of solving by substitution. You should practise several of these types of questions.

Rewrite: $2^{2x+1} - 5(2^x) + 2 = 0$

as: $2y^2 - 5y + 2 = 0$

$(2y - 1)(y - 2) = 0$

$y = \dfrac{1}{2}$	$y = 2$
$y = 2^{-1}$	$y = 2$
$2^x = 2^{-1}$	$2^x = 2^1$
$x = -1$	$x = 1$

Solve the equation $3^{x+2} - 82 + 3^{2-x} = 0$.

Solution

Let $y = 3^x$.

Write in terms of y: 3^{x+2}

$(3^x)(3^2)$

$(3^x)(9)$

$9y$

3^{2-x}

$(3^2)(3^{-x})$

$(9)\left(\dfrac{1}{3^x}\right)$

$\dfrac{9}{y}$

Rewrite: $3^{x+2} - 82 + 3^{2-x} = 0$

as: $\quad 9y - 82 + \dfrac{9}{y} = 0$

$9y^2 - 82y + 9 = 0$ (multiply all terms by y)

$(9y - 1)(y - 9) = 0$

$y = \dfrac{1}{9}$ $y = 9$

$y = 9^{-1}$ $y = 3^2$

$3^x = (3^2)^{-1}$ $3^x = 3^2$

$3^x = 3^{-2}$ $3^x = 3^2$

$x = -2$ $x = 2$

key point

Remember that the question asked to solve for x, so once we have the values for y we must continue on and find x.

Logarithms

A **logarithm** ('log' for short) is an index (exponent).

Given any two positive numbers a and b, there exists a third number, c, such that $a = b^c$.

The number c is said to be the log of a to the base b.

The general rule of logs is:

$$a = b^c \Leftrightarrow \log_b a = c$$

Example

Evaluate the following:

(i) $\log_7 343$

(ii) $\log_{27} \dfrac{1}{3}$

Solution

(i) Let $\log_7 343 = x$.

$$343 = 7^x$$

$$7^3 = 7^x$$

$$3 = x$$

$$\therefore \log_7 343 = 3$$

(ii) Let $\log_{27} \dfrac{1}{3} = x$.

$$\dfrac{1}{3} = 27^x$$

$$3^{-1} = 3^{3x}$$

$$-1 = 3x$$

$$-\dfrac{1}{3} = x$$

$$\therefore \log_{27} \dfrac{1}{3} = -\dfrac{1}{3}$$

key point

You can use the $\boxed{\log_\square \square}$ button on your calculator to find the value of questions such as $\log_7 343$.

Natural logarithm

There are many constants in mathematics. The one you are probably most familiar with is π. Another constant is called e and it has a value of $2 \cdot 71828 \ldots$. A log to the base e ($\log_e x$) is called a natural log. Natural logs obey the same rules as logs to any other base. $\log_e x$ is written as $\ln x$.

Rules of logarithms

(See the booklet of tables and formula, indices and logarithms, page 21.)

Where $a, b \in \mathbb{R}$; $p, q \in \mathbb{Q}$; $a^p, a^q \in \mathbb{Q}$; $a, b \neq 0$:

○ $\log_a(xy) = \log_a x + \log_a y$ ○ $\log_a\left(\dfrac{1}{x}\right) = -\log_a x$

○ $\log_a\left(\dfrac{x}{y}\right) = \log_a x - \log_a y$ ○ $\log_a(a^x) = x$

○ $\log_a x^q = q \log_a x$ ○ $a^{\log_a x} = x$

○ $\log_a 1 = 0$ ○ $\log_b x = \dfrac{\log_a x}{\log_a b}$

It is vital that you are very familiar with the rules of logarithms. They can appear in questions involving algebra, functions, differential calculus and integration.

(2016 Q.4 (b))

Given $\log_a 2 = p$ and $\log_a 3 = q$, where $a > 0$, write each of the following in terms of p and q:

(i) $\log_a \dfrac{8}{3}$ **(ii)** $\log_a \dfrac{9a^2}{16}$

Solution

(i) $\log_a \dfrac{8}{3}$

$\log_a 8 - \log_a 3$ $\left(\log \dfrac{a}{b} = \log a - \log b\right)$

$\log_a 2^3 - \log_a 3$

$3\log_a 2 - \log_a 3$ $(\log a^n = n\log a)$

$3p - q$ $(\log_a 2 = p, \quad \log_a 3 = q)$

(ii) $\log_a \dfrac{9a^2}{16}$

$\log_a 9a^2 - \log_a 16$ $\left(\log \dfrac{a}{b} = \log a - \log b\right)$

$\log_a 9 + \log_a a^2 - \log_a 16$ $(\log ab = \log a + \log b)$

$\log_a 3^2 + \log_a a^2 - \log_a 2^4$

$2\log_a 3 + 2\log_a a - 4\log_a 2$ $(\log a^n = n\log a)$

$2\log_a 3 + 2(1) - 4\log_a 2$ $(\log_a a = 1)$

$2q + 2 - 4p$ $(\log_a 2 = p, \quad \log_a 3 = q)$

Logarithm equations

There are two methods for solving an equation involving logs.

Method 1

> Get a single log on **both** sides in the equation, equate the expressions and solve, i.e. write the equation in the form $\log_b x = \log_b y \Rightarrow x = y$ and solve.

Method 2

> Get a single log in the equation and then change from log form to index form, i.e. write the equation in the form $\log_b a = c \Rightarrow a = b^c$.

Make sure all logs have the same base. If necessary, use the **change of base** law:

$$\log_b x = \frac{\log_a x}{\log_a b}$$

Example

Solve the equation $\log_2(x + 6) - \log_2(x + 2) = 1$.

Solution

$\log_2(x + 6) - \log_2(x + 2) = 1$

$$\log_2\left(\frac{x + 6}{x + 2}\right) = 1 \qquad \left(\text{use rule: } \log_a\left(\frac{x}{y}\right) = \log_a x - \log_a y\right)$$

$$\frac{x + 6}{x + 2} = 2^1 \qquad (\text{use general rule: } \log_b a = c \Rightarrow a = b^c)$$

$$\frac{x + 6}{x + 2} = 2$$

$$x + 6 = 2(x + 2)$$

$$x + 6 = 2x + 4$$

$$2 = x$$

Example

Solve the equation $\log_e(x + 1) + \log_e(x - 1) = \log_e 3$.

Solution

$$\log_e(x + 1) + \log_e(x - 1) = \log_e 3$$
$$\log_e(x + 1)(x - 1) = \log_e 3 \qquad \text{(use rule: } \log_a(xy) = \log_a x + \log_a y\text{)}$$
$$\log_e(x^2 - 1) = \log_e 3$$
$$x^2 - 1 = 3$$
$$x^2 = 4$$
$$x = \pm 2$$

key point

Logs are defined only for positive numbers. Therefore, reject any solutions that give rise to a log of a negative number in the **original** equation.

Check solutions:

$x = 2$	$x = -2$
$\log_5(2 + 1) + \log_5(2 - 1) = \log_5 3$	$\log_5(-2 + 1) + \log_5(-2 - 1) = \log_5 3$
Results in log of positive numbers, so accept $x = 2$.	Results in log of negative numbers, so reject $x = -2$.

exam Q

Given that $p = \log_c x$, express $\log_c \sqrt{x} + \log_c(cx)$ in terms of p.

Solution

$$\log_c \sqrt{x} + \log_c(cx)$$
$$\log_c x^{\frac{1}{2}} + \log_c c + \log_c x \qquad \text{(use rules: } \log_a(xy) = \log_a x + \log_a y\text{)}$$
$$\frac{1}{2}\log_c x + 1 + \log_c x \qquad \text{(use rules: } \log_a x^q = q \log_a x \text{ and } \log_a(a^x) = x\text{)}$$
$$\frac{1}{2}p + 1 + p \qquad \text{(let } \log_c x = p\text{)}$$
$$\frac{3}{2}p + 1$$

Sound is a wave in the air; the loudness of the sound is related to the intensity of the wave.

Type of sound	Intensity
Whisper	100
Background noise in a quiet rural area	1,000
Normal conversation	1,000,000
Rock concert	1,000,000,000,000

Sound volume is usually not measured in intensity, but in loudness, which is given by the formula

$$L = 10 \log_{10} I$$

where L is the loudness (measured in decibels, dB), and I is the intensity.

(i) What is the loudness, in decibels, of a whisper?

(ii) The quietest sound a human being can hear is intensity 1.
What is the loudness of that sound?

(iii) If sound A is 30 decibels higher than sound B, how much more intense is it?

Solution

(i) Whisper, $I = 100$

$$L = 10 \log_{10} I$$
$$L_{whisper} = 10 \log_{10} (100)$$
$$L_{whisper} = 10(2)$$
$$L_{whisper} = 20 \ dB$$

(ii) Quietest sound, $I = 1$

$$L = 10 \log_{10} I$$
$$L_{quietest\ sound} = 10 \log_{10} (1)$$
$$L_{quietest\ sound} = 10(0)$$
$$L_{quietest\ sound} = 0 \ dB$$

(iii) $L_A = 10 \log_{10} I_A$

$$L_B = 10 \log_{10} I_B$$
$$L_A - L_B = 30$$
$$10 \log_{10} I_A - 10 \log_{10} I_B = 30 \quad (\div 10)$$
$$\log_{10} I_A - \log_{10} I_B = 3$$
$$\log_{10} \frac{I_A}{I_B} = 3 \quad \left(\text{use rule: } \log_a\left(\frac{x}{y}\right) = \log_a x - \log_a y \right)$$
$$\frac{I_A}{I_B} = 10^3$$
$$\frac{I_A}{I_B} = 1,000$$
$$I_A = 1,000(I_B)$$

Thus, the intensity of source A is 1,000 times the intensity of source B.

(2013 Q.3)

Scientists can estimate the age of certain ancient items by measuring the proportion of carbon-14, relative to the total carbon content in the item. The formula used is $Q = e^{-\frac{0.693t}{5730}}$, where Q is the proportion of carbon-14 remaining and t is the age, in years, of the item.

(a) An item is 2,000 years old. Use the formula to find the proportion of carbon-14 in the item.

(b) The proportion of carbon-14 in an item found at Lough Boora, County Offaly, was 0·3402. Estimate, correct to two significant figures, the age of the item.

Solution

(a) Find Q when $t = 2000$:

$Q = e^{-\frac{0.693t}{5730}}$ $\qquad$ Let $t = 2000$

$Q = e^{-\frac{0.693(2000)}{5730}}$

$Q = e^{-\frac{1386}{5730}}$

$Q = 0.7851$

Therefore 0·7851 of the carbon-14 is remaining.

(b) Find t when $Q = 0.3402$:

$$Q = e^{-\frac{0.693t}{5730}} \qquad\qquad \text{Let } Q = 0.3402$$

$$0.3402 = e^{-\frac{0.693t}{5730}}$$

$$\ln 0.3402 = \ln e^{-\frac{0.693t}{5730}} \qquad \text{(natural log both sides)}$$

$$\ln 0.3402 = -\frac{0.693t}{5730}\ln e \qquad \text{(use rule: } \log_a x^q = q \log_a x\text{)}$$

$$\ln 0.3402 = -\frac{0.693t}{5730} \qquad \text{(since ln e = 1)}$$

$$5730(\ln 0.3402) = -0.693t \qquad \text{(multiply both sides by 5730)}$$

$$\frac{5730(\ln 0.3402)}{-0.693} = t \qquad \text{(divide both sides by } -0.693\text{)}$$

$$8915.165 = t$$

$$8,900 \text{ years} = t \qquad \text{(to two significant figures)}$$

Solve the simultaneous equations: $\log_3 x + \log_3 y = 2$
$\log_3 (2y - 3) - 2\log_9 x = 1$

Solution

Use rules of logs:

$$\log_3 x + \log_3 y = 2$$

$$\log_3 xy = 2 \qquad \text{(rule: } \log_a (xy) = \log_a x + \log_a y\text{)}$$
$$xy = 3^2$$
$$xy = 9 \qquad \text{①}$$

$$\log_3 (2y - 3) - 2\log_9 x = 1$$

$$\log_3 (2y - 3) - 2\left(\frac{\log_3 x}{\log_3 9}\right) = 1 \qquad \left(\text{rule: } \log_b x = \frac{\log_a x}{\log_a b}\right)$$

$$\log_3 (2y - 3) - 2\left(\frac{\log_3 x}{2}\right) = 1 \qquad \text{(use calculator to find } \log_3 9\text{)}$$

$$\log_3 (2y - 3) - \log_3 x = 1$$

$$\log_3\left(\frac{2y - 3}{x}\right) = 1 \qquad \left(\text{rule: } \log_a \left(\frac{x}{y}\right) = \log_a x - \log_a y\right)$$

$$\frac{2y - 3}{x} = 3^1 \qquad \text{(rule: } \log_b a = c \implies a = b^c\text{)}$$

$$\frac{2y - 3}{x} = 3$$

$$2y - 3 = 3x \qquad \text{②}$$

Solve the equations:

Linear equation ②

$$2y - 3 = 3x$$
$$\frac{2y - 3}{3} = x$$

Quadratic equation ①

$$xy = 9$$
$$\left(\frac{2y - 3}{3}\right)y = 9 \qquad (\times 3)$$
$$(2y - 3)y = 27$$
$$2y^2 - 3y = 27$$
$$2y^2 - 3y - 27 = 0$$
$$(2y - 9)(y + 3) = 0$$
$$2y - 9 = 0 \quad y + 3 = 0$$
$$y = \frac{9}{2}, \quad y = -3$$

Substitute $y = \dfrac{9}{2}$

$$2y - 3 = 3x$$
$$2\left(\frac{9}{2}\right) - 3 = 3x$$
$$9 - 3 = 3x$$
$$6 = 3x$$
$$2 = x$$

$$x = 2, \quad y = \frac{9}{2}$$

Answer: $\left(2, \dfrac{9}{2}\right)$

Reject $y = -3$, as it results in a log of negative numbers.

(2017 Q.7 (a)–(e))

Sometimes it is possible to predict the future population in a city using a function.

The population in Sapphire City, over time, can be predicted using the following function:

$$p(t) = Se^{0 \cdot 1t} \times 10^6$$

The population in Avalon, over time, can be predicted using the following function:

$$q(t) = 3 \cdot 9e^{kt} \times 10^6$$

In the functions above, t is time, in years; $t = 0$ is the beginning of 2010; and both S and k are constants.

(a) The population in Sapphire City at the beginning of 2010 is 1,100,000 people. Find the value of S.

(b) Find the predicted population in Sapphire City at the beginning of 2015.

(c) Find the predicted change in the population in Sapphire City during 2015.

(d) The predicted population in Avalon at the beginning of 2011 is 3,709,795 people. Write down and solve an equation in k to show that $k = -0 \cdot 05$, correct to 2 decimal places.

(e) Find the year during which the populations in both cities will be equal.

Solution

(a) At the beginning of 2010, $t = 0$:

$$p(t) = Se^{0 \cdot 1t} \times 10^6$$

$$p(0) = Se^{0 \cdot 1(0)} \times 10^6$$

$$p(0) = Se^0 \times 10^6$$

$$p(0) = S(1) \times 10^6 \qquad\qquad [p(0) = 1,100,000]$$

$$1100000 = S \times 10^6$$

$$\frac{1100000}{10^6} = S$$

$$1 \cdot 1 = S$$

(b) At the beginning of 2015, $t = 5$:

$$p(t) = 1 \cdot 1e^{0 \cdot 1t} \times 10^6$$

$$p(5) = 1 \cdot 1e^{0 \cdot 1(5)} \times 10^6$$

$$p(5) = 1 \cdot 1e^{0 \cdot 5} \times 10^6$$

$$p(5) = 1 \cdot 813593 \times 10^6$$

Therefore, the population at the beginning of 2015 is 1,813,593.

(c) At the beginning of 2016, $t = 6$:

$p(t) = 1 \cdot 1 e^{0 \cdot 1 t} \times 10^6$

$p(6) = 1 \cdot 1 e^{0 \cdot 1(6)} \times 10^6$

$p(6) = 1 \cdot 1 e^{0 \cdot 6} \times 10^6$

$p(6) = 2 \cdot 00433068 \times 10^6$

$p(6) = 2004330 \cdot 68$

Therefore, the population at the beginning of 2016 is 2,004,330.

The change in population during 2015 $= 2004330 - 1813593$

$= 190{,}737$ people

(d) At the beginning of 2011, $t = 1$:

$$q(t) = 3 \cdot 9 e^{kt} \times 10^6$$

$$q(1) = 3 \cdot 9 e^{k(1)} \times 10^6$$

$$q(1) = 3 \cdot 9 e^{k} \times 10^6 \qquad [q(1) = 3{,}709{,}795]$$

$$3709795 = 3 \cdot 9 e^{k} \times 10^6$$

$$\frac{3709795}{3 \cdot 9 \times 10^6} = e^k$$

$$0 \cdot 951229487 = e^k$$

$$\ln(0 \cdot 951229487) = k$$

$$-0 \cdot 0499999 = k$$

$$-0 \cdot 05 = k$$

(e) When the populations are equal:

$$p(t) = q(t)$$

$$1 \cdot 1 e^{0 \cdot 1 t} \times 10^6 = 3 \cdot 9 e^{-0 \cdot 05 t} \times 10^6$$

$$1 \cdot 1 e^{0 \cdot 1 t} = 3 \cdot 9 e^{-0 \cdot 05 t}$$

$$1 \cdot 1 e^{0 \cdot 1 t} = \frac{3 \cdot 9}{e^{0 \cdot 05 t}}$$

$$1 \cdot 1 (e^{0 \cdot 1 t})(e^{0 \cdot 05 t}) = 3 \cdot 9$$

$$e^{0 \cdot 1 t + 0 \cdot 05 t} = \frac{3 \cdot 9}{1 \cdot 1}$$

$$e^{0 \cdot 15 t} = \frac{3 \cdot 9}{1 \cdot 1}$$

$$0 \cdot 15 t = \ln\left(\frac{3 \cdot 9}{1 \cdot 1}\right)$$

$$t = \frac{\ln\left(\dfrac{3 \cdot 9}{1 \cdot 1}\right)}{0 \cdot 15}$$

$$t = 8 \cdot 43778 \dots$$

Therefore, during 2018, the populations will be equal.

6 Functions and Graphing Functions

aims

☐ To learn what a function is and become familiar with the notation associated with functions

☐ To be able to form composite functions

☐ To be able to graph functions of various forms and use the graphs to find the solution to given questions

☐ To be able to recognise injective, surjective and bijective functions

☐ To learn how to find the inverse of a function

☐ To be able to graph the inverse of a function

Introduction

A function is a rule that changes input into output. A relation is any set of ordered pairs. A function is defined as a set of ordered pairs (a relation) in which no two ordered pairs have the same first element.

> **key point**
>
> A function must give exactly one unique output for each input.
> A **function** is also called a **mapping** or simply a **map**.

The set of input numbers is called the **domain**. The set of output numbers is called the **range**.

The set of **all possible outputs** is called the **codomain**. In general, the range is a subset of the codomain. However, sometimes the range and the codomain are the same.

Consider the function f shown:
$f = \{(1, a), (2, b), (3, d), (4, d)\}$ from set X to set Y.

Domain: The set of elements from which the arrows leave: $\{1, 2, 3, 4\}$.

Range: The set of elements where the arrows arrive: $\{a, b, d\}$.

Codomain: The **possible** set of elements into which the arrows go: $\{a, b, c, d, e\}$.

Consider the function:

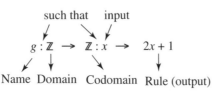

A domain or range described as:

$$[p, q) \text{ means } \{p \leq x < q\}$$

That is, the square bracket means p is included. The rounded bracket means q is not included.

exam focus

(see booklet of formulae and tables, page 23)
It is vital that you are familiar with the basic **number systems**:
$\mathbb{N} = \{1, 2, 3, \ldots\}$, the set of natural numbers.
$\mathbb{Z} = \{\ldots -2, -1, 0, 1, 2, \ldots\}$, the set of integers.
$\mathbb{Q} = \left\{\text{fractions, } \dfrac{p}{q}, p, q \in \mathbb{Z}, q \neq 0\right\}$, the set of rational numbers.

$\mathbb{R}\backslash\mathbb{Q}$ = the set of irrational numbers, e.g. $\sqrt{3}$, π, etc.

Composite functions

When one function is followed by another function, the result is a **composite** function.

Applying function g after applying function f is written in three different ways:

  1. $g \circ f(x)$ **2.** $gf(x)$ **3.** $g[f(x)]$

All are pronounced 'g after f' and mean 'do f followed by g'.

Example

$f(x) = x^2 + 3$ and $g(x) = 2x - 1$, where $x \in \mathbb{R}$.

(i) Evaluate $fg(3)$.

(ii) Evaluate $g[f(-2)]$.

(iii) Find the values for x for which $f \circ g(x) = 12$.

(iv) Find $f^2(x)$ in terms of x.

Note: $f^2(x) = ff(x)$

Solution

(i) $fg(3) = f(2(3) - 1)$
$= f(6 - 1)$
$= f(5)$
$= (5)^2 + 3$
$= 25 + 3$
$= 28$

(ii) $g[f(-2)] = g[(-2)^2 + 3]$
$= g[4 + 3]$
$= g[7]$
$= 2(7) - 1$
$= 14 - 1$
$= 13$

(iii) $f \circ g(x) = 12$
$f(2x - 1) = 12$
$(2x - 1)^2 + 3 = 12$
$4x^2 - 4x + 1 + 3 = 12$
$4x^2 - 4x + 4 - 12 = 0$
$4x^2 - 4x - 8 = 0$
$x^2 - x - 2 = 0$
$(x + 1)(x - 2) = 0$
$x = -1 \quad \text{or} \quad x = 2$

(iv) $f^2(x) = f f(x)$
$= f(x^2 + 3)$
$= (x^2 + 3)^2 + 3$
$= x^4 + 6x^2 + 9 + 3$
$= x^4 + 6x^2 + 12$

The number of people who visit a local circus can be modelled by $A(d) = 3500d - 400d^2 - 1000$, where $A(d)$ represents the attendance at the circus d days after it opens. The profit made by the circus can be modelled by $P(a) = 2a - 2500$, where $P(a)$ represents the profit in euros for the circus on a day when a people attend.

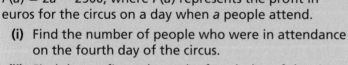

(i) Find the number of people who were in attendance on the fourth day of the circus.

(ii) Find the profit made on the fourth day of the circus.

(iii) Use these functions to find a new function that will give the profit made by the circus d days after the circus opens.

(iv) How much profit does the circus make on the third day of the circus?

Solution

(i) Find the value of $A(d)$ when $d = 4$:
$$A(4) = 3500(4) - 400(4)^2 - 1{,}000$$
$$= 14000 - 6400 - 1{,}000$$
$$= 6600$$
Therefore, 6,600 people attended the circus on the fourth day.

(ii) Find the value of $P(a)$ when $a = 6600$:
$$P(6600) = 2(6600) - 2500$$
$$= 13200 - 2500$$
$$= 10700$$
Therefore, profit on day 4 was €10,700.

(iii) To find the profit in terms of d, we need to find $P \circ A(d)$.

$$P(a) = 2a - 2500$$
$$P(A(d)) = 2(A(d)) - 2500$$
$$= 2(3500d - 400d^2 - 1000) - 2500$$
$$= 7000d - 800d^2 - 2000 - 2500$$
$$= 7000d - 800d^2 - 4500$$

(iv) To find the profit on the third day, find the value of $P \circ A(d)$ when $d = 3$.

$$P(A(3)) = 7000(3) - 800(3)^2 - 4500$$
$$= 21000 - 7200 - 4500$$
$$= 9300$$

Therefore, the profit on day 3 was €9,300.

Graphing functions

You must be able to graph a given function and recognise the graphs of certain functions. To graph a function, find points which satisfy the function by substituting values in for x (inputs) and finding the corresponding y values (outputs). Plot these points and join them up to obtain the graph of the function.

key point

To better understand the graphs of functions, you should practise graphing functions on a graphing calculator or graphing software, such as Geogebra (free to download from www.geogebra.org).

To recognise if a graph represents a function, use the vertical line test.

VERTICAL LINE TEST

If any vertical line (the red line in the picture) cuts the graph at only one point, then the graph represents a function.

If any vertical line (the red line in the picture) cuts the graph at more than one point, then the graph does **not** represent a function.

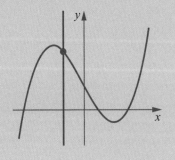

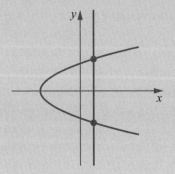

Example

Use the vertical line test to determine if each of the following is the graph of a function where $x \in \mathbb{R}$.

(i)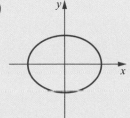

(ii)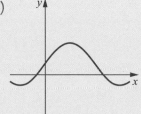

(iii)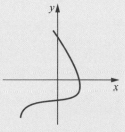

Solution

  (i) A vertical line would cut the graph twice, therefore it is not a function.

 (ii) A vertical line would only cut the graph once, therefore it is a function.

(iii) A vertical line would cut the graph more than once in some places, therefore it is not a function.

Continuous functions

A function is continuous when its graph is a single unbroken curve. To recognise a function which is not continuous (discontinuous), look out for holes, jumps or vertical asymptotes (where the function heads up or down towards infinity). More on this in Differential Calculus III.

The graph of a continuous function can be drawn without lifting your pen off the page.

Example

State whether the following functions are continuous or discontinuous. Give a reason for your answer.

Solution

(i)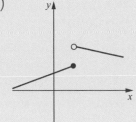

(ii)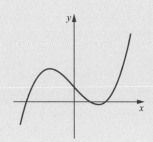

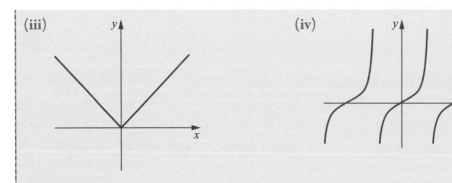

(iii)

(iv)

Solution

  (i) Discontinuous, because there is a hole in the graph and the graph jumps.

 (ii) Continuous, because the graph is a single unbroken curve.

(iii) Continuous, because the graph is a single unbroken curve.

(iv) Discontinuous, because there is a gap in the graph.

If a function $f(x)$ is continuous at a particular input value, $x = a$, then $\lim\limits_{x \to a} f(x) = f(a)$.

The converse is also true, i.e. if a function has a limit at a value, it is continuous at that value.

Linear functions

A linear function is usually given by $f: x \to ax + b$, where $a, b \in \mathbb{Q}, x \in \mathbb{R}$. To graph a linear function, you need two points or a point and the slope of the line.

If the coefficient of the x part is positive ($a > 0$), the graph is **increasing**.	If the coefficient of the x part is zero ($a = 0$), the graph is **horizontal**.	If the coefficient of the x part is negative ($a < 0$), the graph is **decreasing**.

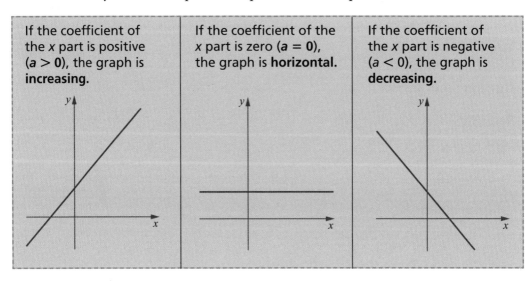

Graphing linear functions is covered extensively under the topic of coordinate geometry of the line, which can be found in the Less Stress More Success Leaving Certificate Higher Level Paper 2 book.

Quadratic functions

A quadratic function is usually given by $f: x \rightarrow ax^2 + bx + c$, where $a, b, c \in \mathbb{Q}, x \in \mathbb{R}$ and $a \neq 0$. Because of its shape, quite a few points are needed to accurately graph a quadratic function.

If the coefficient of the x^2 part is positive $(a > 0)$, the graph has a $\cup$ **shape**.	If the coefficient of the x^2 part is negative $(a > 0)$, the graph has a $\cap$ **shape**.
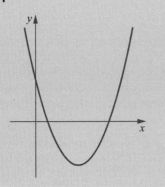	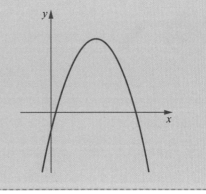

The nature of the roots of a quadratic equation

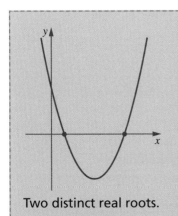	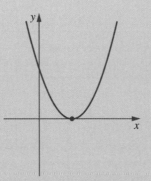	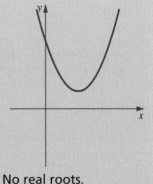
Two distinct real roots. $b^2 - 4ac > 0$	Two real roots, both of which are equal. $b^2 - 4ac = 0$	No real roots. $b^2 - 4ac < 0$

Note: $b^2 - 4ac$ is known as the discriminant.

Completing the square

Completing the square means taking any quadratic polynomial in the form $px^2 + qx + r$ and expressing it in the form $p(x + a)^2 + b$ for some a and b. The procedure for how to complete the square was covered in Chapter 2: Quadratic and Cubic Equations.

Once a quadratic equation is in its square form, you can easily find the minimum or maximum point on the curve, as:

- The minimum value of an expression in the form $p(x + a)^2 + b$ is b. This occurs when $x + a = 0 (x = -a)$.
- The maximum value of an expression in the form $b - p(x + a)^2$ is b. This occurs when $x + a = 0 (x = -a)$.

Maximum and minimum points can also be found by using differential calculus.

Example

(i) Express $x^2 - 8x - 3 = 0$ in the form $(x - p)^2 + q = 0$.

(ii) Hence, find the coordinates of the minimum point on the graph.

Solution

(i) Half of the x term is -4. Add and subtract $(-4)^2 = 16$ to the equation.

$$x^2 - 8x + 16 - 16 - 3 = 0$$
$$x^2 - 8x + 16 - 19 = 0$$
$$(x - 4)(x - 4) - 19 = 0$$
$$(x - 4)^2 - 19 = 0$$

(ii) The minimum point on the graph occurs when the part in brackets equals zero:

$$x - 4 = 0$$
$$x = 4$$

The minimum value of the graph is the number on its own:

Minimum value $= -19$

Putting these two pieces of information together tells us that the minimum point on the graph is at $(4, -19)$.

(2017 Q.1)

(a) Write the function $f(x) = 2x^2 - 7x - 10$, where $x \in \mathbb{R}$, in the form $a(x + h)^2 + k$, where a, h, and $k \in \mathbb{Q}$

(b) Hence, write the minimum point of f.

(c) **(i)** Explain why f must have two real roots.

(ii) Write the roots of $f(x) = 0$ in the form $p \pm \sqrt{q}$, where p and $q \in \mathbb{Q}$.

Solution

(a) Using the method of undetermined coefficients:

$$2x^2 - 7x - 10 = a(x + h)^2 + k$$
$$2x^2 - 7x - 10 = a(x^2 + 2xh + h^2) + k$$
$$2x^2 - 7x - 10 = ax^2 + 2axh + ah^2 + k$$

> **key point**
>
> The 'completing the square' method could also have been used to solve part (a).

Compare like terms:

$$2x^2 - 7x - 10 = ax^2 + 2axh + ah^2 + k$$

x^2 terms:	x terms:	Constants:
$2x^2 = ax^2$	$-7x = 2axh$	$-10 = ah^2 + k \quad \left(a = 2, h = -\dfrac{7}{4}\right)$
$2 = a$	$-7 = 2ah \quad (a = 2)$	$-10 = (2)\left(-\dfrac{7}{4}\right)^2 + k$
	$-7 = 2(2)h$	$-10 = (2)\left(\dfrac{49}{16}\right) + k$
	$-7 = 4h$	$-10 = \dfrac{49}{8} + k$
	$-\dfrac{7}{4} = h$	$-10 - \dfrac{49}{8} = k$
		$-\dfrac{129}{8} = k$

Therefore, $2x^2 - 7x - 10 = 2\left(x - \dfrac{7}{4}\right)^2 - \dfrac{129}{8}$

(b)
$$f(x) = 2\left(x - \frac{7}{4}\right)^2 - \frac{129}{8}$$

The minimum point of f occurs when the part in brackets equals zero:

Minimum value is the final value in the square form:

> **key point**
>
> The word 'hence' in part (b) means that calculus cannot be use to solve this part.

$$x - \frac{7}{4} = 0$$

$$f(x) = 2\left(x - \frac{7}{4}\right)^2 - \frac{129}{8}$$

$$x = \frac{7}{4}$$

minimum value $= -\dfrac{129}{8}$

Therefore, minimum point is: $\left(\dfrac{7}{4}, -\dfrac{129}{8}\right)$

(c) (i) *f* must have two real roots, as it is a U-shape quadratic graph and has its minimum point, $\left(\dfrac{7}{4}, -\dfrac{129}{8}\right)$, below the *x*-axis.

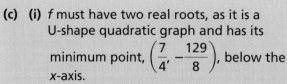

Therefore, it must cross the *x*-axis twice and so has two real roots.

Alternatively, we could have shown that

$$b^2 - 4ac \geq 0$$
$$(-7)^2 - 4(2)(-10) \geq 0$$
$$49 + 89 \geq 0$$
$$138 \geq 0$$

Therefore, the roots of the function are real.

(ii) We can use the quadratic formula to solve for *x*, but since the function is already in square form, we can solve it as follows:

$$f(x) = 2\left(x - \frac{7}{4}\right)^2 - \frac{129}{8}$$

$$0 = 2\left(x - \frac{7}{4}\right)^2 - \frac{129}{8}$$

$$\frac{129}{8} = 2\left(x - \frac{7}{4}\right)^2$$

$$\frac{129}{16} = \left(x - \frac{7}{4}\right)^2$$

$$\pm\sqrt{\frac{129}{16}} = x - \frac{7}{4}$$

$$\pm\frac{\sqrt{129}}{4} = x - \frac{7}{4}$$

$$\frac{7}{4} \pm \frac{\sqrt{129}}{4} = x$$

The graph shows two functions.
The equations of these functions are:

Line: $3x - 5y + 12 = 0$
Curve: $y = 2x^2 + 3x - 2$

(i) Use the graph to estimate the points where the line intersects the curve.

(ii) Solve the equations simultaneously to find the two points of intersection.

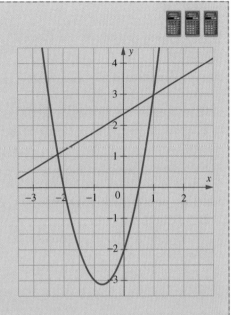

Solution

(i) Estimated points of intersection:
(1, 3) and (−2·3, 1·1).

(ii) Rearrange the linear equation to get y on its own:

$$3x - 5y + 12 = 0$$
$$3x + 12 = 5y$$
$$\frac{3x + 12}{5} = y$$

Linear equation = Quadratic equation

$$y = y$$

$$\frac{3x + 12}{5} = 2x^2 + 3x - 2 \qquad (\times 5)$$

$$3x + 12 = 5(2x^2 + 3x - 2)$$

$$3x + 12 = 10x^2 + 15x - 10$$

$$0 = 10x^2 + 12x - 22 \qquad (\div 2)$$

$$0 = 5x^2 + 6x - 11$$

$$0 = (5x + 11)(x - 1)$$

$5x + 11 = 0$	$x - 1 = 0$
$5x = -11$	$x = 1$
$x = -\dfrac{11}{5}$	
$x = -2\cdot2$	

Substitute the values for x into the linear equation to find values for y:

$x = -2\cdot2$

$$\frac{3x + 12}{5} = y$$

$$\frac{3(-2\cdot2) + 12}{5} = y$$

$$\frac{-6\cdot6 + 12}{5} = y$$

$$\frac{5\cdot4}{5} = y$$

$$1\cdot08 = y$$

$x = 1$

$$\frac{3x + 12}{5} = y$$

$$\frac{3(1) + 12}{5} = y$$

$$\frac{3 + 12}{5} = y$$

$$\frac{15}{5} = y$$

$$3 = y$$

Points of intersection:

(−2·2, 1·08)   and   (1, 3)

Transforming graphs in the vertical direction

Adding a constant to a function moves the graph of the function vertically **upwards** by that constant.

In the diagram, $f(x) + 2$ is two units above $f(x)$.

Subtracting a constant from a function moves the graph of the function vertically **downwards** by that constant.

In the diagram, $f(x) - 1$ is one unit below $f(x)$.

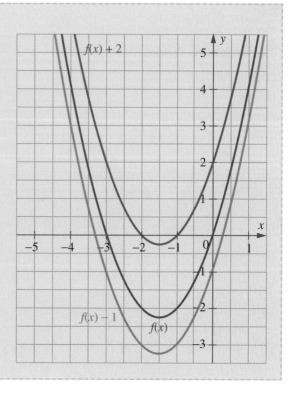

Cubic functions

A cubic function is usually given by $f : x \rightarrow ax^3 + bx^2 + cx + d$, where $a, b, c, d \in \mathbb{Z}$, $x \in \mathbb{R}$ and $a \neq 0$. Because of its shape, quite a few points are needed to accurately graph a cubic function.

If the coefficient of the x^3 part is positive ($a > 0$), the graph **starts by increasing**.	If the coefficient of the x^3 part is negative ($a < 0$), the graph **starts by decreasing**.
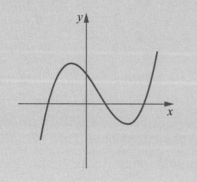	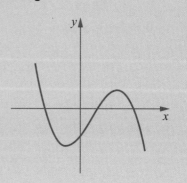

The nature of the roots of a cubic equation

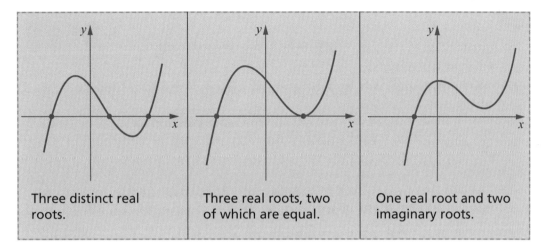

| Three distinct real roots. | Three real roots, two of which are equal. | One real root and two imaginary roots. |

key point

Two cubic equations with the same roots

Consider the polynomials:

$f(x) = x^3 - 2x^2 - x + 2$

$g(x) = 2x^3 - 4x^2 - 2x + 4$

Factorising each function gives:

$f(x) = (x + 1)(x - 1)(x - 2)$

$g(x) = 2(x + 1)(x - 1)(x - 2)$

The two functions have the same roots: -1, 1 and 2. Thus, they both cross the x-axis at these points.

However, the $g(x)$ function also has an integer factor 2, which causes the graph to be double the height of the $f(x)$ graph.

The integer factor acts as an amplification factor.

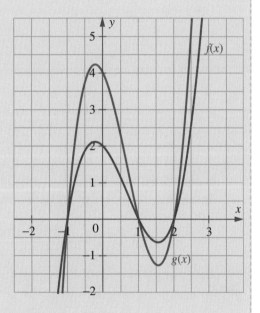

The function $f(x) = x^3 - 2x^2 - 5x + 6$ has three integer roots.

(i)   Find the three roots.

(ii) The function $g(x) = (x + 1)^3 - 2(x + 1)^2 - 5(x + 1) + 6$. Find the three roots of the function $g(x)$.

(iii) Sketch the graphs of $f(x)$ and $g(x)$ on the same axes and scale.

(iv) Comment on the relationship between $f(x)$ and $g(x)$.

Solution

(i) Use trial and error to find an integer root. The root will be a factor of 6. We need to try only those values which are factors of 6, i.e. ±1, ±2, ±3, ±6.

$f(1) = (1)^3 - 2(1)^2 - 5(1) + 6 = 1 - 2 - 5 + 6 = 0$

$\therefore x = 1$ is a root and so $(x - 1)$ is a factor.

Divide $(x^3 - 2x^2 - 5x + 6)$ by $(x - 1)$.

$$
\begin{array}{r}
x^2 - x - 6 \\
x - 1 \overline{\smash{\big)}\; x^3 - 2x^2 - 5x + 6} \\
\underline{-\, x^3 \pm x^2} \\
-x^2 - 5x \\
\underline{\pm\, x^2 \mp x} \\
-6x + 6 \\
\underline{\pm\, 6x \mp 6} \\
0
\end{array}
$$

Solve:

$x^2 - x - 6 = 0$

$(x - 3)(x + 2) = 0$

$x = 3$ and $x = -2$

Thus, the roots of $f(x)$ are -2, 1 and 3.

(ii) The $g(x)$ function is the same as the $f(x)$ function, but the x term has been replaced with $(x + 1)$.

Therefore, the roots of $f(x)$ are now equal to $(x + 1)$. To get the roots for the $g(x)$ function:

$\quad x + 1 = -2 \qquad\quad x + 1 = 1 \qquad\quad x + 1 = 3$

$\quad\quad\quad x = -3 \qquad\qquad\quad x = 0 \qquad\qquad\quad x = 2$

Roots of $g(x) = -3$, 0, 2

(iii) To graph the functions:

1. Since both start with a positive x^3 term, both graphs begin by increasing (rising).

2. The graphs cross the x-axis at their roots.

3. To better draw the graphs, we need to find where the graphs cross the y-axis.

At the y-axis, $x = 0$: $f(0) = (0)^3 - 2(0)^2 - 5(0) + 6$

$\qquad\qquad\qquad\qquad\qquad = 0 - 0 - 0 + 6$

$\qquad\qquad\qquad\qquad\qquad = 6 \qquad\qquad$ Thus, $f(x)$ crosses the y-axis at $(0, 6)$.

At the y-axis, $x = 0 : g(0) = (0 + 1)^3 - 2(0 + 1)^2 - 5(0 + 1) + 6$

$$= (1)^3 - 2(1)^2 - 5(1) + 6$$
$$= 1 - 2 - 5 + 6$$
$$= 0 \qquad \text{Thus, } g(x) \text{ crosses the } y\text{-axis at } (0, 0).$$

Combining all of this information, sketch the graphs as follows.

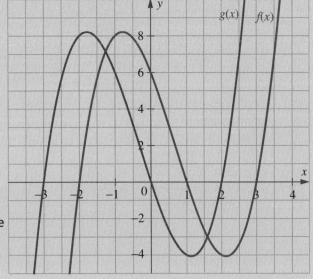

(iv) The $g(x)$ graph is the same as the $f(x)$ graph, but has been shifted one unit to the left. This means that adding one unit to x in the $f(x)$ function causes the graph to shift one unit to the left.

key point

Transforming graphs in the horizontal direction

Adding a constant to the x-part of a function moves the graph of the function horizontally to the **left** by that constant. In the diagram, $f(x + 2)$ is two units to the left of $f(x)$.

Subtracting a constant from the x-part of a function moves the graph of the function horizontally to the **right** by that constant. In the diagram, $f(x - 1)$ is one unit to the right of $f(x)$.

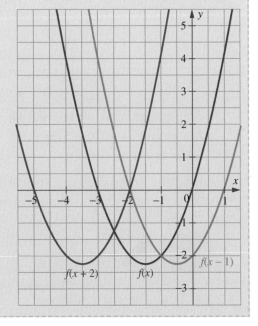

(2014 Q.1)

(a) The graph of a cubic function $f(x)$ cuts the x-axis at $x = -3$, $x = -1$ and $x = 2$, and the y-axis at $(0, -6)$, as shown. Verify that $f(x)$ can be written as

$$f(x) = x^3 + 2x^2 - 5x - 6$$

(b) (i) The graph of the function $g(x) = -2x - 6$ intersects the graph of the function $f(x)$.

Let $f(x) = g(x)$ and solve the resulting equation to find the coordinates of the points where the graphs of $f(x)$ and $g(x)$ intersect.

(ii) Draw the graph of the function $g(x) = -2x - 6$ on the diagram above.

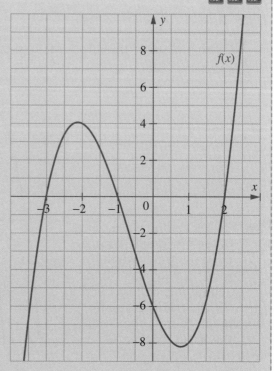

Solution

(a) Roots of the function are: $x = -3$ $x = -1$ $x = 2$

Factors of the function are: $(x + 3)$ $(x + 1)$ and $(x - 2)$

$$f(x) = a(x + 3)(x + 1)(x - 2)$$
$$f(x) = a(x + 3)(x^2 - 2x + 1x - 2)$$
$$f(x) = a(x + 3)(x^2 - x - 2)$$
$$f(x) = a(x^3 - x^2 - 2x + 3x^2 - 3x - 6)$$
$$f(x) = a(x^3 + 2x^2 - 5x - 6)$$

To find a, substitute in the point $(0, -6)$:

$$f(0) = a((0)^3 + 2(0)^2 - 5(0) - 6)$$
$$-6 = a(-6)$$
$$1 = a$$
$$\therefore f(x) = x^3 + 2x^2 - 5x - 6$$

This part (a) was worth 15 marks. 10 of those marks were awarded for writing $(x + 3)(x + 1)(x - 2)$.

(b) (i)

$$f(x) = g(x)$$
$$x^3 + 2x^2 - 5x - 6 = -2x - 6$$
$$x^3 + 2x^2 - 3x = 0$$
$$x(x^2 + 2x - 3) = 0$$
$$x(x + 3)(x - 1) = 0$$

$x = 0$	$x + 3 = 0$	$x - 1 = 0$
$x = 0$	$x = -3$	$x = 1$
$y = -2x - 6$	$y = -2x - 6$	$y = -2x - 6$
$y = -2(0) - 6$	$y = -2(-3) - 6$	$y = -2(1) - 6$
$y = -6$	$y = 6 - 6$	$y = -2 - 6$
	$y = 0$	$y = -8$
$(0, -6)$	$(-3, 0)$	$(1, -8)$

(ii) $g(x)$ intersects $f(x)$ at the points $(0, -6)$, $(-3, 0)$ and $(1, -8)$.

Plotting these on the graph gives:

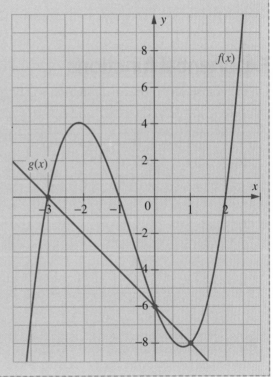

Graphing polynomials of higher powers

As the highest power increases, the graph may have more turning points.

The *maximum* number of turning points is one fewer than the highest power.

A function in the form
$$f(x) = ax^4 + bx^3 + cx^2 + dx + e$$
has at most **three** turning points:

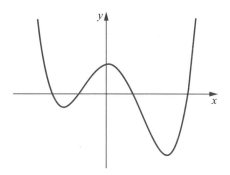

A function in the form
$$f(x) = ax^5 + bx^4 + cx^3 + dx^2 + ex + f$$
has at most **four** turning points:

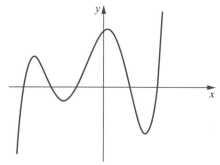

Exponential functions

On our course, an exponential function will be given in the form $f : x \longrightarrow ab^x$, where a is the y-intercept, $x \in \mathbb{R}$ and $b \in \mathbb{R}^+$ and $b > 0$ (b must be a positive real number) and $a \neq 0$.

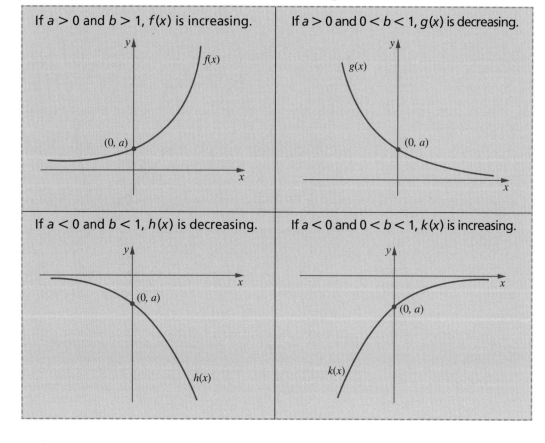

If $a > 0$ and $b > 1$, $f(x)$ is increasing.

If $a > 0$ and $0 < b < 1$, $g(x)$ is decreasing.

If $a < 0$ and $b < 1$, $h(x)$ is decreasing.

If $a < 0$ and $0 < b < 1$, $k(x)$ is increasing.

key point

The diagram shows the graphs of three exponential functions in the form $f(x) = ab^x$.

The curve intersects the y-axis at (0, 5) and this point is called the focal point.

The bigger the value for b, the sharper the graph will rise (or fall).

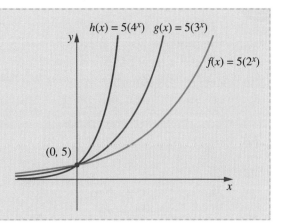

$h(x) = 5(4^x)$ $g(x) = 5(3^x)$

$f(x) = 5(2^x)$

(0, 5)

Example

Use the graph of the function $f : x \rightarrow ab^x$ to answer the following.

(i) Is this graph increasing or decreasing?

(ii) Is the value of a positive or negative? Explain your answer.

(iii) Is the value of b less than or greater than 1?

(iv) Give the domain and range for the function.

Solution

(i) Reading the graph from left to right, we can see that the graph is increasing.

(ii) The value of a is the y-intercept. Since the y-intercept is below the x-axis, it is negative. Therefore, the value of a must be negative.

(iii) Since a is negative and the graph is increasing, then $0 < b < 1$.

(iv) The domain is the set of all real numbers, thus the domain $= \mathbb{R}$.
The range is the set of negative real numbers, thus the range $= \mathbb{R}^-$.

Graph the function $f(x) = 2^x$ in the domain $0 \leq x \leq 5$.

Use the graph to estimate:

(i) $2^{1.5}$ (ii) $2^{3.5}$

(iii) $f^2(2)$ (iv) $\log_2 5$

(v) $\log_2 22$

key point

This is a good opportunity to use a graphic calculator or graphing software, such as Geogebra.

Solution

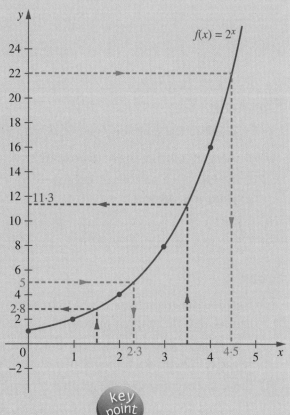

(i) To find $2^{1.5}$, find y when $x = 1.5$. From the graph, $y = 2.8$ when $x = 1.5$. Therefore, $2^{1.5} = 2.8$.

(ii) To find $2^{3.5}$, find y when $x = 3.5$. From the graph, $y = 11.3$ when $x = 3.5$. Therefore, $2^{3.5} = 11.3$.

(iii) $f^2(2) = f(f(2))$
$= f(4)$
$= 16$

(iv) To find the value of $\log_2 5$, use rules of logs:
$\log_a b = c \Longleftrightarrow b = a^c$
$\log_2 5 = x \Longleftrightarrow 5 = 2^x$
From the graph, $x = 2.3$ when $y = 5$.
Therefore, $\log_2 5 = 2.3$.

(v) To find the value of $\log_2 22$, use rules of logs:
$\log_a b = c \Longleftrightarrow b = a^c$
$\log_2 22 = x \Longleftrightarrow 22 = 2^x$
From the graph, $x = 4.5$ when $y = 22$.
Therefore, $\log_2 22 = 4.5$.

key point

Note: $\log_2 y = x$ is the inverse of $y = 2^x$

Exponential function (e^x)

The number e has proven to be of great importance to mathematics, with applications that include number theory, probability, biological and physical sciences, engineering and finance.

The diagrams show the graphs of $y = e^x$ and $y = e^{-x}$.

Both graphs meet the y-axis at $(0, 1)$.

For functions $y = e^x$ and $y = e^{-x}$, the domain is $x \in \mathbb{R}$ and the range is $y \in \mathbb{R}$ and $y > 0$.

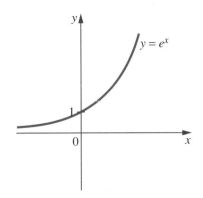

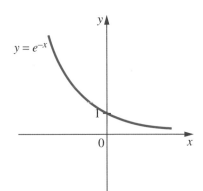

$y = e^x$ represents
exponential growth

$y = e^{-x}$ represents
exponential decay

A radioactive substance is decaying. Initially 5 kg of the radioactive substance was present and four weeks later half of it remained. The mass, R kg, of the radioactive substance at time t weeks can be modelled by $R(t) = R_0 e^{-kt}$, where $t \geq 0$.

(i) State the value of R_0.

(ii) Find the value of k, correct to three decimal places.

(iii) Sketch the graph of R against t for $t \in \mathbb{R}$ and $0 \leq t \leq 10$.

(iv) Find, correct to one decimal place, how long it will take for 60% of the substance to decay.

Solution

(i) R_0 is the value of $R(t)$ when $t = 0$. This is the mass at the start.
Therefore, $R_0 = 5$ kg.

(ii) When $t = 4$, $R(t)$ is 2·5 kg:

$$R(t) = R_0 e^{-kt}$$

$$2{\cdot}5 = 5e^{-k(4)}$$

$$\frac{1}{2} = e^{-4k} \qquad \text{(divide both sides by 5)}$$

$$\ln\frac{1}{2} = -4k \qquad \text{(}\log_a b = c \Longleftrightarrow b = a^c\text{)}$$

$$\frac{\ln\frac{1}{2}}{-4} = k \qquad \text{(use calculator to evaluate left side)}$$

$$0{\cdot}173 = k$$

(iii) $R(t) = R_0e^{-kt}$

$R(t) = 5e^{-(0.173)t}$

T	$5e^{-(0.173)t}$	R(t)
0	$5e^{-(0.173)(0)}$	5
1	$5e^{-(0.173)(1)}$	4·21
2	$5e^{-(0.173)(2)}$	3·54
3	$5e^{-(0.173)(3)}$	2·98
4	$5e^{-(0.173)(4)}$	2·5

T	$5e^{-(0.173)t}$	R(t)
5	$5e^{-(0.173)(5)}$	2·11
6	$5e^{-(0.173)(6)}$	1·77
7	$5e^{-(0.173)(7)}$	1·49
8	$5e^{-(0.173)(8)}$	1·25
9	$5e^{-(0.173)(9)}$	1·05
10	$5e^{-(0.173)(10)}$	0·89

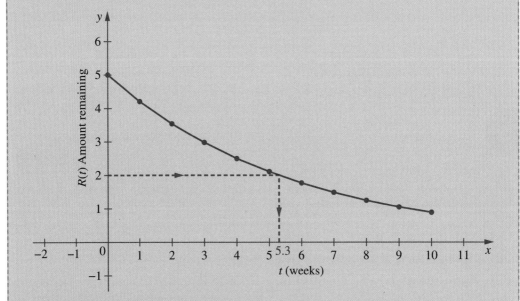

(iv) 60% of 5 kg is 3 kg. Therefore, to find the time for 60% to decay means to find the time when 2 kg remains.

Using the graph to find the value for t when $R(t) = 2$ kg is $t = 5.3$ weeks.

Logarithmic functions

On our course, a logarithmic function will be given in the form $f: x \rightarrow \log_a x$, where $x \in \mathbb{R}$ and $a \in \mathbb{R}^+$ ($\mathbb{R}^+$ is the set of all positive, real numbers).

If $a > 1$, $f(x)$ is increasing.

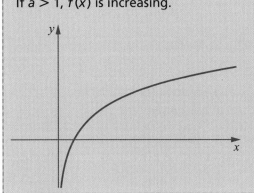

If $0 < a < 1$, $f(x)$ is decreasing.

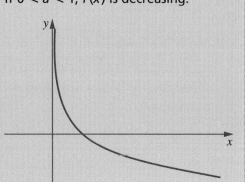

key point

The domain is restricted to only positive real numbers because we cannot take the logarithm of zero or of a negative number.

For the graph of a logarithmic function: Domain: $(0, \infty) = \{0 < x < \infty\}$ and Range: $(-\infty, \infty) = \{-\infty < x < \infty\}$

Example

The diagram shows the graph of $y = f(x)$ where f is a logarithmic function.

Which of the following represents $f(x)$?

(i) $f(x) = \log_6(x - 3)$

(ii) $f(x) = \log_3(x - 3)$

(iii) $f(x) = \log_3(x + 3)$

(iv) $f(x) = \log_6(x + 3)$

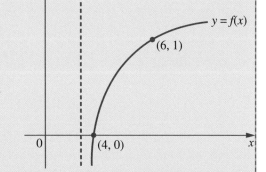

Solution

We must find which of the functions is satisfied by **both** points $(4, 0)$ and $(6, 1)$.

(i) Find $f(4) = \log_6(4 - 3)$
$\qquad = \log_6(1) = 0$
Therefore, $(4, 0)$ satisfies function (a).

(ii) Find $f(4) = \log_3(4 - 3)$
$\qquad = \log_3(1) = 0$
Therefore, $(4, 0)$ satisfies function (b).

(iii) Find $f(4) = \log_3(4 + 3)$
$\qquad = \log_3(7) \neq 0$
Therefore, $(4, 0)$ does **not** satisfy function (c).

(iv) Find $f(4) = \log_6(4 + 3)$
$\qquad = \log_6(7) \neq 0$
Therefore, $(4, 0)$ does **not** satisfy function (d).

The point $(4, 0)$ satisfies **(i)** and **(ii)**. Now see which of these is satisfied by the point $(6, 1)$:

(i) Find $f(6) = \log_6(6 - 3)$
$$= \log_6(3) \neq 1$$

Therefore, $(6, 1)$ does **not** satisfy function **(a)**.

(ii) Find $f(6) = \log_3(6 - 3)$
$$= \log_3(3) = 1$$

Therefore, $(6, 1)$ satisfies function **(b)**.

Thus, the graph represents the function **(ii)**: $f(x) = \log_3(x - 3)$.

(2018 Q.7)

The time, in days of practice, it takes Jack to learn to type x words per minute (wpm) can be modelled by the function:

$$t(x) = k\left[\ln\left(1 - \frac{x}{80}\right)\right], \text{ where } 0 \leq x \leq 70, x \in \mathbb{R}, \text{ and } k \text{ is a constant.}$$

(a) Based on the function $t(x)$, Jack can learn to type 35 wpm in 35·96 days. Write the function above in terms of k and hence show that $k = -62\cdot5$, correct to 1 decimal place.

(b) Find the number of wpm that Jack can learn to type with 100 days of practice. Give your answer correct to the nearest whole number.

(c) Complete the table below, correct to the nearest whole number and hence draw the graph of $t(x)$ for $0 \leq x \leq 70, x \in \mathbb{R}$.

x (wpm)	0	10	20	30	40	50	60	70
$t(x)$ (days)								

(d) A simpler function that could be used to model the number of days needed to attain x wpm is $p(x) = 1\cdot5x$

Using the same axis and scale, draw the graph of $p(x)$ for $0 \leq x \leq 70, x \in \mathbb{R}$,

(e) Let $h(x) = p(x) - t(x)$

Use your graphs to estimate the solution to $h(x) = 0$ for $x > 0$

Solution

(a) $t(x) = k\left[\ln\left(1 - \frac{x}{80}\right)\right]$

$t(x) = 35\cdot96, x = 35, k = ?$

$$35\cdot96 = k\left[\ln\left(\cdot1 - \frac{35}{80}\right)\right]$$

$$35\cdot96 = k\left[\ln\left(\frac{45}{80}\right)\right]$$

$$\frac{35 \cdot 96}{\ln\left(\frac{45}{80}\right)} = k$$

$$-62 \cdot 4995 = k$$

$$-62 \cdot 5 = k$$

(b) $t(x) = -62 \cdot 5\left[\ln\left(1 - \frac{x}{80}\right)\right]$ $t(x) = 100, x = ?$

$$100 = -62 \cdot 5\left[\ln\left(1 - \frac{x}{80}\right)\right]$$

$$\frac{100}{-62 \cdot 5} = \ln\left(1 - \frac{x}{80}\right)$$

$$e^{-\frac{100}{62 \cdot 5}} = 1 - \frac{x}{80}$$

$$\frac{x}{80} = 1 - e^{-\frac{100}{62 \cdot 5}}$$

$$x = 80\left(1 - e^{-\frac{100}{62 \cdot 5}}\right)$$

$$x = 68 \cdot 848$$

After 100 days, Jack would be able to type 69 wpm.

(c) Completing the table:

x (wpm)	0	10	20	30	40	50	60	70
$t(x)$ (days)	8	10	18	29	43	61	87	130

Graph the function:

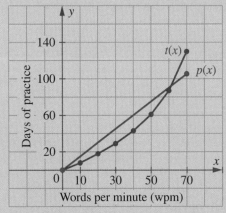

(d) $p(x) = 1 \cdot 5x$ is a linear function.

Find the first and last point within the domain:

$p(0) = 1 \cdot 5(0)$	$p(70) = 1 \cdot 5(70)$
$p(0) = 0$	$p(70) = 105$
$(0, 0)$	$(70, 105)$

These points are plotted on the graph above and joined to show $p(x)$.

(e) $h(x) = p(x) - t(x)$ and $h(x) = 0$ and $x < 0$

$0 = p(x) - t(x)$

$t(x) = p(x)$

From the graph, we can see that $t(x) = p(x)$ when $x = 63$ wpm.

Injective, surjective and bijective functions

INJECTIVE FUNCTION (ONE-TO-ONE MAPPING)

A function in which each input corresponds to only one output and each output corresponds to only one input.

There can be elements in the codomain which do not have a corresponding input (they are not 'busy'). Therefore, the range does not necessarily equal the codomain.

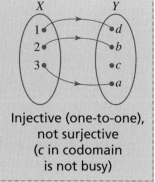

Injective (one-to-one), not surjective (c in codomain is not busy)

SURJECTIVE FUNCTION (MANY-TO-ONE MAPPING)

A function in which every output has *at least* one input. This means that every element in the codomain is busy. Therefore, the range and the codomain are equal.

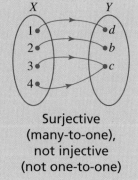

Surjective (many-to-one), not injective (not one-to-one)

BIJECTIVE FUNCTION (PERFECT ONE-TO-ONE MAPPING)

A function which is **both injective and surjective.**

This means there is a perfect one-to-one correspondence between the domain and codomain.

key point

A function has an inverse if it is bijective.

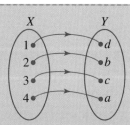

Bijective, injective and surjective (perfect one-to-one)

Example

The function g from set A to set B is shown.

(i) Is g a function? Explain.

(ii) Is g injective? Explain.

(iii) Is g surjective? Explain.

(iv) Explain why g is not bijective.

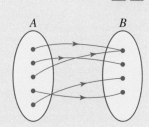

Solution

(i) Yes, g is a function, as only one arrow comes from each element of the domain (set A).

(ii) No, g is not injective, as the mapping is not one-to-one. There are two inputs in set A that have the same output in set B.

(iii) Yes, g is surjective, as the range and the codomain are equal. All elements in set B have an input from set A.

(iv) In order for g to be bijective, it must be both injective **and** surjective. The function g is surjective but not injective, therefore it is not bijective.

HORIZONTAL LINE TEST

Injective function	**Surjective function**
If any horizontal line (red lines in picture) intersects the graph of a function **at most once**, then the graph is an injective function (one-to-one mapping).	If a horizontal line (red lines in picture) intersects the graph of a function **at least once**, so all of the elements of the co-domain are in use, then the graph is a surjective function (many-to-one mapping).

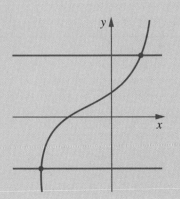

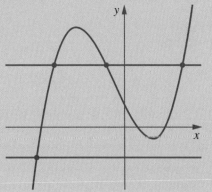

key point

Restricted domain

The graph shows the function $f(x)$. Using a horizontal line test we can see that $f(x)$ is neither injective nor surjective. If the horizontal line goes below the x-axis, it does not touch the graph at all.

To make $f(x)$ **injective**, both the domain and the codomain could be restricted to $\mathbb{R}^+$.

To make $f(x)$ **surjective**, the codomain could be restricted to $\mathbb{R}^+$.

To make $f(x)$ **bijective**, it must be *both* injective and surjective. Therefore, both the domain and the codomain could be restricted to $\mathbb{R}^+$.

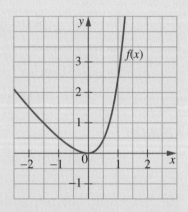

It is vital that you are fully aware of how restricting a domain and codomain of a function can change the nature of the function.

exam Q

The graph of the function $f : R \rightarrow R : x \rightarrow x^2 - 3x - 4$ is shown.

(i) What is the range of the function?

(ii) Explain why f is not injective.

(iii) Suggest a domain for f to make the function injective.

(iv) Explain why f is not surjective.

(v) Suggest a codomain to make the function, f, surjective.

(vi) Give a restricted domain for which $f(x)$ is bijective.

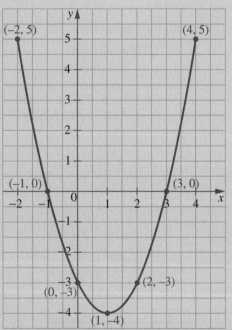

Solution

(i) The lowest y-value of the graphed function is $y = -4$.
∴ The range of the function is $y \geq -4$ or $[-4, \infty)$.

(ii) f is not injective, as any horizontal line in the given range will intersect the curve at more than one point.

Alternatively, we could say that -2 is mapped onto 5 and 4 is also mapped onto 5, therefore the function is not a one-to-one mapping and so it is not injective.

(iii) If the domain was restricted to $x \geq 1$, we get the right-hand side of the graph only and a horizontal line will intersect it at one point only, and so it is injective.

(iv) f is not surjective, as the range of f is $y \geq -4$ and the codomain of f is $\mathbb{R}$. Since the codomain and the range are not equal, f is not surjective.

(v) If the codomain is restricted to $y \geq -4$, then the codomain and the range are the same and thus f would be surjective.

(vi) In order for $f(x)$ to be bijective, it must be both injective and surjective. Therefore, $f(x)$ will be bijective when the domain is restricted to $x \geq 1$ and the codomain is restricted to $y \geq -4$.

From the above question you can see that restricting a domain or range can cause a function to become injective, surjective or bijective.

Inverse functions

A function, $f(x)$, must give exactly one unique output for each input. A function that 'reverses' or 'undoes' the result of $f(x)$ is called its inverse and is denoted by $f^{-1}(x)$. For an inverse function, $f^{-1}(x)$, to exist, the $f(x)$ must be bijective.

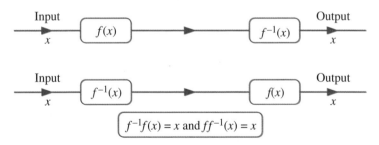

To find the inverse of a function, do the following:

> **1.** Let $f(x) = y$.
> **2.** Express x in terms of y (x on its own).
> **3.** Replace x with $f^{-1}(x)$, and replace y with x.

Example

Find the inverse of the function $f(x) = \dfrac{x}{1 - x}$.

Solution

Let $f(x) = y$:

$$y = \frac{x}{1 - x}$$

Rearrange to get x in terms of y:

$$y(1 - x) = x$$
$$y - xy = x$$
$$y = x + xy$$
$$y = x(1 + y)$$
$$\frac{y}{1 + y} = x$$

Replace y with x and x with $f'(x)$:

$$\frac{x}{1 + x} = f^{-1}(x)$$

Therefore, the inverse of $f(x)$ is

$$f^{-1}(x) = \frac{x}{1 + x}$$

key point

Changing the subject of a formula from algebra can be an essential skill when finding the inverse of a function.

Graphing the inverse of a function

If f is a one-to-one function, the graphs of $y = f(x)$ and $y = f^{-1}(x)$ are reflections of each other in the line $y = x$. In general, if the point (a, b) is on $y = f(x)$, then the point (b, a) is on $y = f^{-1}(x)$.

The domain of $f(x)$ is the range of $f^{-1}(x)$ and the range of $f(x)$ is the domain of $f^{-1}(x)$.

Any point of intersection between $f(x)$ and $f^{-1}(x)$ will be in the line $y = x$.

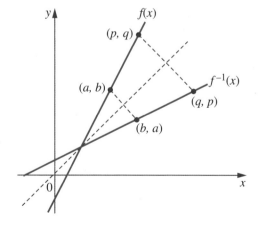

The diagram shows the graph of a function.

(i) Given the graph is of a one-to-one function, draw the graph of its inverse function.

(ii) Use your graph to estimate the two points where the function and its inverse intersect.

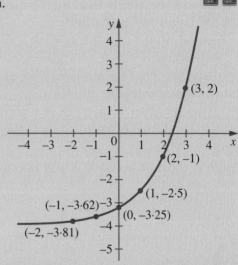

Solution

(i) Reverse the coordinates of each point on the given function to find the points on the inverse function.

Plot these new points.

Join these points to draw the graph of the inverse function (red graph).

(ii) Draw the line $y = x$ through the origin (green line).

By observation, we estimate the function and its inverse intersect at the points $(-4, -4)$ and $(3·3, 3·3)$.

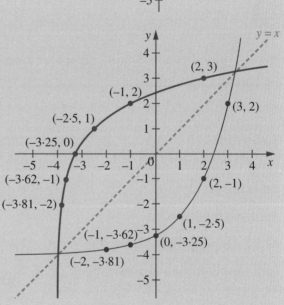

Exponential functions and logarithmic functions are the inverse of each other

In general, $f(x) = a^x$ and $f(x) = \log_a x$ are inverses of each other.

$f(x) = e^x$ and $f(x) = \ln x$ are inverses of each other. One 'undoes' the other.

$$e^{\ln x} = x \quad \text{and} \quad \ln e^x = x$$

For e^x, the domain is $x \in \mathbb{R}$ and the range is $y \in \mathbb{R}$, $y > 0$.

For $\ln x$, the domain is $x \in \mathbb{R}$ and the range is $y \in \mathbb{R}$, $x > 0$.

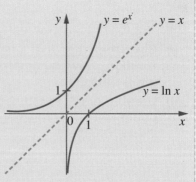

$f(x) = \log_e(x - 2)$, $x > \dfrac{1}{2}$ and $g(x) = e^x + 2$, where $x \in \mathbb{R}$ are two functions.

Show that $f(x)$ and $g(x)$ are inverse functions.

Solution

Find the inverse of $f(x)$: $\qquad\qquad\qquad f(x) = \log_e(x - 2)$

Let $f(x) = y$: $\qquad\qquad\qquad\qquad\quad y = \log_e(x - 2)$

Applying the log rule: $\qquad\qquad\qquad e^y = x - 2 \qquad\qquad (\log_a b = c \Leftrightarrow b = a^c)$

Rearrange to get x in terms of y: $\quad e^y + 2 = x$

Replace y with x and x with $f^{-1}(x)$: $\quad e^x + 2 = f^{-1}(x) \qquad\qquad (g(x) = e^x + 2)$

$$g(x) = f^{-1}(x)$$

Therefore, the inverse of $f(x)$ is $g(x)$ and similarly the inverse of $g(x)$ is $f(x)$.

(2016 Q.5 (b))

(i) Show that $f(x) = 3x - 2$, where $x \in \mathbb{R}$, is an injective function.

(ii) Given that $f(x) = 3x - 2$, where $x \in \mathbb{R}$, find a formula for f^{-1}, the inverse functions of f. Show your work.

Solution

(i) $f(x) = 3x - 2$ is a linear function.

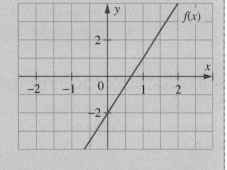

When graphed, this function would be a straight line with a slope of $+3$ and with a y-intercept of -2.

Any horizontal line will intersect the $f(x)$ graph exactly once, at all values of x. Therefore, $f(x)$ is injective.

Alternative method:

Let
$$f(a) = f(b)$$
$$3a - 2 = 3b - 2$$
$$3a = 3b$$
$$a = b$$

This means there is only one output for each input.

Therefore, the function is injective.

(ii) $f(x) = 3x - 2$

$\quad\quad y = 3x - 2$ (change $f(x)$ to y)

$y + 2 = 3x$

$\dfrac{y + 2}{3} = x$ (get x on its own)

$\dfrac{x + 2}{3} = f^{-1}(x)$ (change y to x and x to $f^{-1}(x)$)

7 Binomial Theorem

aims

☐ To be able to expand expressions of the form $(p + q)^n$ using the binomial theorem

☐ To see pattern in a binomial expansion

☐ To be able to write down the middle term, a particular term, or the general term in a binomial expansion

☐ To be well prepared for Bernoulli trials in probability

Introduction: looking for pattern

We are often required to expand binomial expressions of the form $(p + q)^n$. Binomial expansions may be required in algebra, complex numbers, pattern, probability and other topics.

key point

A binomial expression has only two terms, e.g. p and q.

We can use ordinary algebraic multiplication to show that:

$$(1 + p)^1 = 1 + p$$

$$(1 + p)^2 = (1 + p)(1 + p) = 1 + 2p + p^2$$

$$(1 + p)^3 = (1 + p)(1 + p)^2 = 1 + 3p + 3p^2 + p^3$$

$$(1 + p)^4 = (1 + p)(1 + p)^3 = 1 + 4p + 6p^2 + 4p^3 + p^4 \text{ and so on.}$$

The coefficients of the terms in these expansions can be written as a triangle:

```
              1       1
          1       2       1
      1       3       3       1
  1       4       6       4       1
...     ...     ...     ...     ...     ...
```

This triangular array of numbers is known as Pascal's triangle.

The next row is obtained like this:

```
    1          4           6           4          1
1      (1 + 4)     (4 + 6)     (6 + 4)     (4 + 1)     1
1          5          10          10          5          1
```

Now consider expansions of $(p + q)^n$.

If $n = 1$, then $(p + q)^1 = \binom{1}{0}p^1q^0 + \binom{1}{1}p^0q^1 = p + q$

If $n = 2$, then $(p + q)^2 = \binom{2}{0}p^2q^0 + \binom{2}{1}p^1q^1 + \binom{2}{2}p^0q^2 = p^2 + 2pq + q^2$

If $n = 3$, then $(p + q)^3 = \binom{3}{0}p^3q^0 + \binom{3}{1}p^2q^1 + \binom{3}{2}p^1q^2 + \binom{3}{3}p^0q^3$

$$= p^3 + 3p^2q + 3pq^2 + q^3$$

The general formula for the expansion of $(p + q)^n$ is:

$$(p + q)^n = \binom{n}{0}p^nq^0 + \binom{n}{1}p^{n-1}q^1 + \binom{n}{2}p^{n-2}q^2 + \cdots + \binom{n}{n-1}p^1q^{n-1} + \binom{n}{n}p^0q^n$$

This is known as the binomial expansion. It can be found in the booklet of formulae and tables on page 20.

- It is very useful to notice and identify the pattern when working on a binomial expansion.

- A general term for the coefficient of the $(r + 1)^{th}$ term in the expansion of $(p + q)^n$ is $\dfrac{n!}{r!(n-r)!}$.

- A general term, $(r + 1)^{th}$ term, in the expansion of $(p + q)^n$ is $\dfrac{n!}{r!(n-r)!}\,p^{n-r}q^r$.   (see booklet of formulae and tables, page 20)

- Your calculator has a button with nCr on it. It is important to know the notations $\binom{n}{r}$, ^nC_r and nCr all mean the same.

Simple binomial expansions

Example

Find the coefficient of the x^3 term in the expansion $(1 + x)^{10}$.

Solution

We expand $(1 + x)^{10}$ until we meet the x^3 term

$$(1 + x)^{10} = \binom{10}{0}(1)^{10}x^0 + \binom{10}{1}(1)^9x^1 + \binom{10}{2}(1)^8x^2 + \binom{10}{3}(1)^7x^3 + \cdots$$

Answer: $\binom{10}{3}(1)^7 = \binom{10}{3} = 120$ from calculator or $\binom{10}{3} = \dfrac{10 \times 9 \times 8}{1 \times 2 \times 3}$

$$= 120 \text{ by hand.}$$

Example

Expand fully $(1-3x)^4$.

Solution

$$(1-3x)^4 = \binom{4}{0}(-3x)^0 + \binom{4}{1}(-3x)^1 + \binom{4}{2}(-3x)^2 + \binom{4}{3}(-3x)^3 + \binom{4}{4}(-3x)^4$$

$$= \quad 1 \quad - \quad 12x \quad + \quad 54x^2 \quad - \quad 108x^3 \quad + \quad 81x^4$$

key point

- A minus sign in an expansion often causes candidates problems.
- As $(1)^4 = 1$, $(1)^3 = 1$ etc., we can ignore the 1 when expanding in the above example.

Example

Expand $(2 - 5x)^5$ in ascending powers of x.

Solution

$(2-5x)^5$

$$= \binom{5}{0}(2)^5(-5x)^0 + \binom{5}{1}(2)^4(-5x)^1 + \binom{5}{2}(2)^3(-5x)^2 + \binom{5}{3}(2)^2(-5x)^3 + \binom{5}{4}(2)^1(-5x)^4 + \binom{5}{5}(2)^0(-5x)^5$$

$$= 32 - 400x + 2{,}000x^2 - 5{,}000x^3 + 6{,}250x^4 - 3{,}125x^5$$

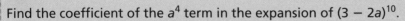

Find the coefficient of the a^4 term in the expansion of $(3 - 2a)^{10}$.

Solution

For an initial attempt we could expand $(3 - 2a)^{10}$ until we meet the a^4 term.

Hence, we write:

$$\binom{10}{0}(3)^{10} + \binom{10}{1}(3)^9(-2a)^1 + \binom{10}{2}(3)^8(-2a)^2 + \binom{10}{3}(3)^7(-2a)^3 + \binom{10}{4}(3)^6(-2a)^4 + \cdots$$

the required term.

With practice you can find particular terms in a binomial expansion without working out the whole expansion.

Finally, $\binom{10}{4}(3)^6(-2a)^4 = (210)(729)(16a^4) \Rightarrow$ coefficient of $a^4 = 2{,}449{,}440$.

Find the value of the middle term of the binomial expansion of $\left(\dfrac{2}{x} - x^2\right)^6$.

Solution

'The power of 6' indicates there are *seven* terms in this expansion. Hence, the middle term is the fourth term.

$$\binom{6}{0}\left(\frac{2}{x}\right)^6(-x^2)^0 + \binom{6}{1}\left(\frac{2}{x}\right)^5(-x^2)^1 + \binom{6}{2}\left(\frac{2}{x}\right)^4(-x^2)^2 + \binom{6}{3}\left(\frac{2}{x}\right)^3(-x^2)^3 + \cdots$$

Again, with practice you may decide to simply write out the middle term.

$$\text{Answer} = \binom{6}{3}\left(\frac{2}{x}\right)^3(-x^2)^3 = 20\left(\frac{8}{x^3}\right)(-x^6) = -160x^3$$

In the binomial expansion of $(1 + kx)^6$, the coefficient of x^4 is 240.
Find the two possible real values of k.

Solution

$$(1 + kx)^6 = \binom{6}{0} + \binom{6}{1}(kx)^1 + \binom{6}{2}(kx)^2 + \binom{6}{3}(kx)^3 + \binom{6}{4}(kx)^4 \cdots$$

By observation, the required term $= \binom{6}{4}(kx)^4 = 15k^4x^4$.

The coefficient of x^4 is $240 \Rightarrow 15k^4 = 240$
$$k^4 = 16$$
$$\therefore k = \pm 2$$

Notice the hint in the question:
find two values of k.

Find the value of the term which is independent of x in the
expansion of $\left(x^2 - \dfrac{1}{x} \right)^9$.

Solution

$$\left(x^2 - \frac{1}{x} \right)^9 = \binom{9}{0}(x^2)^9 + \binom{9}{1}(x^2)^8\left(-\frac{1}{x}\right)^1 + \binom{9}{2}(x^2)^7\left(-\frac{1}{x}\right)^2 + \binom{9}{3}(x^2)^6\left(-\frac{1}{x}\right)^3 + \binom{9}{4}(x^2)^5\left(-\frac{1}{x}\right)^4 \cdots$$

$$= x^{18} - 9x^{15} + 36x^{12} - 84x^9 + 126x^6 \cdots$$

Can you see the pattern? The next term has an x^3 while the following
term has $x^0(=1)$, i.e. is independent of x.

Hence, by observation the seventh term $\binom{9}{6}(x^2)^3\left(-\dfrac{1}{x}\right)^6$ is the

required term $= 84$.

An alternative, more sophisticated solution requires the general term of the expansion:

$$= \binom{9}{r}(x^2)^{9-r}\left(-\frac{1}{x}\right)^r$$

$$= \binom{9}{r}x^{18-2r}(-1)^r(x^{-r})$$

$$= (-1)^r\binom{9}{r}x^{18-2r-r}$$

The term independent of x will have no x term. In order for this to be the case, the x must have a power of zero.

key point

Independent of $x \Rightarrow x^0$.

$$\therefore \ 18 - 2r - r = 0 \quad \text{comparing indices}$$

$$18 = 3r$$

$$6 = r$$

Hence, we have $\binom{9}{6}(x^2)^{9-6}\left(-\frac{1}{x}\right)^6$

$$= 84x^6\left(\frac{1}{x^6}\right) = 84$$

8 Complex Numbers I

aims

□ To know what a complex number is and develop the skills required to answer exam questions on complex numbers

□ To handle $(i)^n$ where $n \in \mathbb{Z}$ and associated questions on sequences and series

□ To know how to perform the operations, addition, subtraction, multiplication and division of complex numbers

□ To be able to solve quadratic and cubic equations with coefficients that are real and/or complex

Introduction

A **complex number** z is a number of the form $a + bi$, $a, b \in \mathbb{R}$ and $i = \sqrt{-1}$. a is called the real part of z and b is called the imaginary part of z.

Adding and subtracting imaginary numbers

Imaginary numbers are added in the usual way and hence $4i + 6i = 10i$
They are also subtracted in the usual way and hence $4i - 6i = -2i$

Multiplying imaginary numbers

When we multiply two imaginary numbers we need to consider the fact that powers of i can be simplified as follows:

$$i^2 = i \times i = \sqrt{-1} \times \sqrt{-1} = -1$$
$$i^3 = i^2 \times i = -1 \times i = -i$$
$$i^4 = i^2 \times i^2 = -1 \times -1 = 1$$
$$i^5 = i^4 \times i = 1 \times i = i$$

This pattern now continues and is shown in the diagram:

Every fourth multiple comes a full circle.

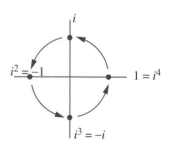

Example

Simplify each of the following: **(i)** i^{13} **(ii)** i^{98} **(iii)** i^{-17}

Solution

> **key point**
>
> Use $i^4 = 1$ to simplify expressions with multiple powers of i.

(i) $i^{13} = i^4 i^4 i^4 i$

$i^{13} = (1)(1)(1)i$

$i^{13} = i$

(ii) $i^{98} = i^{96}(i^2)$

$i^{98} = (i^4)^{24}(i^2)$

$i^{98} = (1)i^2$

$i^{98} = i^2$

$i^{98} = -1$

(iii) $i^{-17} = \dfrac{1}{i^{17}} = \dfrac{1}{i^{16}i}$

$i^{-17} = \dfrac{1}{(1)i} = \dfrac{1}{i}$

$i^{-17} = \dfrac{1}{i} \times \dfrac{i}{i} = \dfrac{i}{i^2} = -i$

exam Q

$\mu_1, \mu_2, \mu_3, \mu_4, \ldots$ is a sequence where $\mu_n = i^n$ and $i = \sqrt{-1}$.

Evaluate $\mu_1, \mu_2, \mu_3, \mu_4$ and μ_5. Hence or otherwise, evaluate $\displaystyle\sum_1^{22}\mu_n$.

Solution

$\mu_1 = i^1 = i$

$\mu_2 = i^2 = -1$

$\mu_3 = i^3 = -i$

$\mu_4 = i^4 = 1$

$\mu_5 = i^5 = i \;\; (= \mu_1)$

Notice $\mu_1 + \mu_2 + \mu_3 + \mu_4 = i - 1 - i + 1 = 0$.

$$\sum_1^{22}\mu_n = (\mu_1 + \mu_2 + \mu_3 + \mu_4) + \cdots + (\mu_{17} + \mu_{18} + \mu_{19} + \mu_{20}) + \mu_{21} + \mu_{22}$$

$$= \qquad 0 \qquad\quad + \cdots + \qquad\qquad 0 \qquad\qquad + \mu_{21} + \mu_{22}$$

$$= i - 1$$

exam focus

> The above example is a typical exam question in that the successful solution requires the candidate to link knowledge from different sections of the course, in this case, complex numbers with sequences and series.

Operations

Addition, subtraction and multiplication are the same as in ordinary algebra, except i^2, i^3 and i^4 are replaced by -1, $-i$ and 1, respectively.

Equality: If two complex numbers are equal, then:

real parts = real parts   and   imaginary parts = imaginary parts

(e.g. if $a + bi = c + di$, then $a = c$ and $b = d$).

Example

Find integers p and q such that

$$(p + 3i)(q - i) = 13 + i.$$

Solution

$$(p + 3i)(q - i) = 13 + i$$
$$pq - pi + 3qi - 3i^2 = 13 + i$$
$$pq - pi + 3qi + 3 = 13 + i$$

Real parts equal $\Rightarrow pq + 3 = 13$ and i parts equal $\Rightarrow -p + 3q = 1$

$$pq = 10 \qquad \text{and} \qquad 3q - 1 = p$$

Hence, $(3q - 1)q = 10 \Rightarrow 3q^2 - q - 10 = 0$

$$(3q + 5)(q - 2) = 0$$

Now $3q + 5 = 0$ $\boxed{\text{or}}$ $q - 2 = 0$

$q = -\dfrac{5}{3}$ reject, not integer $\boxed{\text{or}}$ $q = 2$

$$2p = 10 \Rightarrow p = 5$$

Find the two complex numbers $a + ib$ such that $(a + ib)^2 = 15 - 8i$ where $a, b \in \mathbb{R}$.

Solution

$$(a + ib)^2 = 15 - 8i$$
$$a^2 + 2abi + i^2b^2 = 15 - 8i \quad \text{(remove the brackets)}$$
$$a^2 + 2abi - b^2 = 15 - 8i$$
$$\text{R} \quad \text{I} \quad \text{R} \qquad \text{R} \quad \text{I} \quad \text{(identify real and imaginary parts)}$$

Real parts = Real parts   Imaginary parts = Imaginary parts

$$a^2 - b^2 = 15 \quad ①$$ $$2ab = -8 \quad ②$$

Solving between equation ① and ②

② $2ab = -8$ ① $\quad a^2 - b^2 = 15$

$\quad ab = -4$ $a^2 - \left(\dfrac{-4}{a}\right)^2 = 15 \quad \left[\text{replace } b \text{ with } \dfrac{-4}{a}\right]$

$\quad b = \dfrac{-4}{a}$

put this into equation ① $a^2 - \dfrac{16}{a^2} = 15$

$\qquad a^4 - 16 = 15a^2$

$\qquad a^4 - 15a^2 - 16 = 0$

$\qquad (a^2 - 16)(a^2 + 1) = 0$

$\qquad a^2 - 16 = 0 \qquad \text{or} \quad a^2 + 1 = 0$

$\qquad\qquad a^2 = 16 \quad \text{or} \qquad\qquad a^2 = -1$

$\qquad\qquad a = \pm 4 \quad \text{or} \qquad\qquad a = \pm i$

As $a, b \in \mathbb{R}$, the result $a = \pm i$ is rejected.

Now $b = -\dfrac{4}{a}$ gives

$a = 4$	$a = -4$
$b = -\dfrac{4}{4}$	$b = -\dfrac{4}{-4}$
$b = -1$	$b = 1$
$a = 4, b = -1$	$a = -4, b = 1$

Thus, $(4 - i)^2 = 15 - 8i$

or $\quad(-4 + i)^2 = 15 - 8i$

Another way of asking the same question is:

If $\quad a + ib = \sqrt{15 - 8i}$, find the values of a and b where $a, b \in \mathbb{R}$

or if $\quad z = \sqrt{15 - 8i}$, find all the values of z.

Conjugate of a complex number

Where $z = a + bi$, the conjugate of $z = \bar{z} = a - bi$ (only change the sign of the imaginary part).

e.g. if $z = -2 - 5i$, then $\quad \bar{z} = -2 + 5i$

Division: multiply the top and bottom by the conjugate of the bottom.

$$\text{e.g. } \frac{p + qi}{a + bi} \quad \text{becomes} \quad \frac{(p + qi)(a - bi)}{(a + bi)(a - bi)}$$

(2015 Q.4 (a))

The complex numbers z_1, z_2 and z_3 are such that $\dfrac{2}{z_1} = \dfrac{1}{z_2} + \dfrac{1}{z_3}$, $z_2 = 2 + 3i$ and $z_3 = 3 - 2i$, where $i^2 = -1$.

Write z_1 in the form $a + bi$, where $a, b \in \mathbb{Z}$.

Solution

$$\frac{1}{z_2} = \frac{1}{2 + 3i} = \frac{(1)(2 - 3i)}{(2 + 3i)(2 - 3i)} \qquad \text{(conjugate multiplication)}$$

$$= \frac{2 - 3i}{4 - 6i + 6i - 9i^2}$$

$$= \frac{2 - 3i}{4 + 9}$$

$$= \frac{2 - 3i}{13}$$

Likewise

$$\frac{1}{z_3} = \frac{1}{3 - 2i} = \frac{(1)(3 + 2i)}{(3 - 2i)(3 + 2i)} \qquad \text{(conjugate multiplication)}$$

$$= \frac{3 + 2i}{9 + 6i - 6i - 4i^2}$$

$$= \frac{3 + 2i}{9 + 4}$$

$$= \frac{3 + 2i}{13}$$

Hence

$$\frac{2}{z_1} = \frac{1}{z_2} + \frac{1}{z_3} \text{ becomes}$$

$$\frac{2}{z_1} = \frac{2 - 3i}{13} + \frac{3 + 2i}{13}$$

$$\frac{2}{z_1} = \frac{5 - i}{13}$$

$$\frac{z_1}{2} = \frac{13}{5 - i} \qquad \qquad \text{(invert both sides)}$$

$$z_1 = \frac{26}{5 - i}$$ (multiply both sides by 2)

$$z_1 = \frac{(26)(5 + i)}{(5 - i)(5 + i)}$$ (conjugate multiplication)

$$z_1 = \frac{26(5 + i)}{25 + 5i - 5i - i^2}$$

$$z_1 = \frac{26(5 + i)}{25 + 1}$$

$$z_1 = 5 + i$$

This question was awarded 15 marks (5% of the paper). It was generally badly answered. This type of question will be examined again.

Polynomial equations with complex roots

Conjugate roots theorem

If all the coefficients of a polynomial equation are real, then all complex roots occur as conjugate pairs.

It is vital to remember that the conjugate roots theorem can only be used if all the coefficients in the equation are real.

e.g. can be used with $z^2 + 6z + 13 = 0$ or $2z^3 - 7z^2 + 16z - 15 = 0$

cannot be used with $2iz^2 + (6 + 2i)z + (3 - 6i) = 0$ or $z^3 + 10iz - 4 = 0$

(2016 Q.1 (a))

$(-4 + 3i)$ is one root of the equation $az^2 + bz + c = 0$, where $a, b, c \in \mathbb{R}$, and $i^2 = -1$.

Write the other root.

Solution

Since $a, b, c \in \mathbb{R}$ the other root is the conjugate of $(-4 + 3i) = -4 - 3i$.

This question was awarded 5 marks. The vast majority of candidates were awarded full marks.

Example

Construct a quadratic equation with real coefficients and root $4 + i$.

Solution

We can form a quadratic equation with known roots by using

$$z^2 - \text{(sum of roots)}z + \text{(product of roots)} = 0$$

If $4 + i$ is a root, then in this case $4 - i$ is also a root.

The equation is

$$z^2 - (4 + i + 4 - i)z + (4 + i)(4 - i) = 0$$
$$z^2 - 8z + 17 = 0$$

(2016, Q.1 (c))

(1 + *i*) is a root of the equation

$$z^2 + (-2 + i)z + 3 - i = 0$$

Find its other root in the form *m* + *ni*, where *m, n* ∈ ℝ, and $i^2 = -1$.

Solution

There are at least five possible solution methods for this question. The following solution was a very popular one with candidates.

Find the roots of the equation using the quadratic formula.

a = 1

b = −2 + *i*

c = 3 − *i*

$$z = \frac{-b \pm \sqrt{b^2 - 4ac}}{2a}$$ (see *booklet of formulae and tables*, page 20)

$$z = \frac{-(-2 + i) \pm \sqrt{(-2 + i)^2 - 4(1)(3 - i)}}{2(1)}$$

$$z = \frac{2 - i \pm \sqrt{4 - 4i - 1 - 12 + 4i}}{2}$$

$$z = \frac{2 - i \pm \sqrt{-9}}{2}$$

$$z = \frac{2 - i \pm 3i}{2}$$

$$z = \frac{2 - i + 3i}{2} \text{ or } z = \frac{2 - i - 3i}{2}$$

$$z = 1 + i \text{ or } z = 1 - 2i$$

One root is not the conjugate of the other because not all the coefficients in the quadratic equation were real.

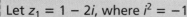

(2014 Q.2 (a))

Let $z_1 = 1 - 2i$, where $i^2 = -1$

The complex number z_1, is a root of the equation $2z^3 - 7z^2 + 16z - 15 = 0$

Find the other two roots of the equation.

Solution

$z_1 = 1 - 2i$ is a root/solution then $\bar{z}_1 = 1 + 2i$ also root/solution.

We can form a quadratic equation by using

$$z^2 - (\text{sum of roots})\, z + (\text{product of roots}) = 0$$

$$z^2 - (1 - 2i + 1 + 2i)z + (1 - 2i)(1 + 2i) = 0$$

Hence $z^2 - 2z + 5 = 0$ is a factor

This means $(z^2 - 2z + 5)(az + b) = 2z^3 - 7z^2 + 16z - 15$

Multiply to get:

$$az^3 + bz^2 - 2az^2 - 2bz + 5az + 5b = 2z^3 - 7z^2 + 16z - 15$$

Compare coefficients

Coefficients of z^3: $a = 2$

　　　Constants: $5b = -15$

　　　　　　$b = -3$

Third factor $az + b$ is now $2z - 3$

$$\text{Third root: } z = \frac{3}{2} \text{ root/solution}$$

Therefore the other two roots are $1 + 2i$ and $\dfrac{3}{2}$.

This question was generally poorly answered.
It is certain to be asked again.

9 Complex Numbers II

☐ To be able to represent complex numbers on an Argand diagram
☐ To apply modulus and argument of complex numbers when they are required
☐ To write a + *ib* in polar form and apply De Moivre's theorem when and as required
☐ To know and apply the two special applications of multiplication and division of two complex numbers in polar form
☐ To find roots of complex numbers
☐ To understand geometrical transformations of complex numbers

Argand diagram and modulus

Argand diagram

The Argand diagram is a coordinated plane where a complex number can be plotted. The real values are marked along the horizontal axis and the imaginary values are marked along the vertical axis.

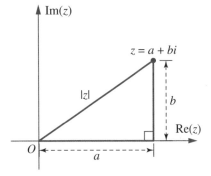

Modulus of a complex number

The **modulus** of a complex number is the **distance from the origin to the point representing the complex number on the Argand diagram**.

The point z represents the complex number $a + bi$.

The modulus of z is the distance from the origin, O, to the complex number $a + bi$.

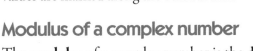

If $z = a + bi$, then
$$|z| = |a + bi| = \sqrt{a^2 + b^2}.$$

If $z = a + bi$, then the modulus of z is written $|z|$ or $|a + bi|$

Using the theorem of Pythagoras, $|z| = \sqrt{a^2 + b^2}$.

key point

1. *i* **never** appears when the modulus formula is used.
2. The modulus of a complex number is **always positive**.
3. Before using the formula, a complex number must be in the form $a + bi$.

Example

If $z = 4 - 2i$

(i) Find $\bar{z}$

(ii) Find $|z|$

(iii) Represent z, $\bar{z}$ and $|z|$ on an Argand diagram.

Solution

(i) $z = 4 - 2i$ then $\bar{z} = 4 + 2i$

(ii) $|z| = |4 - 2i| = \sqrt{(4)^2 + (-2)^2} = \sqrt{16 + 4} = \sqrt{20} = 2\sqrt{5}$

(iii)

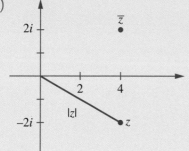

key point

Heavy line = $|Z|$

Example

Given $z_1 = -4 + 3i$ and $z_2 = 1 - i$, find the following in surd form.

(i) $|z_1 z_2|$ (ii) $\left|\dfrac{z_1}{z_2}\right|$

key point

In general, for all complex numbers z and w

(i) $|zw| = |z||w|$ and (ii) $\left|\dfrac{z}{w}\right| = \dfrac{|z|}{|w|}$

Solution

$|z_1| = |-4 + 3i| = \sqrt{(-4)^2 + (3)^2} = \sqrt{16 + 9} = \sqrt{25} = 5$

$|z_2| = |1 - i| = \sqrt{(1)^2 + (-1)^2} = \sqrt{1 + 1} = \sqrt{2}$

Then (i) $|z_1 z_2| = |z_1||z_2| = 5\sqrt{2}$

(ii) $\left|\dfrac{z_1}{z_2}\right| = \dfrac{|z_1|}{|z_2|} = \dfrac{5}{\sqrt{2}} = \dfrac{5(\sqrt{2})}{\sqrt{2}(\sqrt{2})} = \dfrac{5\sqrt{2}}{2}$

Polar coordinates and the polar form of a complex number

Polar coordinates

Consider the complex number $z = x + yi$. The position of z on the Argand diagram can be given by Cartesian, or rectangular, coordinates, (x, y). An alternative way of describing the position of z is to give its modulus, r, and its **argument**, θ. Where θ can be in degrees or radians, (r, θ) are called the polar coordinates of the complex number.

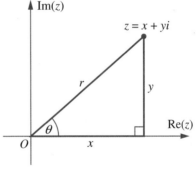

The argument of $z = \arg(z) = \theta = \tan^{-1}\left(\dfrac{y}{x}\right)$.

The argument, θ, is the **angle between the positive real axis** and the line from the origin to the point $z = x + yi$.

key point

Drawing a diagram can clarify your thought process and be a very good aid in calculating θ.

The polar form of the complex number $z = x + yi$ is $z = r(\cos\theta + i\sin\theta)$.

Example

Write down the polar coordinates of the points A, D, E and H shown in the diagram for $0 \leq \theta \leq 2\pi$ and $r > 0$.

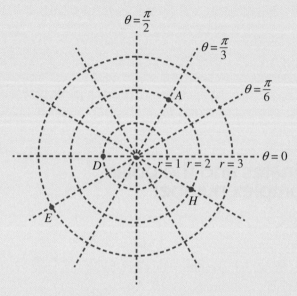

Solution

Use $r(\cos \theta + i \sin \theta)$ four times

$$A = 2\left(\cos\frac{\pi}{3} + i \sin\frac{\pi}{3}\right)$$

$$D = 1(\cos \pi + i \sin \pi)$$

$$E = 3\left(\cos\frac{7\pi}{6} + i \sin\frac{7\pi}{6}\right)$$

$$H = 2\left(\cos\frac{11\pi}{6} + i \sin\frac{11\pi}{6}\right)$$

Sometimes we are given a number in polar form, $r(\cos \theta + i \sin \theta)$, and asked to write it in Cartesian form, $x + yi$ (sometimes referred to as rectangular form). Again, it is good practice to draw a diagram.

Example

Express $4\left(\cos\frac{5\pi}{6} + i \sin\frac{5\pi}{6}\right)$ in the form $x + yi$.

Solution

$$\frac{5\pi}{6} = \frac{5(180°)}{6} = 150°$$

$$\cos 150° = -\frac{\sqrt{3}}{2}$$

$$\sin 150° = \frac{1}{2}$$

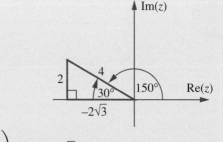

$$\therefore 4\left(\cos \frac{5\pi}{6} + i \sin \frac{5\pi}{6}\right)$$

$$= 4\left(\cos 150° + i \sin 150°\right) = 4\left(-\frac{\sqrt{3}}{2} + \frac{1}{2}i\right) = -2\sqrt{3} + 2i$$

key point

If your calculator is in radian mode, you do not have to change the radians into degrees.

$$\cos \frac{5\pi}{6} = -\frac{\sqrt{3}}{2} \quad \text{and} \quad \sin \frac{5\pi}{6} = \frac{1}{2}$$

Example

Express $z = 2\sqrt{3} + 2i$ in polar form, i.e in the form $r(\cos \theta + i \sin \theta)$

Solution

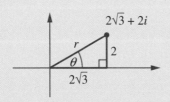

key point

- Show $2\sqrt{3} + 2i$ on an Argand diagram
- $2\sqrt{3} + 2i$ is in the first quadrant

$$r^2 = (2\sqrt{3})^2 + (2)^2 = 12 + 4 = 16$$

$$r = 4$$

$$\tan \theta = \frac{\text{opp}}{\text{adj}} = \frac{2}{2\sqrt{3}} = \frac{1}{\sqrt{3}}$$

$$\theta = \tan^{-1}\left(\frac{1}{\sqrt{3}}\right) = 30°\left(= \frac{\pi}{6}\right)$$

$$z = r(\cos \theta + i \sin \theta) = 4(\cos 30° + i \sin 30°)$$

exam Q

Given $z = -2\sqrt{3} + ki$ where $k \in \mathbb{R}$, find $|z|$ when Arg(z) is given as $\dfrac{4\pi}{3}$.

Solution
To find $|z| = |-2\sqrt{3} + ki|$ we first find the value of k.

Step 1: Plot $z = -2\sqrt{3} + ki$ on an Argand diagram.

$$\text{Arg}(z) = \frac{4\pi}{3} = 240°$$

$\Rightarrow z$ in third quadrant

Step 2: Arg$(z) = 240° \Rightarrow \alpha = 240 - 180 = 60°$

$$\tan \alpha = \tan 60 = \frac{k}{2\sqrt{3}}$$

$$\sqrt{3} = \frac{k}{2\sqrt{3}}$$

$$6 = k$$

[third quadrant (negative value)]

We then have $z = -2\sqrt{3} + ki = -2\sqrt{3} - 6i$.

$$|z| = |-2\sqrt{3} - 6i| = \sqrt{(2\sqrt{3})^2 + (-6)^2}$$

$$= \sqrt{12 + 36} = \sqrt{48} = 4\sqrt{3}$$

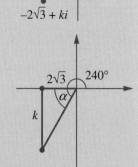

key point

Two special properties of polar coordinates:

1. $r_1(\cos A + i \sin A)r_2(\cos B + i \sin B) = r_1 r_2(\cos(A + B) + i \sin(A + B))$

2. $\dfrac{r_1(\cos A + i \sin A)}{r_2(\cos B + i \sin B)} = \dfrac{r_1}{r_2}\Big[\cos(A - B) + i \sin(A - B)\Big]$

Example

If $z_1 = 5\left(\cos\dfrac{4\pi}{3} + i \sin\dfrac{4\pi}{3}\right)$ and $z_2 = 2\left(\cos\dfrac{\pi}{3} + i \sin\dfrac{\pi}{3}\right)$, evaluate:

(i) $z_1 z_2$ (ii) $\dfrac{z_1}{z_2}$

Give your answers in the form $x + iy$ where $x, y \in \mathbb{R}$.

Solution

(i) $z_1z_2 = \left[5\left(\cos\dfrac{4\pi}{3} + i\sin\dfrac{4\pi}{3}\right)\right]\left[2\left(\cos\dfrac{\pi}{3} + i\sin\dfrac{\pi}{3}\right)\right]$

$\qquad = 10\left[\cos\left(\dfrac{4\pi}{3} + \dfrac{\pi}{3}\right) + i\sin\left(\dfrac{4\pi}{3} + \dfrac{\pi}{3}\right)\right]$

$z_1z_2 = 10\left[\cos\dfrac{5\pi}{3} + i\sin\dfrac{5\pi}{3}\right]$

$z_1z_2 = 10\left[\dfrac{1}{2} - i\dfrac{\sqrt{3}}{2}\right] = 5 - i5\sqrt{3}$

(ii) $\dfrac{z_1}{z_2} = \dfrac{5\left(\cos\dfrac{4\pi}{3} + i\sin\dfrac{4\pi}{3}\right)}{2\left(\cos\dfrac{\pi}{3} + i\sin\dfrac{\pi}{3}\right)} = \dfrac{5}{2}\left[\cos\left(\dfrac{4\pi}{3} - \dfrac{\pi}{3}\right) + i\sin\left(\dfrac{4\pi}{3} - \dfrac{\pi}{3}\right)\right]$

$\qquad\qquad = \dfrac{5}{2}\left[\cos\pi + i\sin\pi\right]$

$\qquad\qquad = \dfrac{5}{2}\left[-1 + 0\right] = -\dfrac{5}{2}$

key point

Arg $(z_1)(z_2)$ = Arg z_1 + Arg z_2

Arg $\left(\dfrac{z_1}{z_2}\right)$ = Arg z_1 − Arg z_2

De Moivre's theorem

De Moivre's theorem states:

$[r(\cos\theta + i\sin\theta)]^n = r^n(\cos n\theta + i\sin n\theta)$, where $n \in \mathbb{Q}$.   (see *booklet of formulae and tables*, page 20)

The theorem is named after the French mathematician Abraham de Moivre (1667–1754).

exam focus

You could be asked to prove De Moivre's theorem, for $n \in \mathbb{N}$, using induction. Proof by induction is covered in the methods of proof chapter.

Example

Use De Moivre's theorem to evaluate:

(i) $(\cos 15° + i\sin 15°)^9$

(ii) $[\sqrt{2}(\cos 18° + i\sin 18°)]^5$

Solution

(i) $(\cos 15° + i\sin 15°)^9$

$= \cos(9 \times 15°) + i\sin(9 \times 15°)$

$= \cos 135° + i\sin 135°$

$= -\dfrac{1}{\sqrt{2}} + i\dfrac{1}{\sqrt{2}}$

(ii) $[\sqrt{2}(\cos 18° + i\sin 18°)^5]$

$= (\sqrt{2})^5[\cos(5 \times 18°) + i\sin(5 \times 18°)]$

$= 4\sqrt{2}[\cos 90° + i\sin 90°]$

$= 4\sqrt{2}[0 + i]$

$= 4\sqrt{2}i$

Powers of complex numbers

Evaluating $(a + bi)^n$ where $a, b \in \mathbb{R}$ and $n \in \mathbb{N}$ by direct multiplication is very awkward for $n > 3$. However, the calculation can be greatly simplified by using De Moivre's theorem.

To evaluate a large power such as $(a + bi)^n$:

(i)   Write $a + bi$ in polar form

(ii) Use De Moivre's theorem

(iii) Simplify the answer

After using De Moivre's theorem, the angle may be very large positive or very large negative. We can add or subtract full circles to bring it back within range.

(2017 Q.2)

$z = -\sqrt{3} + i$, where $i^2 = -1$

(a) Use De Moivre's theorem to write z^4 in the form $a + b\sqrt{c}i$, where $a, b,$ and $c \in \mathbb{Z}$.

(b) The complex number w is such that $|w| = 3$ and w makes an angle of $30°$ with the positive sense of the real axis. If $t = zw$, write t in its simplest form.

Solution

key point

Show $-\sqrt{3} + i$ on an Argand diagram

(a) $r^2 = 1^2 + (\sqrt{3})^2 = 1 + 3 = 4$

$r = 2$

$\tan \alpha = \dfrac{\text{opp}}{\text{adj}} = \dfrac{1}{\sqrt{3}}$

$\alpha = \tan^{-1}\left(\dfrac{1}{\sqrt{3}}\right) = 30°$

$\theta = 180° - \alpha = 180° - 30° = 150°$

Now $z = -\sqrt{3} + i = r(\cos\theta + i\sin\theta)$

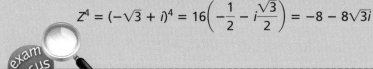

$z = -\sqrt{3} + i = 2(\cos 150° + i\sin 150°)$

$z^4 = (-\sqrt{3} + i)^4 = (2(\cos 150° + i\sin 150°))^4$

$z^4 = (-\sqrt{3} + i)^4 = 2^4(\cos 4(150°) + i\sin 4(150°))$

$z^4 = (-\sqrt{3} + i)^4 = 16(\cos 600° + i\sin 600°)$ by De Moivre's theorem

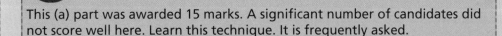

$$z^4 = (-\sqrt{3} + i)^4 = 16\left(-\dfrac{1}{2} - i\dfrac{\sqrt{3}}{2}\right) = -8 - 8\sqrt{3}i$$

exam focus

This (a) part was awarded 15 marks. A significant number of candidates did not score well here. Learn this technique. It is frequently asked.

(b) $w = r(\cos\theta + i\sin\theta)$

$w = 3(\cos 30° + i\sin 30°)$

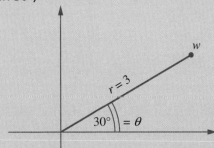

From part (a) $z = 2(\cos 150° + i \sin 150°)$

$$t = zw = 2(\cos 150° + i \sin 150°)3(\cos 30° + i \sin 30°)$$
$$= 6(\cos 180° + i \sin180°) \qquad \text{(adding the angles)}$$
$$= 6(-1 + 0)$$
$$= -6$$

This (b) part was awarded 10 marks. It was badly answered; candidates often did not notice the link to z from part (a).

Trigonometrical identities

De Moivre's theorem is very popular with examiners. They use it to link trigonometry, complex numbers and the binomial expansion.

An essential skill is to be capable of expanding (or multiplying out directly) expressions of the form:

$$(\cos \theta + i \sin \theta)^3$$

The chapter on binomial theorem covers this in more detail.

Example

Use De Moivre's theorem to prove $\sin 3\theta = 3 \sin \theta - 4 \sin^3\theta$.

Solution

$(\cos \theta + i \sin \theta)^3 = \cos 3\theta + i \sin 3\theta$ (by De Moivre's theorem)

$(\cos \theta + i \sin \theta)^3 = \cos^3\theta + 3i \cos^2\theta \sin \theta - 3\cos \theta \sin^2\theta - i \sin^3\theta$

         (by binomial expansion or multiplication in algebra)

Imaginary part of De Moivre's theorem = Imaginary part of binomial expansion

$$\therefore \sin 3\theta = 3\cos^2\theta \sin\theta - \sin^3\theta$$

$$\sin 3\theta = 3(1 - \sin^2\theta)\sin\theta - \sin^3\theta \quad \text{(see \textit{booklet of formulae and tables}, page 13)}$$

$$\sin 3\theta = 3\sin\theta - 3\sin^3\theta - \sin^3\theta$$

$$\sin 3\theta = 3\sin\theta - 4\sin^3\theta$$

Equating the real parts in the previous example also proves
$\cos 3\theta = 4\cos^3\theta - 3\cos\theta$.

Finding roots of complex numbers

From trigonometry, we know that:

$$\cos\theta = \cos(\theta + n(360°)) = \cos(\theta + 2n\pi), \text{ where } n \in \mathbb{Z}$$

$$\sin\theta = \sin(\theta + n(360°)) = \sin(\theta + 2n\pi), \text{ where } n \in \mathbb{Z}$$

Thus, we can write for $n \in \mathbb{Z}$:

$$r(\cos\theta + i\sin\theta) = r[\cos(\theta + n(360°)) + i\sin(\theta + n(360°))] = r[\cos(\theta + 2n\pi) + i\sin(\theta + 2n\pi)]$$

When a complex number is written in the form $r[\cos(\theta + n(360°)) + i\sin(\theta + n(360°))]$, the complex number is said to be written in **general polar form**.

Method for finding roots of a complex number:

1. Write the number in polar form.
2. Write the number in general polar form.
3. Apply De Moivre's theorem.
4. Let $n = 0, 1, 2, \ldots$ (as required).

Candidates perform very badly when attempting to write a complex number in general polar form. It requires a bit of work. You can do it!

(2012 Q.3 (a))

The complex number z has modulus $5\frac{1}{16}$ and argument $\frac{4\pi}{9}$. Find in polar form, the four complex fourth roots of z. (That is, find the four values of w for which $w^4 = z$.)

Solution

$$w^4 = z = \frac{81}{16}(\cos 80° + i \sin 80°)$$

key point

$$5\frac{1}{16} = \frac{81}{16} \text{ and } \frac{4\pi}{9} = 80°$$

And $w^4 = z = \frac{81}{16}(\cos(80° + 360°n) + i\sin(80° + 360°n))$ where $n \in \mathbb{Z}$

$$w = z^{\frac{1}{4}} = \left[\frac{81}{16}(\cos(80° + 360°n) + i \sin(80° + 360°n))\right]^{\frac{1}{4}}$$

$$w = z^{\frac{1}{4}} = \left(\frac{81}{16}\right)^{\frac{1}{4}}(\cos(80° + 360°n) + \sin(80° + 360°n))^{\frac{1}{4}}$$

$$w = z^{\frac{1}{4}} = \frac{81^{\frac{1}{4}}}{16^{\frac{1}{4}}}\left(\cos\frac{1}{4}(80° + 360°n) + i\sin\frac{1}{4}(80° + 360°n)\right) \text{ by De Moivre's theorem}$$

$$w = z^{\frac{1}{4}} = \frac{3}{2}(\cos(20° + 90°n) + i \sin(20° + 90°n))$$

$$n = 0: z_0 = \frac{3}{2}(\cos(20° + 0°) + i \sin(20° + 0°)) = \frac{3}{2}(\cos 20° + i \sin 20°)$$

$$n = 1: z_1 = \frac{3}{2}(\cos(20° + 90°) + \sin(20° + 90°)) = \frac{3}{2}(\cos 110° + i \sin 110°)$$

$$n = 2: z_2 = \frac{3}{2}(\cos(20° + 180°) + i \sin(20° + 180°)) = \frac{3}{2}(\cos 200° + i \sin 200°)$$

$$n = 3: z_3 = \frac{3}{2}(\cos(20° + 270°) + i \sin(20° + 270°)) = \frac{3}{2}(\cos 290° + i \sin 290°)$$

This question was awarded 20 marks (= $6\frac{2}{3}$% of paper). The standard of answering was very poor.

A low partial credit of 14 marks ($4\frac{2}{3}$%) was awarded for any reasonable first step, e.g:

$$\cos\frac{4\pi}{9} + i\sin\frac{4\pi}{9} \text{ or } \cos 80° + i \sin 80° \text{ got 14 marks!}$$

Many candidates got 0 out of 20 marks. Shrewd candidates, who made a reasonable first step, got 14 out of 20 marks.

This type of question could be asked again.

Geometrical transformations of complex numbers
Rotations

> A **rotation** turns a point through an angle about a fixed point.

An **anticlockwise** turn is described as a **positive rotation**.	A **clockwise** turn is described as a **negative rotation**.
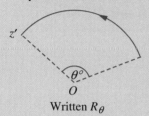 Written R_θ	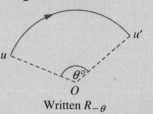 Written $R_{-\theta}$

Example

(i) Given $\mu = -2 - i$, plot the following on an Argand diagram:
$\mu, i\mu, i^2\mu, i^3\mu, i^4\mu$.

(ii) Give a geometrical interpretation of how to find the position of $i\mu$, $i^2\mu$ and $i^3\mu$ in relation to μ.

Solution

(i) $\mu = -2 - i$

$i\mu = i(-2 - i) = -2i - i^2 = 1 - 2i$

$i^2\mu = -1(-2 - i) = 2 + i$

$i^3\mu = -i(-2 - i) = 2i + i^2 = -1 + 2i$

$i^4\mu = 1(-2 - i) = -2 - i = \mu$

(ii) $i\mu$ is found by rotating μ 90° anticlockwise.

$i^2\mu$ is found by rotating μ 180° anticlockwise.

or $i^2\mu$ is found by central symmetry in the origin.

$i^3\mu$ is found by rotating μ 270° anticlockwise.

$i^4\mu = \mu$ is a rotation of 360°.

Every time a complex number is multiplied by i, the complex number is rotated by 90 degrees anticlockwise.

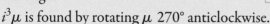

- All the above rotations are about the origin.
- Multiplication by i^1, i^2, i^3, i^4 results in an anticlockwise (positive) rotation.

Parallelogram

If z_1 and z_2 are two complex numbers, then z_1, z_2 and $z_1 + z_2$ form a parallelogram with the origin.

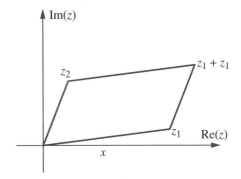

Sample paper

Four complex numbers, z_1, z_2, z_3 and z_4, are shown on the Argand diagram. They satisfy the following conditions:

$z_2 = iz_1$

$z_3 = kz_1$, where $k \in \mathbb{R}$

$z_4 = z_2 + z_3$

The same scale is used on both axes.

(i) Match the indicated points A, B, C, D on the diagram with the given complex numbers z_1, z_2, z_3, z_4.

(ii) Write down the approximate value of k.

Solution

(i) $z_2 = iz_1 \Rightarrow z_2$ is the image of z_1 by a rotation of 90° anticlockwise.

By observation of the given Argand diagram the only possible such rotation maps $C \rightarrow A$

$\therefore C = z_1$ and $A = z_2$

Next, $z_3 = kz_1 \Rightarrow z_3$ is a multiple of z_1. This means the origin, z_1 and z_3 are in the same straight line. By observation, $D = z_3$.

Hence, by elimination, $B = z_4$.

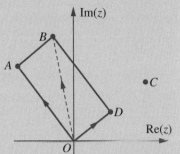

Alternatively, since we are given $z_4 = z_2 + z_3$, you may decide the shape $ABDO$, where O is the origin, forms a parallelogram. Then using the parallelogram rule,
we state $B = A + D \Rightarrow B = z_2 + z_3$.
Hence, $B = z_4$.

(ii) By observation from the diagram, $D = z_3$ is approximately midway between O and C
$\Rightarrow k$ is approximately $\frac{1}{2}$.

Dilations (enlargements)

If a complex number is multiplied by k, where $k \in \mathbb{R}$, then its modulus will be multiplied by k. In other words, if a complex number is multiplied by 2 (dilation by a factor of 2), then its distance from the origin will be twice as far from the origin as the original complex number.

If a complex number is multiplied by $\frac{1}{3}$ (dilation by a factor of $\frac{1}{3}$), then its distance from the origin will be one-third the distance from the origin as the original complex number.

Composition of rotations and dilations

If a complex number is multiplied by ki, where $k \in \mathbb{R}$, its modulus (distance from the origin) will by multiplied by k **and** it will be rotated by 90°. This is called a composition of a dilation and a rotation.

key point

If a non-zero complex number, z_1, is multiplied by another non-zero complex number, z_2, the result is a composition of a dilation and a rotation. This leads to:

1. Dilation (enlargement or transformation) by a factor of $|z_2|$ about the origin.
2. A rotation of $\mathrm{Arg}(z_2)$ about the origin.

Outward and inward spirals

If $\|z\| > 1$, then when a complex number is repeatedly multiplied by itself, it will spiral outwards (from the origin).	If $\|z\| < 1$, then when a complex number is repeatedly multiplied by itself, it will spiral inwards (towards the origin).
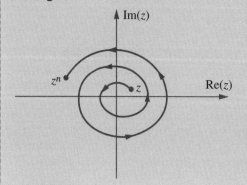	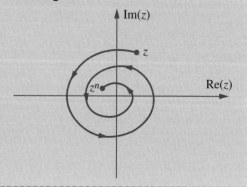

If $\|z\| = 1$, then when a complex number z is repeatedly multiplied by itself, it will always stay on a circle of radius 1.

Example

The planet Delaya orbits the star Alderaan. The Argand diagram below can be used to model positions in space relative to Alderaan where the position of Alderaan itself is represented by the origin.

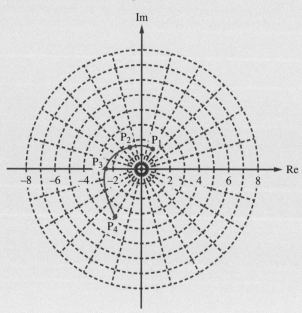

A deep space probe is launched from Delaya such that its position (P) relative to Alderaan on the diagram after t years can be modelled by the following equation

$$P(t) = (1·4)^t \left(\cos\frac{t\pi}{3} + i \sin\frac{t\pi}{3} \right)$$

P_1, P_2, P_3 and P_4 represent the positions of the probe after 1, 2, 3 and 4 years as shown on the diagram.

Each unit on the map represents 40 million km.

(i) Write down the distance from Delaya to Alderaan and mark the position of Delaya on the diagram.

(ii) Mark on the Argand diagram the points P_5 and P_6 the positions of the probe after 5 and 6 years.

(iii) How far away from Alderaan will the probe be after 4·8 years? Give your answer to the nearest million km.

(iv) The orbit of the planet Phantasia is approximately 3,850 million km from Alderaan. How many years will it take the probe to reach Phantasia's orbit? Give your answer to one decimal place.

Solution

(i) and (ii)

When $t = 0$

$$P(0) = (1·4)^0(\cos 0 + i\sin 0) = 1(1 + 0) = 1 \text{ unit} = 40 \text{ million km}$$

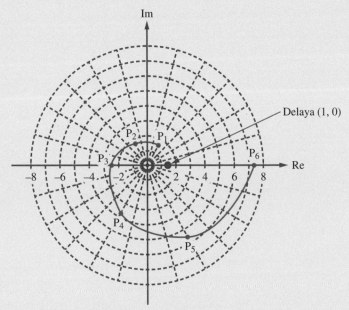

(iii) $P(4·8) \rightarrow$ distance $= (1·4)^{4·8} = 5·028$ units
$$= 5·028 \times 40 \text{ million km}$$
$$= 201 \text{ million km}$$

(iv) 3,850 million km $= \dfrac{3850}{40}$ units $= 96 \cdot 25$

Let k = number of years

Then $P(k) = (1 \cdot 4)^k = 96 \cdot 25$

$\quad \ln(1 \cdot 4)^k = \ln 96 \cdot 25$ (take ln of both sides)

$\quad k\ln(1 \cdot 4) = \ln 96 \cdot 25$ (see *booklet of formulae and tables*, page 21)

$\quad\quad\quad\quad k = 13 \cdot 6$ years

Note the links to other topics in the above question. In addition to complex number rotation we have pattern, scale, algebra and logs. Examiners love links between topics.

10 Pattern I

Sequences

A sequence is a particular order in which related things follow each other. For example:

(i) 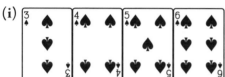 ?

(ii)  ?

(iii)

(iv) 1, 3, 6, 10, ?

Example

Which of these sequences is the odd one out? Justify your answer.

(i) $-3, -7, -11, -15, -19, -23, \ldots$ (iii) $2, 4, 8, 16, 32, 64, \ldots$

(ii) $1, 2, 3, 4, 5, 6, \ldots$ (iv) $1, 1, 2, 3, 5, 8 \ldots$

key point

When answering questions of this type, the important thing is not the sequence that you pick, but the reason why you picked it. In fact, for various reasons, they all could be the odd one out.

Solution

(i) Could be the odd one out because it is the only sequence with negative numbers.

key point

A sequence in which you go from term to term by adding (or subtracting) by the same number each time is called an **arithmetic sequence**.

(ii) Could be the odd one out because it is the list of natural numbers, $\mathbb{N}$. However, it is also an arithmetic sequence, with common difference $d = +1$.

(iii) Could be the odd one out because it is the only sequence that is geometric.

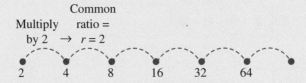

key point

A sequence in which you go from term to term by multiplying (or dividing) by the same number each time is called a **geometric sequence**.

(iv) Could be the odd one out because it is the only sequence with a number repeated.

key point

A sequence where each number is the sum of the previous two is called a **Fibonacci sequence**, that is, $F_{n+1} = F_n + F_{n-1}$ with $F_0 = 1$ and $F_1 = 1$.

Example

Match the following sequences labelled A, B, C and D with the given graphs labelled P, Q, R and S and state the type of sequence in each case.

A: $3, -3, 3, -3, 3, \ldots$

B: $625, 375, 225, 135, 81, \ldots$

C: $8, -6, \dfrac{9}{2}, -\dfrac{27}{8}, \dfrac{81}{32}, \ldots$

D: $43, 36, 29, 22, 15, \ldots$

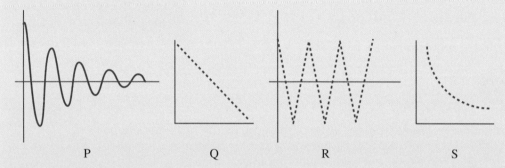

P   Q   R   S

Solution

$A \rightarrow R$ A geometric sequence with common ratio $= r = -1$.

$B \rightarrow S$ A geometric sequence with common ratio $= r = \dfrac{3}{5}$.

$C \rightarrow P$ A geometric sequence with common ratio $= r = -\dfrac{3}{4}$.

$D \rightarrow Q$ An arithmetic sequence with common difference $= d = -7$.

key point

The graph shown could represent

   (i) An arithmetic sequence, with common difference $= d = 0$

or **(ii)** A geometric sequence, with common ratio $= r = 1$.

Examples include $9, 9, 9, 9 \ldots$ [or] $\dfrac{2}{3}, \dfrac{2}{3}, \dfrac{2}{3}, \dfrac{2}{3} \ldots$

Recurrence equations

Sequences are often defined by giving an equation with a given term μ_{n+1} and the preceding term μ_n. This relationship between μ_{n+1} and μ_n is called a recurrence equation. A starting point for the sequence is needed and so the first term (or the first couple of terms) must also be given.

So if $\mu_1 = 2$ and $\mu_{n+1} = \mu_n + 3$

key point

Then when $n = 1$ $\quad \mu_2 = \mu_1 + 3 = 2 + 3 = 5$

When $n = 2$ $\quad \mu_3 = \mu_2 + 3 = 5 + 3 = 8$

When $n = 3$ $\quad \mu_4 = \mu_3 + 3 = 8 + 3 = 11$

When a recurring equation is used, the sequence is said to be defined recursively.

Thus the sequence is 2, 5, 8, 11, etc.

exam Q

(2016 Q.9 (b))

A male bee comes from an unfertilised egg, i.e. he has a female parent but he does not have a male parent. A female bee comes from a fertilised egg, i.e. she has a female parent and a male parent.

(i) The following diagram shows the ancestors of a certain male bee. We identify his generation as G_1 and our diagram goes back to G_4. Continue the diagram to G_5.

G_1	G_2	G_3	G_4	G_5
			Female	
		Female		
Male → Female			Male	
		Male → Female		

(ii) The number of ancestors of this bee in each generation can be calculated by the formula

$$G_{n+2} = G_{n+1} + G_n,$$

where $G_1 = 1$ and $G_2 = 1$, as in the diagram.

Use this formula to calculate the number of ancestors in G_6 and in G_7.

(iii) The number of ancestors in each generation can also be calculated by using the formula

$$G_n = \frac{(1 + \sqrt{5})^n - (1 - \sqrt{5})^n}{2^n \sqrt{5}}$$

Use this formula to verify the number of ancestors in G_3.

Solution

(i)

G_1	G_2	G_3	G_4	G_5
				Female
			Female → Male	Male
		Female		
Male → Female			Male → Female	Female
		Male	Female ← Female	Female
				Male

(ii) $G_{n+2} = G_{n+1} + G_n$

$n = 1 \rightarrow G_3 = G_2 + G_1$

$n = 2 \rightarrow G_4 = G_3 + G_2$

$n = 3 \rightarrow G_5 = G_4 + G_3$ then $G_5 = 3 + 2 = 5$

$n = 4 \rightarrow G_6 = G_5 + G_4$ then $G_6 = 5 + 3 = 8$

$n = 5 \rightarrow G_7 = G_6 + G_5$ then $G_7 = 8 + 5 = 13$

You must use the formula provided.

(iii) Now $G_n = \dfrac{(1 + \sqrt{5})^n - (1 - \sqrt{5})^n}{2^n\sqrt{5}}$ becomes

$G_3 = \dfrac{(1 + \sqrt{5})^3 - (1 - \sqrt{5})^3}{2^3\sqrt{5}}$ when $n = 3$

$(1 + \sqrt{5})^3 = \binom{3}{0}(1)^3(\sqrt{5})^0 + \binom{3}{1}(1)^2(\sqrt{5})^1 + \binom{3}{2}(1)^1(\sqrt{5})^2 + \binom{3}{3}(1)^0(\sqrt{5})^3$

$= (1)(1)(1) + (3)(1)(\sqrt{5}) + (3)(1)(5) + (1)(1)(5\sqrt{5})$

$= 1 + 3\sqrt{5} + 15 + 5\sqrt{5}$

$= 16 + 8\sqrt{5}$

Refer to *Chapter 7: Binomial Theorem*, if required.

Using the same method $(1 - \sqrt{5})^3 = 1 - 3\sqrt{5} + 15 - 5\sqrt{3} = 16 - 8\sqrt{5}$

$G_3 = \dfrac{16 + 8\sqrt{5} - (16 - 8\sqrt{5})}{8\sqrt{5}} = \dfrac{16\sqrt{5}}{8\sqrt{5}} = 2$

This question was awarded 20 marks. Overall, candidates' performances were patchy. Part (ii) was awarded 10 marks, however, the standard of answering was disappointing.

exam Q

(2018 Q.5 (b))

The first two terms of a sequence are $a_1 = 4$ and $a_2 = 2$.

The general term is defined by $a_n = a_{n-1} - a_{n-2}$, when $n \geq 3$.

Write out the next 6 terms of the sequence **and hence** find the value of a_{2019}

Solution

$$a_n = a_{n-1} - a_{n-2}$$

$n = 3$ then $a_3 = a_2 - a_1 = 2 - 4 = -2$

$n = 4$ then $a_4 = a_3 - a_2 = -2 - 2 = -4$

$n = 5$ then $a_5 = a_4 - a_3 = -4 - (-2) = -2$

$n = 6$ then $a_6 = a_5 - a_4 = -2 - (-4) = 2$

$n = 7$ then $a_7 = a_6 - a_5 = 2 - (-2) = 4$

$n = 8$ then $a_8 = a_7 - a_6 = 4 - 2 = 2$

$n = 9$ then $a_9 = a_8 - a_7 = 2 - 4 = -2$

The first six terms are 4, 2, −2, −4, −2, 2.

The sequence repeats itself every six terms.

$a_6 = a_{2016} = 2$ Why?   Because 2016 is a multiple of 6.

Then $a_{2017} = 4$

And $a_{2018} = 2$

And $a_{2019} = -2$

 exam focus

This question from 2018 exam shows very poor judgement by the examiner. Overall, the standard of answering was extremely poor. As a result, for part (b) above, 3 marks out of a total of 5 marks were awarded for finding a_3. Remember, you must stick to your time budget.

Diverging sequences

The sequence 4, 12, 36, 108 ... is divergent, as its $\mu_n (= T_n)$ has no limit as $n \to \infty$. The rules for convergence are strict. For example $-3, 3, -3, 3, -3, \ldots$ is very predictable, but $\underset{n \to \infty}{\text{Lim}} T_n$ does not exist, as there is no (single) value that T_n approaches as $n \to \infty$, so the sequence is divergent. The following graphs are divergent:

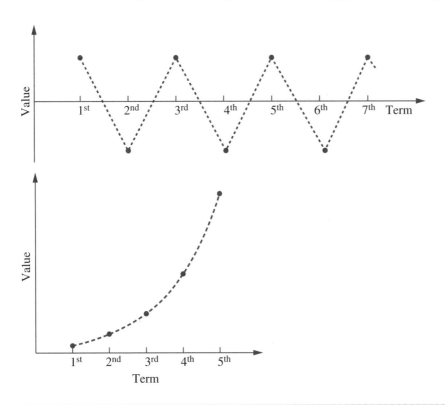

Example

A sequence is to be generated from the iteration formula $\mu_{n+1} = \dfrac{\mu_n + 3}{2}$.

(i) Starting with $\mu_1 = 7$, generate a sequence of seven terms.

(ii) Suggest a possible limit of this sequence.

Solution

(i) $\qquad \mu_{n+1} = \dfrac{\mu_n + 3}{2}$

$n = 1 \implies \mu_2 = \dfrac{\mu_1 + 3}{2} = \dfrac{7 + 3}{2} = 5 \quad$ (given, $\mu_1 = 7$)

$n = 2 \implies \mu_3 = \dfrac{\mu_2 + 3}{2} = \dfrac{5 + 3}{2} = 4$

$$n = 3 \implies \mu_4 = \frac{\mu_3 + 3}{2} = \frac{4 + 3}{2} = 3.5$$

$$n = 4 \implies \mu_5 = \frac{\mu_4 + 3}{2} = \frac{3.5 + 3}{2} = 3.25$$

$$n = 5 \implies \mu_6 = \frac{\mu_5 + 3}{2} = \frac{3.25 + 3}{2} = 3.125$$

$$n = 6 \implies \mu_7 = \frac{\mu_6 + 3}{2} = \frac{3.125 + 3}{2} = 3.0625$$

(ii) The sequence appears to be heading closer and closer to 3. We say the limit of the sequence is 3.

key point

When a sequences **converges** towards a number, it is called a converging sequence. Furthermore, any sequence (or series) that is not convergent must be described as **divergent**.

Differencing

Many investigative and problem-solving questions lead to a sequence of numbers. The technique of differencing is useful in certain situations involving sequences. To observe an application of differencing, we apply the technique to the sequence 2, 10, 30, 68, 130, 222 . . .

To do this:

- Subtract the first number in the sequence from the second.
- Subtract the second number in the sequence from the third.
- Subtract the third number in the sequence from the fourth and so on.

The *second* differences can be found by taking the difference of the differences. The third differences can then be found and so on again.

Hence we find:

	First difference (first change)	Second difference (change of change)	Third difference (change of change of change)
$\mu_1 = 2$			
	8		
$\mu_2 = 10$		12	
	20		6
$\mu_3 = 30$		18	
	38		6
$\mu_4 = 68$		24	
	62		6
$\mu_5 = 130$		30	
	92		
$\mu_6 = 222$			

This technique will help us to find $\mu_n (= T_n)$, the general term in a later example.

To find the general term of a sequence with differencing

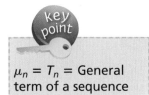

An arithmetic sequence, $\mu_n = kn + h$ where $k, h \in \mathbb{R}$ may also be called a linear sequence. A linear sequence (function) satisfies the condition that the first difference is constant.

A sequence in the form $\mu_n = an^2 + bn + c$ where $a, b, c \in \mathbb{R}$, is called a quadratic sequence. A quadratic sequence (function) satisfies the condition that the second difference is constant.

Similarly, a sequence of the form $\mu_n - pn^3 + qn^2 + rn + s$ where p, q, r and $s \in \mathbb{R}$, is called a cubic sequence. A cubic sequence (function) satisfies the condition that the third difference is constant.

Example

A sequence is $9, 17, 31, 51, 77, 109 \ldots$ and the pattern is continued.

(i) Show that the sequence is not linear (arithmetic)

(ii) Show that the sequence is quadratic

Solution

(i) Since a pattern is not immediately obvious we make use of the technique called differencing in order to help us decide.

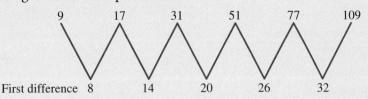

As the first difference is not constant we conclude the sequence is not linear (arithmetic)

(ii)

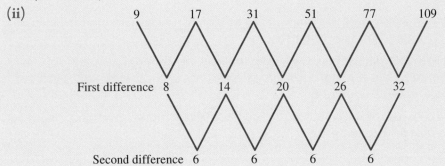

As the second difference is constant we know the sequence is quadratic.

(2013 Q.6)

Shapes in the form of small equilateral triangles can be made using matchsticks of equal length. These shapes can be put together into patterns. The beginning of a sequence of these patterns is show below.

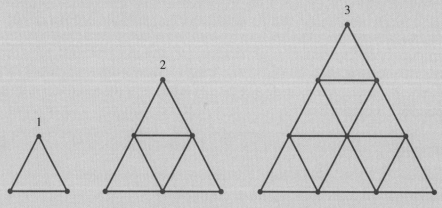

(a) (i) Draw the fourth pattern in the sequence.

(ii) The table below shows the number of small triangles in each pattern and the number of matchsticks needed to create each pattern. Complete the table.

Pattern	1st	2nd	3rd	4th
Number of small triangles	1		9	
Number of matchsticks	3	9		

(b) Write an expression in n for the number of triangles in the nth pattern in the sequence.

(c) Find an expression, in n, for the number of matchsticks needed to turn the $(n-1)^{th}$ pattern into the nth pattern.

(d) The number of matchsticks in the nth pattern in the sequence can be represented by the function $u_n = an^2 + bn$ where $a, b \in \mathbb{Q}$ and $n \in \mathbb{N}$. Find the value of a and the value of b.

(e) One of the patterns in the sequence has 4134 matchsticks. How many small triangles are in that pattern?

Solution

(a) (i)

(ii)

Pattern	1st	2nd	3rd	4th
Number of small triangles	1	4	9	16
Number of matchsticks	3	9	18	30

(b) The number of (small) triangles in the sequence

1, 4, 9, 16 . . .

$(1)^2, (2)^2, (3)^2, (4)^2$ . . .

Then n^{th} pattern has n^2 (small) triangles

(c) To turn pattern 1 into pattern 2 requires six extra matches (3×2)

To turn pattern 2 into pattern 3 requires nine extra matches (3×3)

To turn pattern 3 into pattern 4 requires twelve extra matches (3×4)

To turn pattern 4 into pattern 5 requires fifteen extra matches (3×5)

Then to turn pattern $(n - 1)$ into pattern n requires $3n$ extra matches. Wow!

(d) $u_n = an^2 + bn$

$u_1 = a(1)^2 + b(1) = a + b$

$u_2 = a(2)^2 + b(2) = 4a + 2b$

By observation $u_1 = $ first term $= 3$ matchsticks

$u_2 = $ second term $= 9$ matchsticks

By comparison

$a + b = 3$

$\underline{4a + 2b = 9}$ (multiply by -2)

$-2a - 2b = -6$

$\underline{4a + 2b = 9}$

$2a = 3$

$a = \dfrac{3}{2}$

Substitute $a = \dfrac{3}{2}$ into $a + b = 3$

$\dfrac{3}{2} + b = 3$

$b = \dfrac{3}{2}$

(e) $u_n = an^2 + bn = \dfrac{3}{2}n^2 + \dfrac{3}{2}n$ from part (d)

Given $u_n = 4134$

By comparison $\dfrac{3}{2}n^2 + \dfrac{3}{2}n = 4134$

$3n^2 + 3n = 8268$

$n^2 + n - 2756 = 0$

$(n + 53)(n - 52) = 0$

$n = -53$ or $n = 52$

Reject $n = -53$ since n cannot be negative.

Finally the number of small triangles given by $u_n = n^2$

$u_{52} = 52^2$

$u_{52} = 2704$

11 Pattern II

Arithmetic sequences and series

An example of an arithmetic sequence is: $8, 11, 14, 17, \ldots$

An example of an arithmetic series is: $8 + 11 + 14 + 17 + \cdots$

$\mu_n = T_n$ is the nth term. In the above sequence $\mu_n = 3n + 5$.

S_n is the sum of the first n terms and is written $\sum_{r=1}^{n} \mu_r$. The general form of an arithmetic sequence is written as:

$$a \quad a+d \quad a+2d \quad a+3d \quad a+4d \quad a+5d$$

With $a = $ first term $= \mu_1 = T_1$ and $d = $ common difference.

key point

1. $\mu_n = T_n = a + (n-1)d$

2. $S_n = \dfrac{n}{2}[2a + (n-1)d]$ see *booklet of formulae and tables*, page 22

3. $\mu_n - \mu_{n-1} = \text{constant} = d$

4. If three terms, μ_n, μ_{n+1} and μ_{n+2}, are in arithmetic sequence, then:

$$\mu_{n+2} - \mu_{n+1} = \mu_{n+1} - \mu_n$$

5. μ_n may be determined from S_n by the rule

$$\mu_n = S_n - S_{n-1}$$

Example

Evaluate $\displaystyle\sum_{r=1}^{5}(3n + 5)$.

Solution

$$\sum_{r=1}^{5}(3n + 5) = [3(1)+5] + [3(2)+5] + [3(3)+5] + [3(4)+5] + [3(5)+5]$$
$$= \quad 8 \quad + \quad 11 \quad + \quad 14 \quad + 17 \quad\quad + 20 = 70$$

The population of a type of insect is known to be 250,000 on January 1st in a particular year. Each month the population increases by 80,000.

Find:

(i) The total population on 1 January the following year

(ii) The month in which the population exceeds 7.2×10^5

key point

$$T_1 = \text{Jan 1st}, \ T_2 = \text{Feb 1st}, \ \ldots$$

The growth can be modelled by an arithmetic sequence with first term $a = 250{,}000$ and common difference $d = 80{,}000$.

Solution

(i) For the population at the start of each month use the formula
$$T_n = a + (n - 1)d$$
January 1st of the next year is the start of month number 13.
To calculate $T_{13} \Rightarrow T_{13} = a + (13 - 1)d$
$$T_{13} = 250{,}000 + 12(80{,}000) = 1{,}210{,}000$$

(ii) $7.2 \times 10^5 = 720{,}000$
$$T_n = 250{,}000 + (n - 1)80{,}000$$
$$720{,}000 = 250{,}000 + (n - 1)80{,}000$$
$$470{,}000 = 80{,}000n - 80{,}000$$
$$6.875 = n$$

Hence, the population exceeds 7.2×10^5 during June, i.e. before July 1st.

Example

Ten markers are placed on the ground in a straight line at intervals of 8 metres. During a training session, a player, 8 m from the first marker, has to run to the first marker and back to the start, then run to the second marker and back to the start, and so on in succession until she runs to the tenth marker and back. Calculate the total distance run by the player.

Solution

Diagram

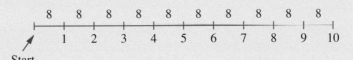

Start

The player runs to the first marker and back. This is a distance of 16 m.

To the second marker and back the distance is 32 m and so on.

Thus, the total distance run is given by:

$$16 + 32 + 48 + 64 + 80 + 96 + 112 + 128 + 144 + 160 = 880 \text{ m}$$

Alternatively, this is obviously an arithmetic series where $a = 16$ and $d = 16$, $n = 10$ and we require S_{10}.

$$S_n = \frac{n}{2}[2a + (n - 1)d]$$

$$S_{10} = \frac{10}{2}[2(16) + (10 - 1)16] \quad [a = 16, d = 16, n = 10]$$

$$= 5[32 + 144]$$

$$= 5[176]$$

$$= 880 \text{ m}$$

(i) Prove that the sum of the first n natural numbers is $\dfrac{n(n + 1)}{2}$.

(ii) If the sum of the first k natural numbers is 2,850, what is the value of k?

Solution

(i) Sum of first n natural numbers $= 1 + 2 + 3 + \cdots + (n - 1) + n$ is given by

$$S_n = \frac{n}{2}[2a + (n - 1)d] \quad \text{with first term } a = 1 \text{ and common difference } d = 1$$

$$S_n = \frac{n}{2}[2(1) + (n - 1)(1)]$$

$$S_n = \frac{n}{2}[2 + n - 1]$$

$$S_n = \frac{n}{2}(n + 1)$$

(ii) $S_k = 2{,}850$ and $S_k = \dfrac{k}{2}(k + 1)$ (from part **(i)**)

$$\therefore\ 2{,}850 = \dfrac{k}{2}(k + 1)$$

$$5{,}700 = k^2 + k \qquad\qquad\text{(multiply both sides by 2)}$$

$$0 = k^2 + k - 5{,}700$$

$$0 = (k - 75)(k + 76)$$

$$\therefore k - 75 = 0 \quad\text{or}\quad k + 76 = 0$$

$$k = 75 \quad\text{or}\quad\qquad k = -76$$

$$\text{Answer}\qquad\qquad\text{Reject}$$

In an arithmetic sequence, the fifth term is -18 and the tenth term is 12.

 (i) Find the first term and the common difference.

(ii) Find the sum of the first 15 terms of the sequence.

Solution

(i) $T_5 = -18 \quad\Rightarrow\quad a + 4d = -18$

  $T_{10} = 12 \quad\Rightarrow\quad \underline{a + 9d = 12} \qquad\qquad \text{(subtract)}$

  $\qquad\qquad\qquad\qquad\quad -5d = -30 \quad\Rightarrow\quad d = 6 \ \text{ and } \ a = -42$

(ii) $S_n = \dfrac{n}{2}[2a + (n - 1)d] \quad \therefore\ S_{15} = \dfrac{15}{2}[-84 + 14(6)] = \dfrac{15}{2}(0) = 0$

Three numbers are in arithmetic sequence. Their sum is 27 and their product is 704.

Find the three numbers.

Solution

Let the three terms be $a - d,\ a,\ a + d$.

Using $a,\ a + d,\ a + 2d$ leads to more complicated algebra.

Given $(a - d) + a + (a + d) = 27$ ① and $(a - d)(a)(a + d) = 704$ ②

$$3a = 27$$

$$a = 9$$

put $a = 9$ into ②

$$(9 - d)(9)(9 + d) = 704$$

$$9(81 - d^2) = 704$$

$$81 - d^2 = \frac{704}{9}$$

$$81 - \frac{704}{9} = d^2$$

$$\frac{25}{9} = d^2$$

$$\pm\frac{5}{3} = d$$

The three terms are $a - d$, a, $a + d$.

If $d = \frac{5}{3}$, terms are $9 - \frac{5}{3}$, 9, $9 + \frac{5}{3}$, i.e. $\frac{22}{3}$, 9, $\frac{32}{3}$.

If $d = \frac{-5}{3}$, terms are $9 + \frac{5}{3}$, 9, $9 - \frac{5}{3}$, i.e. $\frac{32}{3}$, 9, $\frac{22}{3}$.

exam Q (2014 Q.6(a))

The nth term of a sequence is $T_n = \ln a^n$, where $a > 0$ and a is a constant.

(a) (i) Show that T_1, T_2 and T_3 are in arithmetic sequence.

(ii) Prove that the sequence is arithmetic and find the common difference.

Solution

The use of the word 'prove' indicates the examiner is demanding a rigorous solution from the candidate. While the word 'show' is less demanding in terms of the solution.

However, part (i), the easy part, was awarded 10 marks while the more difficult part (ii) was awarded 5 marks. Overall, candidates performed well on (i) and badly on (ii).

(i) $T_n = \ln a^n$

$T_1 = \ln a^1 = 1\ln a$
$T_2 = \ln a^2 = 2\ln a$ see *booklet of formulae and tables*, page 21
$T_3 = \ln a^3 = 3\ln a$ $\log x^q = q \log x$

Now $T_2 - T_1 = 2\ln a - 1\ln a = \ln a$

And $T_3 - T_2 = 3\ln a - 2\ln a = \ln a$

We observe $T_3 - T_2 = T_2 - T_1$

Hence terms are in arithmetic sequence.

(ii) $T_n = \ln a^n = n \ln a$

$T_{n-1} = \ln a^{n-1} = (n - 1)\ln a$

Now $T_n - T_{n-1} = n\ln a - (n - 1)\ln a$

$\qquad\qquad\qquad = n\ln a - n\ln a + \ln a$

$\qquad\qquad\qquad = \ln a$ which is a constant

Common difference: $T_n - T_{n-1} = \ln a$

Hence the sequence is arithmetic.

Geometric sequences and series

An example of a geometric sequence is: $\dfrac{3}{10}, \dfrac{3}{20}, \dfrac{3}{40}, \dfrac{3}{80}, \ldots$

An example of a geometric series is: $\dfrac{3}{10} + \dfrac{3}{20} + \dfrac{3}{40} + \dfrac{3}{80} + \cdots$

In the above sequence, $\mu_n = \left(\dfrac{3}{10}\right)\left(\dfrac{1}{2}\right)^{n-1}$.

The general form of a geometric sequence is written as:

$a \qquad ar \qquad ar^2 \qquad ar^3 \qquad ar^4$

With $a =$ first term $= \mu_1 = T_1$ and $r =$ common ratio.

key point

1. $\mu_n = T_n = ar^{n-1}$

2. $S_n = \dfrac{a(1 - r^n)}{1 - r}$ $\Big\}$ see *booklet of formulae and tables*, page 22

3. $\dfrac{\mu_n}{\mu_{n-1}} = $ constant $= r$

4. If three terms, μ_n, μ_{n+1} and μ_{n+2}, are in geometric sequence, then:

$$\dfrac{\mu_{n+2}}{\mu_{n+1}} = \dfrac{\mu_{n+1}}{\mu_n}$$

5. μ_n may be determined from S_n by the rule

$$\mu_n = S_n - S_{n-1}$$

Example

Evaluate $\displaystyle\sum_{r=3}^{6} \frac{3}{10}\left(\frac{1}{2}\right)^{n-1}$.

Solution $\displaystyle\sum_{r=3}^{6} = \frac{3}{10}\left(\frac{1}{2}\right)^{3-1} + \frac{3}{10}\left(\frac{1}{2}\right)^{4-1} + \frac{3}{10}\left(\frac{1}{2}\right)^{5-1} + \frac{3}{10}\left(\frac{1}{2}\right)^{6-1}$

$$= \frac{3}{10}\left[\frac{1}{4} + \frac{1}{8} + \frac{1}{16} + \frac{1}{32}\right] = \frac{9}{64}$$

The first three terms of a geometric sequence are

$2x - 4,\ x + 1,\ x - 3$.

Find the two possible values of x.

Solution

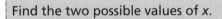

| a | ar | ar^2 | ar^3 | geometric |

$2x - 4 \qquad x + 1 \qquad x - 3$

For geometric sequences, $\dfrac{2^{nd}\ \text{term}}{1^{st}\ \text{term}} = \dfrac{3^{rd}\ \text{term}}{2^{nd}\ \text{term}}\ (= r).$

$$\frac{x + 1}{2x - 4} = \frac{x - 3}{x + 1}$$

$(x + 1)(x + 1) = (x - 3)(2x - 4)$ (multiply both sides by $(2x - 4)(x + 1)$)

$$x^2 + 2x + 1 = 2x^2 - 10x + 12$$

$$0 = x^2 - 12x + 11$$

$$0 = (x - 11)(x - 1)$$

$$\therefore \quad x = 11 \qquad \text{or} \qquad x = 1$$

The question ends at $x = 11$ and $x = 1$. However, the question could have asked you to find the two sequences; then the following would be required:

| a | ar | ar^2 | | a | ar | ar^2 |

$2x - 4 \quad x + 1 \quad x - 3 \qquad\qquad 2x - 4 \quad x + 1 \quad x - 3$

For $x = 11$ $\qquad\qquad$ For $x = 1$

$22 - 4,\ 11 + 1,\ 11 - 3 \qquad\qquad 2 - 4,\ 1 + 1,\ 1 - 3$

$18,\qquad 12,\qquad 8 \qquad\qquad\qquad -2,\qquad 2,\qquad -2$

(2017 Q.4(a))

The amount of a substance remaining in a solution reduces exponentially over time. An experiment measures the percentage of the substance remaining in the solution. The percentage is measured at the same time each day. The data collected over the first 4 days are given in the table below. Based on the data in the table, estimate which is the first day on which the percentage of the substance in the solution will be less than 0·01%.

Day	1	2	3	4
Percentage of substance %	95	42·75	19·2375	8·6569

Solution

We require $T_n = ar^{n-1} < 0.01$

First term $= a = 95$

Common ratio $= r = \dfrac{42.75}{95}$

$= \dfrac{19.2375}{42.75} = \dfrac{9}{20}$

key point

Exponentially = geometric

$95\left(\dfrac{9}{20}\right)^{n-1} < 0.01$

$\left(\dfrac{9}{20}\right)^{n-1} < \dfrac{0.01}{95}$ divide both sides by 95

$(n-1)\ln\left(\dfrac{9}{20}\right) < \ln\left(\dfrac{0.01}{95}\right)$ take ln of both sides

$n - 1 > \dfrac{\ln\left(\dfrac{0.01}{95}\right)}{\ln\left(\dfrac{9}{20}\right)}$ divide both sides by $\ln\left(\dfrac{9}{20}\right)$, which is negative. So we

change the direction of the inequality sign.

$n - 1 > 11.47$

$n > 12.47$

Answer: The percentage of the substance goes to below 0·01% during the 12th day.

 **exam focus**

This question was awarded 15 marks (5% of the paper). It was not well answered. If $r = \dfrac{9}{20}$ then 5 marks awarded, many candidates only got this.

Full marks for 12·47 or 12th day.

An application of sequences and series using $F = P(1 + i)^t$

We have already seen simple in-context applications of sequences and series, e.g. pair of rabbits, insect populations, etc. We now look at a straightforward geometric series question that models population change.

For a more comprehensive treatment applying geometric sequences and series to financial models, see *Chapter 13: Financial Maths II.*

For growth/increasing questions, use $F = P(1 + i)^t$.

For depreciation/decreasing questions, use $F = P(1 - i)^t$.

In January 2013 the polar bear population of the Arctic was estimated at 19,500. This population was considered to be decreasing due to the loss of sea ice habitat caused by climate change at a rate of 4% per annum.

(i) Given that this rate of decline continues, find an estimate (correct to the nearest one hundred) for the Arctic polar bear population in January 2024.

(ii) The World Wildlife Conservation Group states that a population of less than 6,000 polar bears in the wild will make polar bears a critically endangered species. Given that the rate of decrease continued to be 4% per annum, in what year would polar bears become critically endangered?

(iii) The Arctic Watch Organisation suggests that by January 2056 the population of polar bears in the wild will be less than 500 individuals. Calculate the annual rate of decrease used by Arctic Watch to arrive at this figure. (Give your answer in per cent correct to one decimal place.)

Solution

From Jan. 2013 to Jan. 2024 is 11 years ∴ $t = 11$ and the sequence is geometric. Use $(1 - i)$, as the rate is decreasing.

(i)

2013	2014	2015	2016	2017	2018	2019	2020	2021

$P(1-i)^0$ $P(1-i)^1$ $P(1-i)^2$ $P(1-i)^3$ $P(1-i)^4$

Now $F = P(1-i)^t$ where $P = 19{,}500$; $i = 4\% = 0.04$; and $t = 11$

Becomes $F = 19{,}500(0.96)^{11}$

$F = 12{,}400$ to the nearest 100 bears

(ii) Use $F = P(1-i)^t$ where $F = 6{,}000$; $i = 0.04$; and $P = 19{,}500$

$6{,}000 = 19{,}500(0.96)^t$

$0.307692307 = (0.96)^t$ (dividing both sides by 19,500)

$\ln(0.307692307) = t \ln(0.96)$ (take ln of both sides and note ln $A^p = p \ln A$)

$28.873 = t$

That is, in $2013 + 28.873 = 2041.873$

Answer: During 2041 they will become critically endangered in this scenario.

(iii) Again, use $F = P(1-i)^t$ where $F = 500$, $P = 19{,}500$ and

$t = 2056 - 2013 = 43$

$\Rightarrow$ $500 = 19{,}500(1-i)^{43}$

$\dfrac{1}{39} = (1-i)^{43}$ (dividing both sides by 19,500)

$\left(\dfrac{1}{39}\right)^{\frac{1}{43}} = 1 - i$ (take 43rd root of both sides)

$0.918329419 = 1 - i$

$i = 1 - 0.918329419$

$i = 0.082 = 8.2\%$ (percentage correct to one decimal place)

That is to say, the Arctic Watch Organisation is using an annual rate of decrease of 8·2% to estimate the future population of polar bears.

Infinite geometric series

For S_n, the sum of the first n terms, in a geometric series we find the term r^n.

For S_∞, the sum to infinity, in a geometric series we investigate as $n \to \infty$ the term r^n.

In cases where $|r| < 1$, we find expressions such as

$$\left(\frac{1}{2}\right)^n; \quad \left(\frac{2}{3}\right)^n; \quad \left(\frac{19}{20}\right)^n; \quad \left(-\frac{3}{4}\right)^n \text{ etc.}$$

For these cases as $n \to \infty$ the term $r^n \to 0$.

key point

Symbolically: $\lim\limits_{n\to\infty} (\text{proper fraction})^n = 0$

Typically we write:

$$\lim_{n\to\infty}\left(\frac{1}{2}\right)^n = 0; \quad \lim_{n\to\infty}\left(\frac{2}{3}\right)^n = 0; \quad \lim_{n\to\infty}\left(\frac{19}{20}\right)^n = 0 \text{ etc.}$$

Given a geometric series $S_n = a + ar + ar^2 + \ldots + ar^{n-2} + ar^{n-1}$, derive the formula for S_n.

The word 'derive', when used in an exam question, is considered stronger than 'prove', i.e. the examiner is demanding a rigorous solution from the candidate.

Hence, show that $\displaystyle\lim_{n\to\infty} S_n = \frac{a}{1-r}$ when $|r| < 1$.

Solution

$$S_n = a + ar + ar^2 + \cdots + ar^{n-2} + ar^{n-1}$$

(Multiply each term by r) $\quad r\,S_n = \qquad ar + ar^2 + \cdots + ar^{n-2} + ar^{n-1} + ar^n$

$$S_n - r\,S_n = a + 0 + 0 + \cdots + 0 + 0 - ar^n \qquad \text{(subtract)}$$

$$S_n(1-r) = a - ar^n$$

$$S_n = \frac{a(1-r^n)}{1-r}$$

Hence, for the S_n of a geometric series we write

$S_n = \dfrac{a(1-r^n)}{1-r}$ and as $n \to \infty$ we write

$$\lim_{n\to\infty} S_n = \lim_{n\to\infty}\left[\frac{a(1-r^n)}{1-r}\right] = \frac{a(1-0)}{1-r} \qquad \text{(for } |r| < 1,\ \lim_{n\to\infty} r^n = 0)$$

$$S_\infty = \frac{a}{1-r} \qquad\qquad \text{(see \textit{booklet of formulae and tables}, page 22)}$$

Learning the above proof and the technique employed is recommended, as it may be required in the exam.

Recurring decimals as infinite geometric series

Write the recurring decimal 0·63636363 . . . as an infinite geometric series and hence as a fraction.

Solution

0·63636363 · · ·

$$= \frac{63}{100} + \frac{63}{10,000} + \frac{63}{1,000,000} + \cdots$$

This is an infinite geometric series with $a = \frac{63}{100}$ and $r = \frac{1}{100}$.

$$S_\infty = \frac{a}{1 - r}, \quad \text{since } |r| = \frac{1}{100} < 1$$

$$= \frac{\frac{63}{100}}{1 - \frac{1}{100}} = \frac{\frac{63}{100}}{\frac{99}{100}} = \left(\frac{63}{100}\right)\left(\frac{100}{99}\right) = \frac{63}{99} = \frac{7}{11}$$

key point

Candidates should be familiar with the notation $0·\dot{6}\dot{3}$.

That is, $0·\dot{6}\dot{3} = 0·63636363 \ldots$

Exam questions using infinite geometric series

(2015 Q.1)

Mary threw a ball onto level ground from a height of 2 m. Each time the ball hit the ground it bounced back up to $\frac{3}{4}$ of the height of the previous bounce, as shown.

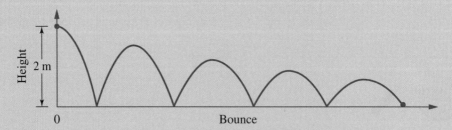

(a) Complete the table below to show the maximum height, in fraction form, reached by the ball on each of the first four bounces.

Bounce	0	1	2	3	4
Height (m)	$\frac{2}{1}$				

(b) Find, in metres, the total vertical distance (up and down) the ball had travelled when it hit the ground for the 5th time. Give your answer in fraction form.

(c) If the ball were to continue to bounce indefinitely, find, in metres, the total vertical distance it would travel.

Solution

(a)

Bounce	0	1	2	3	4
Height (m)	$\dfrac{2}{1}$	$\left(\dfrac{2}{1}\right)\left(\dfrac{3}{4}\right) = \dfrac{3}{2}$	$\left(\dfrac{2}{1}\right)\left(\dfrac{3}{4}\right)\left(\dfrac{3}{4}\right) = \dfrac{9}{8}$	$\left(\dfrac{2}{1}\right)\left(\dfrac{3}{4}\right)^3 = \dfrac{27}{32}$	$\left(\dfrac{2}{1}\right)\left(\dfrac{3}{4}\right)^4 = \dfrac{81}{128}$

> **key point**
>
> Geometric with common ratio $= r = \dfrac{3}{4}$

(b) Vertical distance when it hits the ground for the 5th time

$$= 2(\text{down}) + \frac{3}{2}(\text{up}) + \frac{3}{2}(\text{down}) + \frac{9}{8}(\text{up}) + \frac{9}{8}(\text{down}) + \frac{27}{32}(\text{up})$$
$$+ \frac{27}{32}(\text{down}) + \frac{81}{128}(\text{up}) + \frac{81}{128}(\text{down})$$

$$= 2 + 2\left[\frac{3}{2} + \frac{9}{8} + \frac{27}{32} + \frac{81}{128}\right]$$

$$= 2 + \frac{525}{64} = \frac{653}{64} = 10\frac{13}{14}\text{m}$$

(c) Bounce indefinitely distance

$$= 2 + 2\left[\frac{3}{2} + \frac{9}{8} + \frac{27}{32} + \cdots\right]$$

$$= 2 + S_\infty = 2 + 2\left(\frac{a}{1-r}\right)$$

$$= 2 + 2\left(\frac{\dfrac{3}{2}}{1 - \dfrac{3}{4}}\right) = 2 + 12 = 14 \text{ m}$$

(2016 Q.9 (a))

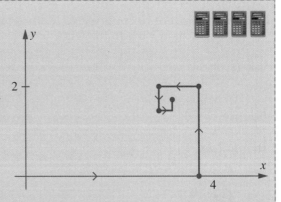

At the first stage of a pattern, a point moves 4 units from the origin in the positive direction along the x-axis. For the second stage, it turns left and moves 2 units parallel to the y-axis. For the third stage, it turns left and moves 1 unit parallel to the x-axis.

At each stage, after the first one, the point turns left and moves half the distance of the previous sstage, as shown.

(i) How many stages has the point completed when the total distance it has travelled, along its path, is 7·9375 units?

(ii) Find the maximum distance the point can move, along its path, if it continues in this pattern indefinitely.

(iii) Complete the second row of the table below showing the changes to the x co-ordinate, the first nine times the point moves to a new position. Hence, or otherwise, find the x co-ordinate and the y co-ordinate of the final position that the point is approaching, if it continues indefinitely in this pattern.

Stage	1st	2nd	3rd	4th	5th	6th	7th	8th	9th
Change in x	+4	0	−1						
Change in y									

Solution

(i) Total distance given by

$$4(\text{right}) + 2(\text{up}) + 1(\text{left}) + \frac{1}{2}(\text{down}) + \frac{1}{4}(\text{right}) + \frac{1}{8}(\text{up}) + \ldots$$

$$4 + 2 + 1 + \frac{1}{2} + \frac{1}{4} + \frac{1}{8} + \ldots$$

Is geometric, first term $a = 4$ common ratio $r = \frac{1}{2}$

$$S_n = \frac{a(1 - r^n)}{1 - r}$$

$$S_n = \frac{4\left(1 - \left(\frac{1}{2}\right)^n\right)}{1 - \frac{1}{2}}$$

$$7 \cdot 9375 = \frac{4\left(1 - \left(\frac{1}{2}\right)^n\right)}{\frac{1}{2}}$$

$$7 \cdot 9375 = 8\left(1 - \left(\frac{1}{2}\right)^n\right)$$

$$7 \cdot 9375 = 8 - 8\left(\frac{1}{2}\right)^n$$

$$8\left(\frac{1}{2}\right)^n = 8 - 7 \cdot 9375$$

$$8\left(\frac{1}{2}\right)^n = \frac{1}{16}$$

$$\frac{1}{2^n} = \frac{1}{128}$$

Therefore, $n = 7$

(ii) $S_\infty = \dfrac{a}{1-r} = \dfrac{4}{1 - \dfrac{1}{2}} = 8$

key point

Indefinitely $\rightarrow S_\infty$

(iii)

Stage	1st	2nd	3rd	4th	5th	6th	7th	8th	9th
Change in x	$+4$	0	-1	0	$\frac{1}{4}$	0	$-\frac{1}{16}$	0	$\frac{1}{64}$
Change in y	0	2	0	$-\frac{1}{2}$	0	$\frac{1}{8}$	0	$-\frac{1}{32}$	0

For x: $4, -1, \dfrac{1}{4}, -\dfrac{1}{16} \cdots$

$a = 4$ and $r = -\dfrac{1}{4}$

$S_\infty = \dfrac{a}{1-r} = \dfrac{4}{1 - \left(-\dfrac{1}{4}\right)} = 3 \cdot 2$

For y: $2, -\dfrac{1}{2}, \dfrac{1}{8}, -\dfrac{1}{32} \cdots$

$a = 2$ and $r = -\dfrac{1}{4}$

$S_\infty = \dfrac{a}{1-r} = \dfrac{2}{1 - \left(-\dfrac{1}{4}\right)} = 1 \cdot 6$

Answer $(3 \cdot 2, 1 \cdot 6)$

exam focus

Part (i) was awarded 10 marks ($3\frac{1}{3}$% of paper) and was well answered.

Part (ii) was awarded 10 marks ($3\frac{1}{3}$% of paper) and was well answered.

Part (iii) was awarded 15 marks (5% of paper) candidates struggled here. It is worth noting that 7 of the 15 marks were awarded for either the x-row or the y-row fully correct.

12 Financial Maths I: Arithmetic

☐ To learn how to calculate percentage mark-up, margin and loss
☐ To learn how to calculate relative error and percentage error
☐ To learn how to calculate compound interest and depreciation
☐ To learn how to calculate income tax

Percentage profit and loss

The percentage profit can be measured as a percentage of the cost price (mark-up) or the selling price (margin).

Mark-up is the profit, as a percentage of the cost price.	Margin is the profit, as a percentage of the selling price.
$\text{Mark-up} = \dfrac{\text{Profit}}{\text{Cost price}} \times 100$	$\text{Margin} = \dfrac{\text{Profit}}{\text{Selling price}} \times 100$

Example

A retailer bought a consignment of DVD players for €12,000. He sold half of them at a 14% mark-up and the other half at a 20% margin. Calculate the total profit made and hence the total selling price.

Solution

$\text{Mark-up} = \dfrac{\text{Profit}}{\text{Cost price}} \times 100$

$14 = \dfrac{\text{Profit}}{6000} \times 100$

$14 = \dfrac{\text{Profit}}{60}$

€840 = Profit

$\text{Margin} = \dfrac{\text{Profit}}{\text{Selling price}} \times 100$

$20 = \dfrac{\text{Profit}}{6000 + \text{profit}} \times 100$

$20(6000 + \text{profit}) = \text{profit} \times 100$

$120000 + 20(\text{profit}) = 100(\text{profit})$

$120000 = 100(\text{profit}) - 20(\text{profit})$

$120000 = 80(\text{profit})$

€1500 = profit

Total profit = €840 + €1,500 = €2,340

Total selling price = €12,000 + €2,340 = €14,340

In selling an item, if a loss is made, the **percentage loss** is calculated as:

$$\text{Percentage loss} = \frac{\text{Loss}}{\text{Cost price}} \times 100$$

Relative error and percentage error

When calculations are being made, errors can occur, especially calculations which involve rounding. It is important to have a measure of the error.

Definitions

Error = |true value − estimate value| and is always considered positive.

$$\text{Relative error} = \frac{\text{Error}}{\text{True value}}$$

$$\text{Percentage error} = \frac{\text{Error}}{\text{True value}} \times 100\%$$

Accumulated error: the collected inaccuracy that can occur when multiple errors are combined.

Example

Four telephone calls cost €3·85, €7·45, €8·40 and €11·55.

(i) John estimates the total cost of the four calls by ignoring the cent part in the cost of each call. Calculate the percentage error in his estimate.

(ii) Anne estimates the total cost of the four calls by rounding the cost of each call to the nearest euro. Calculate the percentage error in her estimate.

Solution

(i) True cost of the phone calls: €3·85 + €7·45 + €8·40 + €11·55 = €31·25.
John ignores the cent part of each value: €3 + €7 + €8 + €11 = €29.
Error = |true value − estimate|
Error = |€31·25 − €29|
Error = €2·25

$$\text{Percentage error} = \frac{\text{Error}}{\text{True value}} \times 100$$

$$\text{Percentage error} = \frac{2·25}{31·25} \times 100 = 7·2\% \text{ error}$$

(ii) True cost of the phone calls: €3·85 + €7·45 + €8·40 + €11·55 = €31·25.

Anne rounds to the nearest euro: €4 + €7 + €8 + €12 = €31.

Error = |true value − estimate|

Error = |€31·25 − €31|

Error = €0·25

$$\text{Percentage error} = \frac{\text{Error}}{\text{True value}} \times 100$$

$$\text{Percentage error} = \frac{0 \cdot 25}{31 \cdot 25} \times 100 = 0 \cdot 8\% \text{ error}$$

Index notation

When dealing with very large or very small numbers it can be easier to perform calculations if the numbers are expressed in the form $a \times 10^n$, where $0 < a < 10$.

A telecommunications company sends a satellite into orbit around Earth. The satellite is to be placed 200 km above the surface of the Earth. An engineer calculates the value for the acceleration due to gravity, g, on the satellite using the formula:

$$g = \frac{GM}{d^2}$$

Where:

G (universal gravitational constant) = $6 \cdot 7 \times 10^{-11}$

M (mass of the Earth) = 6×10^{24} kg

d = distance between the centre of the Earth and the satellite, in metres.

200 km

R

(i) Given that the radius of the Earth is $6 \cdot 37 \times 10^6$ m, find the value of acceleration due to gravity, g, at a point 200 km above the surface of the Earth.

(ii) An error occurs and the satellite is actually placed 240 km above the Earth's surface. Find the percentage error in the engineer's calculation of g, correct to two decimal places.

(iii) In order for the satellite to work at its optimum level, it must be placed at a height where the acceleration due to gravity, g, has a value of 9·3 m/s², with a tolerance of 0·05 m/s². Find the range of values for the height of the satellite, correct to the nearest km.

Tolerance

When making measurements, there is often an allowable percentage error. The tolerance is the amount of error accepted in a given situation.

Solution

(i) $G = 6\cdot7 \times 10^{-11}$ $M = 6 \times 10^{24}$ kg $d = 6\cdot37 \times 10^6 + 200000 = 6570000$

$$g = \frac{GM}{d^2}$$

$$g = \frac{(6\cdot7 \times 10^{-11})(6 \times 10^{24})}{6,570,000}$$

$$g = \frac{4\cdot02 \times 10^{14}}{4\cdot31649 \times 10^{13}}$$

$$g = 9\cdot3131$$

(ii) $G = 6\cdot7 \times 10^{-11}$ $M = 6 \times 10^{24}$ kg $d = 6\cdot37 \times 10^6 + 240,000 = 6610000$

$$g = \frac{GM}{d^2}$$

$$g = \frac{(6\cdot7 \times 10^{-11})(6 \times 10^{24})}{(6610000)^2}$$

$$g = \frac{4\cdot02 \times 10^{14}}{4\cdot36921 \times 10^{13}}$$

$$g = 9\cdot2$$

Error = |true value − estimate|

Error = |9·2 − 9·3131|

Error = 0·1131

$$\text{Percentage error} = \frac{\text{Error}}{\text{True value}} \times 100$$

$$\text{Percentage error} = \frac{0\cdot1131}{9\cdot2} \times 100 = 1\cdot23\%$$

Therefore, the engineer's calculation has a 1·23% error.

(iii) If the satellite is placed so that the value for g is at the lower end of the tolerance:

$$g = 9\cdot25 \quad G = 6\cdot7 \times 10^{-11} \quad M = 6 \times 10^{24} \text{ kg} \quad d = ?$$

$$g = \frac{GM}{d^2}$$

$$9\cdot25 = \frac{(6\cdot7 \times 10^{-11})(6 \times 10^{24})}{d^2}$$

$$9\cdot25 = \frac{4\cdot02 \times 10^{14}}{d^2}$$

$$d^2 = \frac{4\cdot02 \times 10^{14}}{9\cdot25}$$

$$d = \sqrt{\frac{4\cdot02 \times 10^{14}}{9\cdot25}} = 6,592,378\cdot89 \text{ m}$$

exam focus

You could have let the distance equal the radius plus the height, i.e. $d = 6\cdot37 \times 10^6 + H$, and then solve for H. However, this would result in solving a quadratic equation, which would make the algebra part more challenging.

Height above Earth = d − radius

Height above Earth = $6592378 \cdot 89 - 6 \cdot 37 \times 10^6$

Height above Earth = $222{,}378 \cdot 89$ m

If the satellite is placed so that the value for g is at the upper end of the tolerance:

$g = 9 \cdot 35 \qquad G = 6 \cdot 7 \times 10^{-11} \qquad M = 6 \times 10^{24}$ kg $\qquad d = ?$

$$g = \frac{GM}{d^2}$$

$$9 \cdot 35 = \frac{(6 \cdot 7 \times 10^{-11})(6 \times 10^{24})}{d^2}$$

$$9 \cdot 35 = \frac{4 \cdot 02 \times 10^{14}}{d^2}$$

$$d^2 = \frac{4 \cdot 02 \times 10^{14}}{9 \cdot 35}$$

$$d = \sqrt{\frac{4 \cdot 02 \times 10^{14}}{9 \cdot 35}} = 6{,}557{,}030 \cdot 76 \text{ m}$$

Height above Earth = d − radius

Height above Earth = $6557030 \cdot 76 - 6 \cdot 37 \times 10^6$

Height above Earth = $187{,}030 \cdot 76$ m

Thus, the satellite must be placed somewhere between 187 km and 222 km above the surface of the Earth.

Interest

Interest is the sum of money that you pay for borrowing money or that is paid to you for lending money.

When dealing with interest, we use the following symbols:

P = the **principal**, the sum of money borrowed or invested at the beginning of the period.

t = the **time**, the number of weeks/months/years for which the sum of money is borrowed or invested.

i = the **interest rate**, the percentage rate per week/month/year expressed as a fraction or a decimal at which interest is charged.

F = the **final amount**, i.e. the final sum of money, including interest, at the end of the period.

(see *booklet of formulae and tables*, page 30)

Note: per annum = per year.

Annual equivalent rate (AER) and annual percentage rate (APR)
(both percentage rates)
Investments: AER tells you how much your money would earn in exactly one year.
Loans: APR tells you how much your loan will grow by in exactly one year.

Compound interest

When a sum of money earns interest, this interest is often added to the principal to form a new principal. This new principal earns interest in the next year and so on. This is called **compound interest**.

When calculating compound interest, do the following.
Method 1:

Calculate the interest for the **first** year and add this to the principal to form the new principal for the next year. Calculate the interest for **one** year on this new principal and add it on to form the principal for the next year, and so on. The easiest way to calculate each stage is to multiply the principal at the beginning of each year by the factor:

$$(1 + i)$$

This will give the principal for the next year, and so on.

Method 2:
If the number of years is greater than three, then using a formula and a calculator will be much quicker.

Use the formula: $F = P(1 + i)^t$ (see *booklet of formulae and tables*, page 30)

The formula does not work if:
the interest rate, i, is changed during the period
or
money is added or subtracted during the period.

Example

€12,500 is invested in a savings account where the interest is compounded annually with an AER of 3·75%. Calculate the future value of this investment in five years.

Solution

$P = 12500 \qquad i = 3\cdot75\% = \dfrac{3\cdot75}{100} = 0\cdot0375 \qquad t = 5$

$F = P(1 + i)^t$

$F = 12500(1 + 0\cdot0375)^5$

$F = 12500(1\cdot0375)^5$

$F = 15026\cdot25$

The €12,500 investment is worth €15,026·25 in five years' time.

€6,750 is borrowed for a period of 21 months at an APR of 5%.

(i) Convert an APR of 5% to its equivalent monthly rate.

(ii) Find the final value of the €6,750 loan after 21 months.

Solution

(i) Convert the APR to monthly rate:

$1 + \text{APR} = (1 + \text{monthly rate})^{12}$

$1 + 0\cdot05 = (1 + i)^{12}$

$\sqrt[12]{1\cdot05} = 1 + i$

$\sqrt[12]{1\cdot05} - 1 = i$

$0\cdot0040741 = i$

key point

To convert annual rate to monthly rate:

$\left(\sqrt[12]{1 + \text{annual rate}}\right) - 1 = \text{monthly rate}$

(ii) $P = 6750 \qquad i = 0\cdot0040741 \qquad t = 21$

$F = P(1 + i)^t$

$F = 6750(1 + 0\cdot0040741)^{21}$

$F = 6750(1\cdot0040741)^{21}$

$F = 7351\cdot65$

The final value of the €6,750 loan after 21 months is €7,351·65.

key point

In this solution, we could have left the rate as the annual rate and converted the time, t, into a fraction of a year. 21 months $= \frac{21}{12}$ of a year:

$F = 6750(1 + 0\cdot05)^{\frac{21}{12}} = €7{,}351\cdot65$

Continuous compounding

Sometimes the interest is compounded continuously. In this case, the compounding period becomes infinitesimally small and so the growth rate is exponential.

The formula for calculating the final value is:

$$F = Pe^{rt}$$

Where:

F = final value P = principal

r = nominal annual rate t = number of years

(see *booklet of formulae and tables*, page 32)

Example

A sum of money is invested at a nominal annual rate of 6·45%, where the interest is compounded continuously. Find, correct to two decimal places, the time it takes for the sum of money to triple in value.

Solution

Let $P = P$, $r = 0\cdot0645$, $F = 3P$

$$F = Pe^{rt}$$

$$3P = Pe^{(0\cdot0645)t}$$

$$3 = e^{(0\cdot0645)t} \qquad \text{(divide both sides by } P\text{)}$$

$$\log_e 3 = 0\cdot645t \qquad \text{(apply the log function)}$$

$$\ln 3 = 0\cdot0645t$$

$$\frac{\ln 3}{0\cdot0645} = t$$

$$17\cdot03 = t$$

It will take 17·03 years for the investment to triple in value.

Depreciation (reducing balance method)

Over time, material goods (e.g. machinery, vehicles, etc.) lose value as a result of wear and tear, age or obsolescence. This loss of value is known as depreciation.

Reducing balance method

Using the reducing balance method, the cost of the asset is depreciated at a constant rate each year. This method is based on the principle that an asset is more useful in its initial years than in its later years. So instead of spreading the total cost of the asset over its productive lifespan, it is expensed at a constant rate. The depreciated value of an asset can be found by calculating the value at the end of each year or by using the depreciation formula.

Depreciation formula

$$F = P(1 - i)^t$$

Where:

F = final value (net book value, NBV)

P = original value at the start of the period

i = rate, in decimal form

t = number of years   (see *booklet of formulae and tables*, page 30)

Example

A machine which cost €35,650 depreciates to a value of €480 in 10 years. Calculate:

(i) The annual rate of depreciation if the reducing balance method of depreciation is to be used

(ii) The net book value, to the nearest euro, at the end of the sixth year

Solution

(i) Use the depreciation formula, where $F = 480$, $P = 35650$, $t = 10$, $i = ?$

$$F = P(1 - i)^t$$

$$480 = 35650(1 - i)^{10}$$

$$\frac{480}{35650} = (1 - i)^{10}$$

$$\sqrt[10]{\frac{480}{35650}} = 1 - i \qquad \text{(take 10}^{\text{th}} \text{ root of both sides)}$$

$$0 \cdot 6500 = 1 - i$$

$$i = 1 - 0 \cdot 6500$$

$$i = 0 \cdot 35$$

Rate = 35%

(ii) Use the depreciation formula to find the value of the machine after six years:

$$F = ?, \qquad P = 35{,}650, \qquad t = 6, \qquad i = 0 \cdot 35$$

$$F = P(1 - i)^t$$

$$F = 35650(1 - 0 \cdot 35)^6$$

$$F = 35650(0 \cdot 65)^6$$

$$F = 2688 \cdot 68$$

At the end of the sixth year, the machine is worth €2,689.

Olivia bought a new car for €17,800. The rate of depreciation is 16% for the first three years and it then drops to 11%.

(i) Find the value of the car after three years.

(ii) After how many years will the value of the car be €5,250?

Solution

(i) Use the depreciation formula to find the value of the car after three years:

$F = ?, \quad P = 17800, \quad t = 3, \quad i = 0{\cdot}16$

$F = P(1 - i)^t$

$F = 17800(1 - 0{\cdot}16)^3$

$F = 17800(0{\cdot}84)^3$

$F = 10550{\cdot}13$

Value of the car after three years is €10,550·13.

(ii) After three years the value of the car is €10,550·13, so find how many years later the value will be €5,250:

$F = 5250, \quad P = 10550{\cdot}13, \quad t = ?, \quad i = 0{\cdot}11$

$$F = P(1 - i)^t$$

$$5250 = 10550{\cdot}13(1 - 0{\cdot}11)^t$$

$$5250 = 10550{\cdot}13(0{\cdot}89)^t$$

$$\frac{5250}{10550{\cdot}13} = (0{\cdot}89)^t$$

$$\log_{0{\cdot}89}\left(\frac{5250}{10550{\cdot}13}\right) = t$$

$$5{\cdot}9889 = t$$

$$6 = t \quad \text{(to the nearest year)}$$

key point

Notice the use of logarithms in this question.

Six years later the value of the car will be €5,250.

Thus, after nine years the value of the car will be €5,250.

Income tax

The following is called the income tax equation:

gross tax − tax credit = tax payable

Gross tax is calculated as follows:

| Standard rate on all income up to the standard rate cut-off point | + | A higher rate on all income above the standard rate cut-off point |

Deductions on income

All deductions can be divided into two categories: statutory and non-statutory.

Statutory deductions:	Non-statutory deductions:
Compulsory deductions, which must be paid.	Voluntary deductions, which the worker can choose to pay or not pay.
Examples:	**Examples:**
Income tax	Pension contributions
Pay-Related Social Insurance (PRSI)	Trade union subscriptions
Universal Social Charge (USC)	Health insurance payments

Pay-Related Social Insurance (PSRI)

PRSI is made up of social insurance and health contributions. The social insurance part goes to funds to pay for social welfare and benefits in Ireland. The health contribution part goes to the Department of Health and Children to help fund health services in Ireland. The amount of PRSI an employe pays depends on how much they earn and is calculated as a percentage of their earnings. The employer will also pay a contribution to the employee's PRSI payment.

Universal Social Charge (USC)

The Universal Social Charge is a tax payable on gross income. This tax was introduced in 2011 to provide additional income for the state. The rates for USC can be changed in the annual budget. At time of publishing the rates were as follows:

1%	On the first €12,012
3%	On the next €6,656
5·5%	On the next €51,376
8%	On the balance

You are not required to learn off USC rates or PRSI bands. If they are required, you will be given them in the question.

Example

Kevin has a gross yearly income of €62,500. He has a standard rate cut-off point of €29,000 and a tax credit of €4,650. The standard rate of tax is 22% of income up to the standard rate cut-off point and 41% on all income above the standard rate cut-off point. Calculate:

  (i) Kevin's gross tax for the year

 (ii) The amount of tax paid for the year

(iii) The total USC Kevin must pay (based on the previous page)

(iv) Kevin's net pay for the year

Solution

  (i) Gross income: €62,500

              Tax: €29,000 at 22%   +   €33,500 at 41%

              Tax: €6,380   +   €13,735

         Gross tax: €20,115

 (ii) Net tax = gross tax − tax credit

     Net tax = €20,115 − €4,650

     Net tax = €15,465

(iii) USC:

     1% on €12,012 = €   120·12

     3% on €6,656 = €   199·68

     5·5% on €43,832 = €2,410·76

         Total USC = €2,730·56

(iv) Net pay = gross pay − net tax − USC

     Net pay = €62,500 − €15,465 − €2,730·56

     Net pay = €44,304·44

USC rates for this question

1%	On the first €12,012
3%	On the next €6,656
5·5%	On the next €51,376
8%	On the balance

Graham has a gross income of €70,000. His standard rate cut-off point is €28,200. The standard rate of tax is 19% and the higher rate is 41%. He has a tax credit of €3,750. Graham is in PRSI class A1, which means that he does not pay PRSI on the first €127 earned per week, but he pays it at a rate of 4% on all income above that amount (assume a 52-week year). Graham pays trade union subscriptions of €17 every two weeks, health insurance of €99 a month and a pension contribution of €375 per month.

(i) Calculate the total amount of income tax Graham must pay for the year.

(ii) Calculate his USC payment for the year.

(iii) Calculate his PRSI contribution per week, to the nearest cent.

(iv) What is Graham's weekly net income after all deductions?

Solution

(i) Gross income: €70,000

Tax: €28,200 at 19% + €41,800 at 41%

Tax: €5,358 + €17,138

Gross tax: €22,496

Net tax = gross tax − tax credit

Net tax = €22,496 − €3,750

Net tax = €18,746

key point

The USC rates will always be provided in the question.

(ii) USC:

2% on €10,036 = € 200·72

4% on €5,980 = € 239·20

7% on €53,984 = €3,778·88

Total USC = €4,218·80

USC rates for this question

2%	On the first €10,036
4%	On the next €5,980
7%	On the balance

(iii) PRSI:

Weekly income $= \dfrac{70000}{52} = €1{,}346·15$

First €127 is free of PRSI.

Therefore, weekly PRSI = 4% on €1,346·15 − €127 = €1,219·15

Weekly PRSI = €48·77

(iv) Weekly income = €1,346·15

Weekly deductions:

Tax = €360·50   (€18,746 ÷ 52)

USC = € 81·13   (€4,218·80 ÷ 52)

PRSI = € 48·77

Trade union = € 8·50   (€17 ÷ 2)

Health insurance = € 22·85   (€99 × 12 ÷ 52)

Pension = € 86·54   (€375 × 12 ÷ 52)

Total deductions = €608·29

Net income = weekly income − weekly deductions

Net income = €1,346·15 − €608·29

Net income = €737·86

13 Financial Maths II: Applications of Geometric Series

aims

☐ To learn how to apply the sum of a geometric series to periodic investments

☐ To learn how to convert an annual percentage rate to a monthly rate or a monthly rate to an annual rate

☐ To learn how to calculate the current value of an investment bond

☐ To learn how to work with pension funds

☐ To learn how to calculate the regular repayments on an amortised loan

Introduction

Time value of money

This is the value of money when factoring in a given amount of interest earned over a given time period. This is a concept which says it is more valuable to receive a sum of money now than in a year or two, as if you receive it now you can invest it and earn interest on it.

Present value

Also known as present discounted value, this is the value on a given date of a future payment or series of future payments, discounted to reflect the time value of money and other factors such as investment risk, etc. Present value calculations are used, for example, to find the fair market value of a bond, the amount of each regular payment for a given loan, how much money to invest now to receive a specific cash amount in the future and the size of a pension fund required on the date to retirement to give a fixed income every year for a certain number of years.

Discount rate

When future values are brought back to present values at a given rate of interest, the interest rate can be referred to as the discount rate.

Some saving schemes require the investor to save a fixed amount at regular intervals. Certain loan repayment schedules will require the borrower to make regular payments at fixed intervals of time. Calculations involving regular payments require the summation of a geometric series.

Annuities

A form of investment involving a series of periodic equal contributions made by an individual to an account for a specified term. The term 'annuity' is also used for a series of regular payments made to an individual for a specified time.

Payments in periods other than annually

Calculations are the same as for annual payments, but the AER or APR must be treated appropriately.

Method 1	Method 2
• Leave time in years.	• Switch to a different time period.
• Do not change the APR/AER.	• Adjust the APR/AER accordingly.
• Use fractional units of time.	• Use whole number units of time.

Example

The post office offers a savings account with an AER of 4%. Janet deposits €125 at the start of each month for a two-year period. How much will her investment be worth at the end of the two years?

Solution

Method 1: Leave time in years, use fractional units of time

Use the formula: $\qquad F = P(1 + i)^t \qquad$ Let: $P = 125$, $i = 0{\cdot}04$

The first €125 deposit will be in the account for 24 months $\left(\frac{24}{12} \text{ years}\right)$, the second €125 deposit will be in the account for 23 months, etc.

$$F = 125(1{\cdot}04)^{\frac{24}{12}} + 125(1{\cdot}04)^{\frac{23}{12}} + 125(1{\cdot}04)^{\frac{22}{12}} + \cdots + 125(1{\cdot}04)^{\frac{1}{12}}$$

$$F = 125\left[(1{\cdot}04)^{\frac{24}{12}} + (1{\cdot}04)^{\frac{23}{12}} + (1{\cdot}04)^{\frac{22}{12}} + \cdots + (1{\cdot}04)^{\frac{1}{12}}\right]$$

Rewriting the series in ascending order:

$$F = 125\left[(1{\cdot}04)^{\frac{1}{12}} + (1{\cdot}04)^{\frac{2}{12}} + (1{\cdot}04)^{\frac{3}{12}} + \cdots + (1{\cdot}04)^{\frac{24}{12}}\right]$$

The part in the squared brackets is a geometric series, where: $a = (1 \cdot 04)^{\frac{1}{12}}$

$$r = (1 \cdot 04)^{\frac{1}{12}}, n = 24$$

$$S_n = \frac{a(r^n - 1)}{r - 1} \qquad \text{(see \textit{booklet of formulae and tables}, page 22)}$$

$$S_{24} = \frac{(1 \cdot 04)^{\frac{1}{12}}\left[\left((1 \cdot 04)^{\frac{1}{12}}\right)^{24} - 1\right]}{(1 \cdot 04)^{\frac{1}{12}} - 1}$$

$$S_{24} = \frac{1 \cdot 00327374[0 \cdot 0816]}{0 \cdot 00327373978}$$

$$S_{24} = 25 \cdot 00722192$$

So,

$$F = 125(25 \cdot 00722192)$$

$$F = €3,125 \cdot 90$$

Method 2: Change time to months and adjust AER

Adjust AER to find monthly percentage rate:

$$F = P(1 + i)^t$$
$$1 \cdot 04 = 1(1 + i)^{12}$$
$$\sqrt[12]{1 \cdot 04} = 1 + i$$
$$1 \cdot 00327374 = 1 + i$$
$$0 \cdot 00327374 = i$$

The first €125 deposit will be in the account for 24 months, the second €125 deposit will be in the account for 23 months, etc.

$$F = 125(1 \cdot 00327374)^{24} + 125(1 \cdot 00327374)^{23} + \cdots + 125(0 \cdot 00327374)^{1}$$
$$F = 100[(1 \cdot 00327374)^{24} + (1 \cdot 00327374)^{23} + \cdots + (1 \cdot 00327374)^{1}]$$

Rewriting the series in ascending order:

$$F = 125[(1 \cdot 00327374)^{1} + (1 \cdot 00327374)^{2} + \cdots + (1 \cdot 00327374)^{24}]$$

The part in the squared brackets is a geometric series, where: $a = 1 \cdot 00327374$

$$r = 1 \cdot 00327374$$
$$n = 24$$

$$S_n = \frac{a(r^n - 1)}{r - 1}$$

$$S_{24} = \frac{1 \cdot 00327374[(1 \cdot 00327374)^{24} - 1]}{1 \cdot 00327374 - 1}$$

$$S_{24} = \frac{1 \cdot 00327374[0 \cdot 0816]}{0 \cdot 00327374}$$

$$S_{24} = 25 \cdot 00722192$$

So,

$$F = 125(25 \cdot 00722192)$$
$$F = €3,125 \cdot 90$$

What is the difference between saving at the start of the month or the end of the month?

Example

Jack saves €100 at the **start of each month** in his credit union for a calendar year. The interest paid is 4·5% compounded monthly. How much money has Jack saved at the end of the year?

Solution

1st payment

The first payment is in the account for 12 full months, the second is in for 11 full months ... the final payment is in the account for 1 month.

(Express t in fractions of years)

$$F_1 = 100(1·045)^{\frac{12}{12}}$$
$$F_2 = 100(1·045)^{\frac{11}{12}}$$
$$\vdots$$
$$F_{12} = 100(1·045)^{\frac{1}{12}}$$

Take the series as:

$$F_{12} + F_{11} + F_{10} + \cdots + F_2 + F_1$$

Total of the 12 payments is the sum of a geometric series:

$$a = 100(1·045)^{\frac{1}{12}} = 100·3675$$
$$r = (1·045)^{\frac{1}{12}} = 1·003675$$
$$n = 12$$

$$S_{12} = \frac{a(r^{12} - 1)}{r - 1}$$

$$S_{12} = \frac{100·3675((1·003675)^{12} - 1)}{(1·003675) - 1}$$

$$S_{12} = 1{,}229·05$$

Total at end of year: €1,229·05

Example

Jack saves €100 at the **end of each month** in his credit union for a calendar year. The interest paid is 4·5% compounded monthly. How much money has Jack saved at the end of the year?

Solution

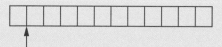

1st payment

The first payment is in the account for 11 full months, the second is in for 10 full months ... the final payment is in the account for 0 months.

(Express t in fractions of years)

$$F_1 = 100(1·045)^{\frac{11}{12}}$$
$$F_2 = 100(1·045)^{\frac{10}{12}}$$
$$\vdots$$
$$F_{12} = 100(1·045)^{\frac{0}{12}}$$

Take the series as:

$$F_{12} + F_{11} + F_{10} + \cdots + F_2 + F_1$$

Total of the 12 payments is the sum of a geometric series:

$$a = 100(1·045)^{\frac{0}{12}} = 100$$
$$r = (1·045)^{\frac{1}{12}} = 1·003675$$
$$n = 12$$

$$S_{12} = \frac{a(r^{12} - 1)}{r - 1}$$

$$S_{12} = \frac{100((1·003675)^{12} - 1)}{(1·003675) - 1}$$

$$S_{12} = 1{,}224·55$$

Total at end of year: €1,224·55

Example

Jason wants to change his car in three years' time. He doesn't want to take out a loan, so instead he decides to deposit a fixed sum at the **end** of each month, for the next three years, in an account that pays 4·8% (AER). If he wants to have €16,000 in three years' time, how much does he have to deposit monthly?

Solution

Use the formula: $F = P(1 + i)^t$ Let: $F = 16000$ $P = x$ $i = 0.048$

Since he is making the deposit at the end of each month, the first deposit will be in the account for 35 months $\left(\frac{35}{12}\text{ years}\right)$, the second deposit will be in the account for 34 months, etc.

$$16000 = x(1\cdot048)^{\frac{35}{12}} + x(1\cdot048)^{\frac{34}{12}} + x(1\cdot048)^{\frac{33}{12}} + \cdots + x(1\cdot048)^{\frac{1}{12}} + x$$

$$16000 = x\left[1 + (1\cdot048)^{\frac{1}{12}} + (1\cdot048)^{\frac{2}{12}} + (1\cdot048)^{\frac{3}{12}} + \cdots + (1\cdot048)^{\frac{35}{12}}\right]$$

The part in the squared brackets is a geometric series, where:

$$a = 1 \quad r = (1\cdot048)^{\frac{1}{12}} \quad n = 36$$

$$S_n = \frac{a(r^n - 1)}{r - 1}$$

$$S_{36} = \frac{1\left[\left((1\cdot048)^{\frac{1}{12}}\right)^{36} - 1\right]}{(1\cdot048)^{\frac{1}{12}} - 1}$$

$$S_{36} = \frac{1[0\cdot151022592]}{(0\cdot00391460763)}$$

$$S_{36} = 38\cdot57924121$$

So,

$$16000 = x(38\cdot57924121)$$

$$€414\cdot73 = x$$

Jason should deposit €414·73 at the end of each month for the next three years to achieve his goal of having €16,000 in three years' time.

Example

A bank offers a 12-year €3,200 bond that will pay €50 at the **end** of every six months for 12 years. Given an APR of 3·75%, calculate a fair market value for this bond.

key point

Solution

Firstly, calculate the present value of a future payment of €3,200, in 12 years' time, at a rate of 3·75% per annum.

> A bond is a certificate issued by a government or a public company promising to repay borrowed money at a fixed rate of interest at a specified time.

$$F = P(1 + i)^t$$

$$3200 = P(1 + 0.0375)^{12}$$

$$\frac{3200}{(1.0375)^{12}} = P$$

$$€2{,}057{\cdot}28 = P$$

Secondly, calculate the present value (PV) of a future payment of €50 at the end of every six months at a rate of 3·75% per annum.

Cost = (PV of €50 at end of one half year) + ⋯ + (PV of €50 at end of 24 half years)

$$\text{Cost} = \frac{50}{(1.0375)^{\frac{1}{2}}} + \frac{50}{(1.0375)^{\frac{2}{2}}} + \frac{50}{(1.0375)^{\frac{3}{2}}} + \cdots + \frac{50}{(1.0375)^{\frac{24}{2}}}$$

$$\text{Cost} = 50\left[\frac{1}{(1.0375)^{\frac{1}{2}}} + \frac{1}{(1.0375)^{\frac{2}{2}}} + \frac{1}{(1.0375)^{\frac{3}{2}}} + \cdots + \frac{50}{(1.0375)^{\frac{24}{2}}}\right]$$

This is the sum of a geometric series where $a = \dfrac{1}{(1.0375)^{\frac{1}{2}}}, r = \dfrac{1}{(1.0375)^{\frac{1}{2}}}, n = 24$

$$S_n = \frac{a(1 - r^n)}{1 - r}$$

$$S_{24} = \frac{\dfrac{1}{(1.0375)^{\frac{1}{2}}}\left(1 - \left(\dfrac{1}{(1.0375)^{\frac{1}{2}}}\right)^{24}\right)}{1 - \dfrac{1}{(1.0375)^{\frac{1}{2}}}}$$

$$S_{24} = \frac{0.9817613873(0.357101022)}{0.01823861265} = 19.22229511$$

$$\text{Cost} = 50(19.22229511) = €961{\cdot}11$$

So the total cost of this bond is: €2,057·28 + €961·11 = €3,018·39.

This means that if an investor purchases this bond now at a fair market value of €3,018·39, they will receive a payment of €50 at the end of each six months for the next 12 years, and also a payment of €3,200 at the end of the 12th year.

(2011 Q.6)

A research company discovers a new drug. A pharmaceutical company says it will buy the rights to the drug now for €55 million or pay €85 million in six years' time for it.

(i) If the interest rate is 4·8%, should the research company sell the rights to the drug now or later? Give a reason for your answer.

(ii) If the interest rate is 9%, what should the company do?

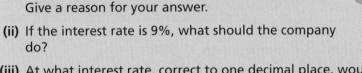

(iii) At what interest rate, correct to one decimal place, would it make no difference for the research company to sell the rights to the drug now or in six years' time?

Solution

(i) Find the present value of €85 million in six years, based on a rate of 4·8%:

$$P = \frac{F}{(1 + i)^t}$$

$$P = \frac{85,000,000}{(1 + 0·048)^6} = 64,158,060·96 = €64·16 \text{ million}$$

The research company should sell in six years' time, because the €85 million is worth €64 million. However, the pharmaceutical company is only offering them €55 million now.

(ii) Find the present value of €85 million in six years, based on a rate of 9%:

$$P = \frac{85,000,000}{(1 + 0·09)^6} = 50,682,722·78 = €50·68 \text{ million}$$

The research company should take the offer now because the €85 million is worth €50·68 million now. However, the pharmaceutical company is offering €55 million now.

(iii) $P = €55$ million $F = €85$ million $t = 6$ $i = ?$

$$P = \frac{F}{(1 + i)^t}$$

$$55 = \frac{85}{(1 + i)^6}$$

$$55(1 + i)^6 = 85$$

$$(1 + i)^6 = \frac{85}{55}$$

$$1 + i = \sqrt[6]{\frac{85}{55}}$$

$$1 + i = 1·075249806$$

$$i = 0·0752 = 7·52\% = 7·5\%$$

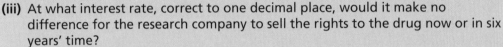

Most lottery games in the USA allow winners of the jackpot prize to choose between two forms of the prize: an annual payments option or a cash value option. In the case of the New York Lotto, there are 26 annual payments in the annual payments option, with the first payment immediately, and the last payment in 25 years' time. The payments increase by 4% each year. The amount advertised as the jackpot prize is the total amount of these 26 payments. The cash value option pays a smaller amount than this.

(i) If the amount of the first annual payment is A, write down, in terms of A, the amount of the second, third, fourth and 26th payments.

(ii) The 26 payments form a geometric series. Use this fact to express the advertised jackpot prize in terms of A.

(iii) Find, correct to the nearest dollar, the value of A that corresponds to an advertised jackpot prize of $21·5 million.

(iv) A winner who chooses the cash value option receives, immediately, the total of the present values of the 26 annual payments. The interest rate used for the present value calculations is 4·78%. We want to find the cash value of the prize referred to in part **(iii)**.

(a) Complete the table below to show the actual amount and the present value of each of the first three annual payments.

Payment number	Time to payment (years)	Actual amount	Present value
1	0		
2	1		
3	2		

(b) Write down, in terms of n, an expression for the present value of the nth annual payment.

(c) Find the amount of prize money payable under the cash value option. That is, find the total of the present values of the 26 annual payments.

Give your answer in millions, correct to one decimal place.

(v) The jackpot described in parts **(iii)** and **(iv)** above was won by an Irish woman recently. She chose the cash value option. After tax, she received $7·9 million. What percentage of tax was charged on her winnings?

Solution

(i) 1st payment $= A$

2nd payment $= A(1·04)$

3rd payment $= A(1·04)^2$

4th payment $= A(1·04)^3$

26th payment $= A(1·04)^{25}$

(ii) Jackpot $= A + A(1 \cdot 04) + A(1 \cdot 04)^2 + A(1 \cdot 04)^3 + \cdots + A(1 \cdot 04)^{25}$

Geometric series where: $a = A$, $r = 1 \cdot 04$, $n = 26$.

$$S_n = \frac{a(r^n - 1)}{r - 1}$$

$$S_{26} = \frac{A((1 \cdot 04)^{26} - 1)}{1 \cdot 04 - 1} = \frac{A((1 \cdot 04)^{26} - 1)}{0 \cdot 04}$$

$$\text{Jackpot} = \frac{A((1 \cdot 04)^{26} - 1)}{0 \cdot 04}$$

(iii) Jackpot $= \$21 \cdot 5$ million $= \$21,500,000$

$$\therefore \quad 21500000 = \frac{A((1 \cdot 04)^{26} - 1)}{0 \cdot 04}$$

$$\frac{0 \cdot 04(21500000)}{(1 \cdot 04)^{26} - 1} = A$$

$$\$485,198 \cdot 68 = A$$

$$\$485,199 = A$$

(iv) (a) *First payment:* They both receive the same first payment, $\$485,199$.

Second payment:

Annual payments option $= \$485,199 \times 1 \cdot 04 = \$504,607$

Cash value option $= \dfrac{\$485,199 \times 1 \cdot 04}{1 \cdot 0478} = \$481,587$

Third payment:

Annual payments option $= \$485,199 \times (1 \cdot 04)^2 = \$524,791$

Cash value option $= \dfrac{\$485,199 \times (1 \cdot 04)^2}{(1 \cdot 0478)^2} = \$478,0002$

Payment number	Time to payment (years)	Actual amount	Present value
1	0	$485,199	$485,199
2	1	$504,607	$481,587
3	2	$524,791	$478,002

(b) nth payment $= \dfrac{\$485,199 \times (1 \cdot 04)^{n-1}}{(1 \cdot 0478)^{n-1}}$

(c) Jackpot $= \$485,199 + \$485,199\left(\dfrac{1 \cdot 04}{1 \cdot 0478}\right) + \$485,199\left(\dfrac{1 \cdot 04}{1 \cdot 0478}\right)^2$

$$+ \cdots + \$485,199\left(\dfrac{1 \cdot 04}{1 \, 0478}\right)^{25}$$

Geometric series: $a = \$485,199, \quad r = \dfrac{1 \cdot 04}{1 \cdot 0478}, \quad n = 26$

$$S_n = \frac{a(r^n - 1)}{r - 1}$$

$$S_{26} = \frac{485199\left(\left(\frac{1\cdot04}{1\cdot0478}\right)^{26} - 1\right)}{\frac{1\cdot04}{1\cdot0478} - 1} = 11508316\cdot44$$

Cash value payment = \$11·5 million

(v) Tax paid = \$11·5 million − \$7·9 million = \$3·6 million

$$\text{Percentage tax paid} = \frac{\text{Tax paid}}{\text{Original prize}} \times 100$$

$$\text{Percentage tax paid} = \frac{3\cdot6}{11\cdot5} \times 100 = 31\cdot3\%$$

key point

Pensions

Pension funds involve making contributions to an annuity before retirement and receiving contributions from an annuity after retirement.

exam Q

Stuart is 35 years old and is planning for his pension. He intends to retire in thirty years' time, when he is 65. First, he calculates how much he wants to have in his pension fund when he retires. Then he calculates how much he needs to invest in order to achieve this. He assumes that in the long run, money can be invested at an inflation adjusted annual rate of 3%, so all calculations should therefore be based on a 3% annual growth rate.

(i) Write down the present value of a future payment of €25,000 in one year's time (i.e. if Stuart wants to receive €25,000 in one year's time, how much should be invest now, given that the interest rate is 3%?).

(ii) Write down, in terms of t, the present value of a future payment of €25,000 in t years' time.

(iii) Stuart wants to have a fund that could, from the date of his retirement, give him a payment of €25,000 at the start of each year for 25 years. Show how to use the sum of a geometric series to calculate the value on the date of retirement of the fund required.

(iv) Stuart plans to invest a fixed amount of money every month in order to generate the fund calculated in part **(iii)**. His retirement is 30 × 12 = 360 months away.

    (a) Find, correct to four significant figures, the rate of interest per month that would, if paid and compounded monthly, be equivalent to an effective annual rate of 3%.

(b) Write down, in terms of n and P, the value on the retirement date of a payment of €P made n months before the retirement date.

(c) If Stuart makes 360 equal payments of €P from now until his retirement, what value of P will give the fund he requires?

(d) If Stuart waits for five years before starting his pension investments, how much will he then have to pay each month in order to generate the same pension fund?

Solution

(i) $P = \dfrac{F}{(1 + i)^t} = \dfrac{25000}{(1 + 0\cdot03)^1} = €24{,}271\cdot8447$

(ii) $P = \dfrac{F}{(1 + i)^t} = \dfrac{25000}{(1\cdot03)^t}$

(iii) The amount of money required in the fund at the start of the retirement must equal the sum of the present values of all the payments from the date of the retirement.

$$\text{Retirement fund} = \frac{25000}{(1\cdot03)^0} + \frac{25000}{(1\cdot03)^1} + \frac{25000}{(1\cdot03)^2} + \frac{25000}{(1\cdot03)^3} + \cdots + \frac{25000}{(1\cdot03)^{24}}$$

This is the sum of a geometric series, where $a = 25000$ and $r = \dfrac{1}{1\cdot03}$.

$$S_{25} = \frac{a(1 - r^n)}{1 - r}$$

$$S_{25} = \frac{25000\left(1 - \left(\frac{1}{1\cdot03}\right)^{25}\right)}{1 - \frac{1}{1\cdot03}}$$

$$S_{25} = €448{,}388\cdot5531$$

(iv) (a) $\qquad\qquad F = P(1 + i)^t$

$\qquad\qquad 1\cdot03 = 1(1 + i)^{12}$

$\qquad\qquad \sqrt[12]{1\cdot03} = 1 + i$

$\qquad\qquad 1\cdot00246627 = 1 + i$

$\qquad\qquad 0\cdot00246627 = i$

Thus, the rate of interest per month that would give an AER of 3% = 0.2466%.

(b) $F = P(1 + i)^t$

$F = P(1 + 0\cdot002466)^t$

(c) $€448{,}388\cdot5531 = P(1 + i)^1 + P(1 + i)^2 + P(1 + i)^3 + \cdots + P(1 + i)^{360}$

$€448{,}388\cdot5531 = P(1\cdot002466)^1 + P(1\cdot002466)^2 + \cdots + P(1\cdot002466)^{360}$

$€448{,}388\cdot5531 = P[(1\cdot002466)^1 + P(1\cdot002466)^2 + P(1\cdot002466)^3 + \cdots$
$\qquad\qquad\qquad\qquad + (1\cdot002466)^{360}]$

This is the sum of a geometric series, where $a = 1\cdot002466$ and $r = 1\cdot002466$.

$$S_n = \frac{a(r^n - 1)}{r - 1}$$

$$S_{360} = \frac{1 \cdot 002466(1 \cdot 002466^{360} - 1)}{1 \cdot 002466 - 1}$$

So,

$$€448,388 \cdot 5531 = P\left[\frac{1 \cdot 002466(1 \cdot 002466^{360} - 1)}{1 \cdot 002466 - 1}\right]$$

$$€448,388 \cdot 5531 = P[580 \cdot 1080215]$$

$$€772 \cdot 94 = P : \text{monthly payments}$$

(d) If Stuart waits for five years, then he will have 25 years to contribute. Thus, the number of monthly contributions = 25 × 12 = 300.

$$€448,388 \cdot 5531 = P[(1 \cdot 002466)^1 + (1 \cdot 002466)^2 + (1 \cdot 002466)^3 + \cdots + (1 \cdot 002466)^{300}]$$

This is the sum of a geometric series, where $a = 1 \cdot 002466$ and $r = 1 \cdot 002466$.

$$S_n = \frac{a(r^n - 1)}{r - 1}$$

$$S_{300} = \frac{1 \cdot 002466(1 \cdot 002466^{300} - 1)}{1 \cdot 002466 - 1}$$

So,

$$€448,388 \cdot 5531 = P\left[\frac{1 \cdot 002466(1 \cdot 002466^{300} - 1)}{1 \cdot 002466 - 1}\right]$$

$$€448,388 \cdot 5531 = P[444 \cdot 5684266]$$

$$€1,008 \cdot 59 = P : \text{monthly payments}$$

Amortised loans

An amortised loan is one which involves paying back a fixed amount at regular intervals over a fixed period of time. Term loans and mortgages are examples of amortised loans. Amortisation is the process by which the loan principal decreases over the life of the loan. With each mortgage payment made, a portion of the payment is applied towards reducing the principal and another portion of the payment is applied towards paying the interest on the loan. At the start of the life of the mortgage, the majority of the repayment will go towards paying the interest and only a small amount will go towards reducing the principal.

To calculate the annual amortisation (repayment) on a mortgage if the interest is compounded annually:

$$A = P\frac{i(1 + i)^t}{(1 + i)^t - 1}$$

Where:

A = annual repayment   i = annual rate, in decimals

P = principal   t = number of years

(see *booklet of formulae and tables*, page 31)

key point

The formula for amortisation is mainly used for loans.

For monthly repayments, adjust *i* to the monthly rate and *t* to the number of months.

Remember:

$$\sqrt[12]{1 + \text{annual rate}} - 1 = \text{monthly rate}$$

exam Q

(2015 Q.6)

(a) Donagh is arranging a loan and is examining two different repayment options.

   (i) Bank A will charge him a monthly interest rate of 0·35%. Find, correct to three significant figures, the annual percentage rate (APR) that is equivalent to a monthly interest rate of 0·35%

   (ii) Bank B will charge him a rate that is equivalent to an APR of 4·5%. Find, correct to three significant figures, the monthly interest rate that is equivalent to an APR of 4·5%.

(b) Donagh borrowed €80,000 at a monthly interest rate of 0·35%, fixed for the term of the loan, from Bank A. The loan is to be repaid in equal monthly repayments over ten years. The first repayments is due one month after the loan is issued. Calculate, correct to the nearest euro, the amount of each monthly repayment.

Solution

(a) (i)

$$F = P(1 + i)^t$$
$$F = 1(1 + 0·0035)^{12}$$

$$1 + (\text{annual rate}) = 1(1·0035)^{12}$$

$$1 + (\text{annual rate}) = 1·0428180072$$

Therefore, the annual rate is 0·0428180072

$$= 4·28180072$$

$$= 4·28\%\quad \text{(to three significant figures)}$$

(ii)
$$F = P(1 + i)^t$$
$$1·045 = 1(1 + i)^{12}$$
$$1·045 = (1 + i)^{12}$$
$$\sqrt[12]{1·045} = 1 + i$$
$$1·0036748094 - 1 = i$$
$$0·0036748094 = i$$
$$0·36748094\% = i$$
$$0·367\% = i \qquad \text{to three significant figures}$$

(b) $P = 80000$, $i = 0·0035$, $t = 120$ months

$$A = P\frac{i(1 + i)^t}{(1 + i)^t - 1}$$

$$A = (80000)\left[\frac{(0·0035)(1 + 0·0035)^{120}}{(1 + 0·0035)^{120} - 1}\right]$$

$$A = 80000\left[\frac{(0·0035)(1·0035)^{120}}{(1·0035)^{120} - 1}\right]$$

$$A = 80000\left[\frac{(0·0035)(1·520845926)}{1·520845926 - 1}\right]$$

$$A = 80000\left[\frac{0·005322960741}{0·520845926}\right]$$

$$A = 817·587$$

$$A = €818 \text{ to the nearest euro}$$

Audrey and Bill plan to get married in five years' time. They estimate that their wedding will cost them €18,500.

(i) How much should Audrey and Bill deposit at the **end** of each month, for the next five years, in an account that pays 4% (AER) in order to have €18,500 saved for their wedding?

(ii) How much did they deposit, in total, to have a final balance of €18,500?

Instead of saving for the wedding, Audrey and Bill decide to look at the option of taking out a loan for the required amount and pay it back in regular repayments over five years.

(iii) Based on an APR of 4%, use the amortisation formula to find how much their monthly repayments would be.

(iv) How much more would the wedding cost Audrey and Bill if they take the option of drawing down a loan instead of saving up for the wedding?

Solution

(i) Use the formula: $F = P(1 + i)^t$ Let: $F = 18500$, $P = x$, $i = 0.04$

Since they are making the deposit at the end of each month, the first deposit will be in the account for 59 months ($\frac{59}{12}$ years), the second deposit will be in the account for 58 months, etc.

$$18500 = x(1 \cdot 04)^{\frac{59}{12}} + x(1 \cdot 04)^{\frac{58}{12}} + x(1 \cdot 04)^{\frac{57}{12}} + \cdots + x(1 \cdot 04)^{\frac{1}{12}} + x$$

$$18500 = x\left[1 + (1 \cdot 04)^{\frac{1}{12}} + (1 \cdot 04)^{\frac{2}{12}} + (1 \cdot 04)^{\frac{3}{12}} + \cdots + (1 \cdot 04)^{\frac{59}{12}}\right]$$

The part in the squared brackets is a geometric series, where:

$$a = 1 \qquad r = (1 \cdot 04)^{\frac{1}{12}} \qquad n = 60$$

$$S_n = \frac{a(r^n - 1)}{r - 1}$$

$$S_{60} = \frac{1\left[\left((1 \cdot 04)^{\frac{1}{12}}\right)^{60} - 1\right]}{(1 \cdot 04)^{\frac{1}{12}} - 1}$$

$$S_{60} = \frac{1[0 \cdot 216652902]}{(0 \cdot 003273739)}$$

$$S_{60} = 66 \cdot 17902351$$

So,

$$18,500 = x(66 \cdot 17902351)$$

$$€279 \cdot 54 = x$$

Audrey and Bill should deposit €279·54 at the end of each month for the next five years to achieve their goal of having €18500 in five years' time.

(ii) Audrey and Bill deposit €279·54 for 60 months.

Total deposited: €279·54 × 60 = €16,772·69.

(iii) Adjust the APR:

$$F = P(1 + i)^t$$
$$1 \cdot 04 = 1(1 + i)^{12}$$
$$\sqrt[12]{1 \cdot 04} = 1 + i$$
$$1 \cdot 00327374 = 1 + i$$
$$0 \cdot 00327374 = i$$

$$A = P \frac{i(1 + i)^t}{(1 + i)^t - 1}$$

$$A = 18500 \left(\frac{0 \cdot 00327374(1 + 0 \cdot 00327374)^{60}}{(1 + 0 \cdot 00327374)^{60} - 1} \right)$$

$$A = 18500 \left(\frac{0 \cdot 00327374(1 \cdot 00327374)^{60}}{(1 \cdot 00327374)^{60} - 1} \right)$$

$$A = 18500(0 \cdot 018384268)$$

Monthly repayments: €340·11.

(iv) If Audrey and Bill take the loan option, they will repay
€340·11 × 60 = €20,406·60.

If Audrey and Bill decide to save, they will have to deposit €16,772·69 (from **(ii)**).

Therefore, the loan option will cost them an additional
€20,406·60 − €16,772·69 = €3,633·91.

(2017 Q.8)

(a) When a loan of €P is repaid in equal repayments of amount
€A, at the end of each of t equal periods of time, where i is the periodic
compound interest rate (expressed as a decimal), the formula below can be
used to find the amount of each repayment:

$$A = P \frac{i(1 + i)^t}{(1 + i)^t - 1}$$

Show how this formula is derived. You may use the formula for the sum of a
finite geometric series.

(b) Alex has a credit card debt of €5,000. One method of clearing this debt is to
make a fixed repayment at the end of each month. The amount of this
repayment is 2·5% of the original debt.

(i) What is the fixed monthly repayment, €A, required to pay the debt of
€5,000?

(ii) The annual percentage rate (APR) charged on debt by the credit card
company is 21·75%, fixed for the term of the debt. Find as a percentage,
correct to 3 significant figures, the monthly interest rate that is equivalent
to an APR of 21·75%

(iii) Assume Alex pays the fixed monthly repayment, €A, each month and does
not have any further transaction on that card. Complete the table below
to show how the balance of the debt of €5,000 is reducing each month for
the first three months, assuming an APR of 21·75%, charged and
compounded monthly.

Payment number	Fixed monthly payment, €A	€A		
		Interest	Previous balance reduced by (€)	New balance of debt (€)
0				5000
1			42·50	4957·50
2				
3				

(iv) Using the formula you derived, or otherwise, find how long it would take to pay off a credit card debt of €5,000, using the repayment method outlined at the beginning of part (b) above.

Give your answer in months, correct to the nearest month.

(v) Alex decides to borrow €5,000 from the local Credit Union to pay off this credit card debt of €5,000. The APR charge for the Credit Union loan is 8·5% fixed for the term of the loan. The loan is to be repaid in equal weekly repayments, at the end of each week, for 156 weeks. Find the amount of each weekly repayment.

(vi) How much will Alex save by paying off the credit card debt using the loan from the Credit Union instead of paying the fixed repayment from part (b)(i) each month to the credit card company?

Solution

(a) P = Sum of present values of all future repayments, A

$$P = \frac{A}{(1 + i)^1} + \frac{A}{(1 + i)^2} + \dots + \frac{A}{(1 + i)^t}$$

Geometric series with first term $a = \dfrac{A}{1 + i}$, $r = \dfrac{1}{1 + i}$

$$S_n = \frac{a(1 - r^n)}{1 - r}$$

$$P = \frac{\dfrac{A}{1 + i}\left(1 - \left(\dfrac{1}{1 + i}\right)^t\right)}{1 - \dfrac{1}{1 + i}} \times \frac{1 + i}{1 + i}$$

$$P = \frac{A\left(1 - \dfrac{1}{(1 + i)^t}\right)}{1 + i - 1}$$

$$P = \frac{A\left(1 - \dfrac{1}{(1 + i)^t}\right)}{i}$$

$$P = \frac{A((1 + i)^t - 1)}{i(1 + i)^t}$$

Therefore,

$$A = P\frac{i(1 + i)^t}{(1 + i)^t - 1}$$

This part (a) was worth only 5 marks. 3 of those marks were awarded for writing $P = \dfrac{A}{1 + i}$.

(b) (i) Monthly repayment = 2·5% of original debt

$$= 2.5\% \text{ of } €5{,}000$$
$$= €125$$

(ii) Based on €1 for one year, the final amount will be €1·2175

$$F = P(1 + i)^t$$
$$1.2175 = 1(1 + i)^{12}$$
$$\sqrt[12]{1.2175} = 1 + i$$
$$\sqrt[12]{1.2175} - 1 = i$$
$$0.016535 = i$$
$$1.6535\% = i$$

Therefore, the monthly rate is 1·65%, to 3 significant figures.

(iii) The monthly interest rate of 1·65%, is charged on the balance due at the start of each month.

This amount of interest is subtracted from the €125 payment and the balance is deducted from the overall amount owed.

Use this information to complete the table:

Payment number	Fixed monthly payment, €A	€A		New balance of debt (€)
		Interest	Previous balance reduced by (€)	
0				5000
1	€125	€82·50	42·50	4957·50
2	€125	€81·80	€43·20	€4914·30
3	€125	€81·09	€43·91	€4870·39

(iv) $A = 125$, $P = 5000$, $i = 0.0165$, $t = ?$

$$A = P\left(\frac{i(1 + i)^t}{(1 + i)^t - 1}\right)$$

$$125 = 5000\left(\frac{0.0165(1 + 0.0165)^t}{(1 + 0.0165)^t - 1}\right)$$

$$125 = 5000\left(\frac{0 \cdot 0165(1 \cdot 0165)^t}{(1 \cdot 0165)^t - 1}\right)$$

$$125 = 82 \cdot 5\left(\frac{(1 \cdot 0165)^t}{(1 \cdot 0165)^t - 1}\right)$$

$$125 = \frac{82 \cdot 5(1 \cdot 0165)^t}{(1 \cdot 0165)^t - 1}$$

$$125((1 \cdot 0165)^t - 1) = 82 \cdot 5(1 \cdot 0165)^t$$

$$125(1 \cdot 0165)^t - 125 = 82 \cdot 5(1 \cdot 0165)^t$$

$$125(1 \cdot 0165)^t - 82 \cdot 5(1 \cdot 0165)^t = 125$$

$$42 \cdot 5(1 \cdot 0165)^t = 125$$

$$(1 \cdot 0165)^t = \frac{125}{42 \cdot 5}$$

$$t = \log_{1 \cdot 0165}\left(\frac{125}{42 \cdot 5}\right)$$

$$t = 65 \cdot 9203$$

Therefore, in 66 months the debt will be paid off.

(v) Find the weekly rate:

$F = €1 \cdot 085, P = €1, t = 52, i = ?$

$$F = P(1 + i)^t$$

$$1 \cdot 085 = 1(1 + i)^{52}$$

$$\sqrt[52]{1 \cdot 085} = 1 + i$$

$$\sqrt[52]{1 \cdot 085} - 1 = i$$

$$0 \cdot 00157 = i$$

$$0 \cdot 157\% = i$$

Parts (b) (i), (ii) and (iii) were worth 10 marks each, while the more challenging part (iv) was only worth 5 marks.

Use the amortisation formula:

$A = ?, P = €5000, i = 0 \cdot 00157, t = 156$

$$A = P\left(\frac{i(1 + i)^t}{(1 + i)^t - 1}\right)$$

$$A = 5000\left(\frac{0 \cdot 00157(1 + 0 \cdot 00157)^{156}}{(1 + 0 \cdot 00157)^{156} - 1}\right)$$

$$A = 5000\left(\frac{0 \cdot 00157(1 \cdot 00157)^{156}}{(1 \cdot 00157)^{156} - 1}\right)$$

$$A = 5000\left(\frac{0 \cdot 0020053198}{0 \cdot 277273769}\right)$$

$$A = €36 \cdot 16$$

Therefore, Alex will need to repay €36·16 per week.

(vi) Credit card repayments = €125 × 66 = €8,250

Credit Union repayments = €36·16 × 156 = €5,640·96

Savings = €8,250 − €5,640·96

= €2,609·04

Parts (b) (v) was worth 10 marks and (b) (vi) was worth 5 marks.

14 Methods of Proof

aims

☐ To learn and understand the different methods of proof
☐ To be able to reproduce an example of a proof by contradiction
☐ To be able to prove that $\sqrt{2}$ is irrational
☐ To be able to use the method of proof by induction

Definitions

An **axiom** is a statement which is assumed to be true and is used as a basis for developing a system.

A **conjecture** is a statement which may be true but has not been proven.

Methods of proof

There are many ways that mathematical statements can be proved (or disproved). These include:

1. Direct proof
   Using definitions, axioms and previous results in a sequential argument.

2. Reductio ad absurdum
   A proposition is disproved by deducing logically that it leads to an absurd result. One common type of this is **proof by contradiction**, where a statement is proved true because it cannot be false.

3. Induction

4. Graphical

exam focus

Proofs can appear in any topic of the maths course. Some are formal proofs, which you must learn off by heart. Others you will have to make up on the spot.

Direct proof

Direct proofs use definitions, axioms and previous results in a sequential argument. All proofs are a sequence of statements leading to the conclusion, but some rely more on words than mathematical symbols.

Example

Given that $ABCD$ is a parallelogram, prove that triangles ABC and ADC are congruent.

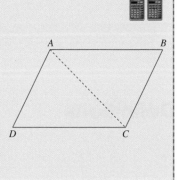

Solution

$\|AD\| = \|BC\|$	(opposite sides of a parallelogram)
$\|DC\| = \|AB\|$	(opposite sides of a parallelogram)
$\|\angle ADC\| = \|\angle CBA\|$	(opposite angles of a parallelogram)
$\therefore \triangle ABC \equiv \triangle ADC$	(SAS)

Using your book of tables and formulae, prove that:

$$(\sin A + \cos A)^2 + (\sin A - \cos A)^2 = 2$$

Solution

$\text{LHS:} = (\sin A + \cos A)^2 + (\sin A - \cos A)^2$ (multiply out)

$= \sin^2 A + 2\sin A\cos A + \cos^2 A + \sin^2 A - 2\sin A\cos A + \cos^2 A$

$= 2\sin^2 A + 2\cos^2 A$

$= 2(\sin^2 A + \cos^2 A)$ (from tables $\sin^2 A + \cos^2 A = 1$)

$= 2(1)$

$= 2 = \text{RHS}$

$\therefore (\sin A + \cos A)^2 + (\sin A - \cos A)^2 = 2$

Reductio ad absurdum

Sometimes, when we are asked to show that a problem has no solution, we go ahead and try to solve it as normal. When we get an absurd answer, we then state that the question has no solution. Absurd answers include statements such as '3 = 0' or values such as $\sqrt{-9}$ when solutions must be real.

Example

Prove that $f(x) = \dfrac{2}{x-3}, x \neq 3$, has no turning points.

Solution

We will pretend that we do not know that the function has no turning points and try to find turning points.

At turning point, $f'(x) = 0$.

$f(x) = \dfrac{2}{x-3}$ Use quotient rule to find $f'(x)$: $u = 2$ $v = x - 3$

$\dfrac{du}{dx} = 0$ $\dfrac{dv}{dx} = 1$

$$f'(x) = \dfrac{v\dfrac{du}{dx} - u\dfrac{dv}{dx}}{v^2}$$

$$f'(x) = \dfrac{(x-3)(0) - (2)(1)}{(x-3)^2}$$

> **key point**
>
> See chapters on Differential Calculus II and III for more on quotient rule and turning points.

$$f'(x) = \dfrac{0 - 2}{(x-3)^2}$$

$$f'(x) = \dfrac{-2}{(x-3)^2}$$

At turning point, $f'(x) = 0$: $0 = \dfrac{-2}{(x-3)^2}$ (multiply both sides by $(x-3)^2$)

$$0 = -2 \qquad \text{(can't solve!)}$$

Thus, there are no values of x for which $f'(x) = 0$.

Therefore, $f(x)$ has no turning points.

Proof by contradiction

One common type of a proof by reductio ad absurdum is **proof by contradiction**, where a statement is proved to be true because it cannot be false.

key point

This method of proof takes a proposition of the form **if** certain conditions **then** a result will follow and examines the consequences of assuming that **if** certain conditions **then** the *opposite* result will follow.

Example

If $\triangle ABC$ is isosceles, then the base angles cannot equal 92°.

Solution

Start by assuming that the opposite is true: the base angles equal 92°.

Proof: If the base angles equal 92°, the sum of the base angles would be
$$92° + 92° = 184°.$$

This contradicts the theorem, which states that the sum of the interior angles of a triangle is 180°.

Therefore, the base angles of an isosceles triangle cannot equal 92°.

Prove that $\sqrt{2}$ is irrational.

Solution

Proof:

Let us assume that the opposite is true: $\sqrt{2}$ is **not** irrational.

You may be asked this proof in the exam.

Thus, $\sqrt{2}$ is rational and can be written as a fraction.

Let $\sqrt{2} = \dfrac{a}{b}$ (where a and b have no common factor, other than 1)

$\Rightarrow$ $2 = \dfrac{a^2}{b^2}$ (squaring both sides)

$\Rightarrow$ $2b^2 = a^2$

Since $2b^2$ is even, a^2 must also be even. So a must be even and can be written as $a = 2k$.

So $2b^2 = (2k)^2$

$\Rightarrow$ $2b^2 = 4k^2$

$\Rightarrow$ $b^2 = 2k^2$

Since $2k^2$ is even, b^2, and therefore b, must be even.

But now we have a and b both even, so they have a common factor of 2.

This is a contradiction, as we know that their highest common factor is 1, so we **cannot** say that $\sqrt{2}$ is rational.

Thus, $\sqrt{2}$ is irrational.

Proof by induction

Proof by induction involves two steps:

1. Proving that the proposition is true for the smallest value of n given in the question. If that number is 1, then we call this $P(1)$.
2. Assuming the proposition is true for $n = k$, prove that the proposition is true for $n = k + 1$. In other words: $P(k) \Rightarrow P(k + 1)$.

key point

If it is true for $n = 1$, then step 2 ensures that it is true for $n = 2$. If it is true for $n = 2$, then step 2 ensures that it is true for $n = 3$ and so on.

We will use **proof by induction** to prove propositions in three areas:

1. **Divisibility**   2. **Series**   3. **Inequalities**

Notes: 1. Proof by induction applies only to propositions that are stated to be true for whole numbers greater than or equal to zero.
2. The proposition is often denoted by $P(n)$. The assumption $P(k)$ must **always** be used in proving that $P(k + 1)$ is true.

Divisibility

These questions require you to prove that a given value is a factor of a given expression. That is, the expression is divisible by the given value.

exam Q

(2016 Q.4 (a))

Prove by induction that $8^n - 1$ is divisible by 7 for all $n \in \mathbb{N}$.

Solution

Step 1: Prove P_1 is true for $n = 1$:

$P_1: 8^1 - 1$

$P_1: 7$, which is divisible by 7

Therefore, P_n is true for $n = 1$.

Step 2: Assume P_k is true

$P_k: 8^k - 1$ is divisible by 7.

Step 3: Prove P_{k+1} is true

$$P_{k+1}: \quad 8^{k+1} - 1$$
$$(8^k)(8^1) - 1$$
$$8(8^k) - 1$$
$$(7 + 1)(8^k) - 1$$
$$7(8^k) + 8^k - 1$$

$7(8^k)$ is divisible by 7

$8^k - 1$ is divisible by 7, if P_k is true.

Therefore, P_{k+1} is true if P_k is true.

Step 4: Since P_1 is true, then P_2 must be true.

Since P_2 is true, then P_3 must be true, etc.

Hence, by the principle of mathematical induction, P_n is true for all $n \in \mathbb{N}$.

Series

These questions require you to prove that the sum of a given series is given by a given expression.

(2014 Q.3)

(a) Prove, by induction, that the sum of the first n natural numbers,

$$1 + 2 + 3 + \cdots + n \text{ is } \frac{n(n + 1)}{2}$$

(b) Hence, or otherwise, prove that the sum of the first n even natural numbers,

$$2 + 4 + 6 + \cdots + 2n, \text{ is } n^2 + n$$

(c) Using the results from **(a)** and **(b)** above, find an expression for the sum of the first n odd natural numbers in its simplest form.

Solution

(a) $p(n): 1 + 2 + 3 + \cdots + n \text{ is } \frac{n(n + 1)}{2}$

Step 1: $P(1): 1 = \frac{1(1 + 1)}{2} = \frac{1(2)}{2} = 1$

$\therefore P(1)$ is true.

Step 2: Assume $P(k)$ is true

$$P(k): 1 + 2 + 3 + \cdots + k = \frac{k(k + 1)}{2}$$

Step 3: Prove $P(k + 1) = \dfrac{(k + 1)(k + 2)}{2}$:

$$P(k + 1): 1 + 2 + 3 + \cdots + k + (k + 1) = \frac{(k + 1)((k + 1) + 1)}{2}$$

$$[1 + 2 + 3 + \cdots + k] + (k + 1) = \frac{(k + 1)(k + 2)}{2}$$

$$\frac{k(k + 1)}{2} + (k + 1) = \frac{(k + 1)(k + 2)}{2}$$

$$\frac{k(k + 1) + 2(k + 1)}{2} = \frac{(k + 1)(k + 2)}{2}$$

$$\frac{(k + 1)(k + 2)}{2} = \frac{(k + 1)(k + 2)}{2}$$

$$\therefore P(k + 1): 1 + 2 + 3 + \cdots + k + (k + 1) = \frac{(k + 1)((k + 1) + 1)}{2}$$

Step 4: Therefore $P(k + 1)$ is true if $P(k)$ is true.

Since $P(1)$ is true, $P(2)$ is true, etc.

Hence, by the principle of mathematical induction, $P(n)$ is true.

(b) $2 + 4 + 6 + 8 + \cdots + 2n$

This is an arithmetic series where $a = 2$ and $d = 2$ and there are n terms.

$$S_n = \frac{n}{2}[2a + (n - 1)d]$$

$$S_n = \frac{n}{2}[2(2) + (n - 1)(2)]$$

$$S_n = \frac{n}{2}[4 + 2n - 2]$$

$$S_n = \frac{n}{2}[2 + 2n]$$

$$S_n = n[1 + n]$$

$$S_n = n + n^2$$

key point

Alternative method:

$$1 + 2 + 3 + \cdots + n = \frac{n(n + 1)}{2}$$

Doubling both sides gives:

$$2 + 4 + 6 + \cdots + 2n = n(n + 1)$$

(c)

$$\left.\begin{array}{c}\text{Sum of first } n \text{ even numbers} \\ + \\ \text{Sum of first } n \text{ odd numbers}\end{array}\right\} = \text{sum of first } 2n \text{ numbers}$$

$$\left.\begin{array}{c}n^2 + n \\ + \\ \text{Sum of first } n \text{ odd numbers}\end{array}\right\} = \frac{2n(2n + 1)}{2}$$

$$(n^2 + n) + \text{Sum of first } n \text{ odd numbers} = \frac{2n(2n + 1)}{2}$$

$$(n^2 + n) + \text{Sum of first } n \text{ odd numbers} = n(2n + 1)$$

$$(n^2 + n) + \text{Sum of first } n \text{ odd numbers} = 2n^2 + n$$

$$\text{Sum of first } n \text{ odd numbers} = 2n^2 + n - n^2 - n$$

$$\text{Sum of first } n \text{ odd numbers} = n^2$$

Prove by induction that:

$$\sum_{r=1}^{n} r(r + 3) = \frac{n}{3}(n + 1)(n + 5)$$

Solution

$P(n)$:

$$\sum_{r=1}^{n} r(r + 3) = \frac{n}{3}(n + 1)(n + 5)$$

Step 1: $P(1)$:   LHS $= r(r + 3) = 1(1 + 3) = 4$

RHS $= \dfrac{n}{3}(n + 1)(n + 5) = \dfrac{1}{3}(1 + 1)(1 + 5) = \dfrac{1}{3}(2)(6) = \dfrac{12}{3} = 4$

LHS = RHS

$\therefore$ $P(1)$ is true.

Step 2: Assume $P(k)$ is true, i.e.

$$\sum_{r=1}^{k} r(r + 3) = \frac{k}{3}(k + 1)(k + 5)$$

$$1(1 + 3) + 2(2 + 3) + \cdots + k(k + 3) = \frac{k}{3}(k + 1)(k + 5)$$

Step 3: Test $P(k + 1)$:

$$\sum_{r=1}^{k+1} r(r + 3) = \frac{k + 1}{3}(k + 1 + 1)(k + 1 + 5)$$

$$\sum_{r=1}^{k+1} r(r + 3) = \frac{k + 1}{3}(k + 2)(k + 6)$$

LHS $= 1(1 + 3) + 2(2 + 3) + \cdots + k(k + 3) + (k + 1)(k + 1 + 3)$

$= [1(1 + 3) + 2(2 + 3) + \cdots + k(k + 3)] + (k + 1)(k + 4)$

$= \left[\dfrac{k}{3}(k + 1)(k + 5)\right] + (k + 1)(k + 4)$ (using our assumption)

$= \dfrac{k(k + 1)(k + 5) + 3(k + 1)(k + 4)}{3}$

$= \dfrac{(k + 1)[k(k + 5) + 3(k + 4)]}{3}$ (take out common factor)

$= \dfrac{(k + 1)[k^2 + 5k + 3k + 12]}{3}$

$= \dfrac{(k + 1)[k^2 + 8k + 12]}{3}$

$= \dfrac{(k + 1)(k + 2)(k + 6)}{3}$

$$= \frac{(k + 1)}{3}(k + 2)(k + 6)$$

LHS = RHS

Step 4: $\therefore$ $P(k + 1)$ is true if $P(k)$ is true.

Hence, by the principle of mathematical induction, $P(n)$ is true.

Inequalities

Inequality propositions can be proved by using a transitive approach:

If $A > B$ and $B > C$, then $A > C$.

We take $P(k)$, which is in the form $A > C$, and deduce a statement in the form $A > B$. We then state that $B > C$ and proceed to prove that this is true. We can then deduce that $A > C$.

Example

Prove by induction that $n! > 2^n$ for all $n \in \mathbb{N}$, $n \geq 4$.

Solution

$P(n)$: $n! > 2^n$ for all $n \in \mathbb{N}$, $n \geq 4$.

Step 1: $P(4)$: LHS $= 4! = 4 \times 3 \times 2 \times 1 = 24$

> Given $n \geq 4$, the smallest value for n is 4.

RHS $= 2^n = 2^4 = 16$

$\therefore$ LHS $>$ RHS

$\therefore$ $P(4)$ is true.

Step 2: Assume $P(k)$ is true, i.e. $k! > 2^k$.

Step 3: Test $P(k + 1)$: $(k + 1)! > 2^{k+1}$

$$k! > 2^k$$
$$(k + 1)k! > 2^k(k + 1)$$
$$(k + 1)! > 2^k(k + 1)$$

Is $2^k(k + 1) > 2^{k+1}$?
$2^k(k + 1) > 2^k(2)$
$(k + 1) > 2$ (true for $k \geq 4$)
$\therefore$ $2^k(k + 1) > 2^{k+1}$

$\therefore$ $(k + 1)! > 2^{k+1}$

Step 4: $\therefore$ $P(k + 1)$ is true if $P(k)$ is true.

Hence, by the principle of mathematical induction, $P(n)$ is true.

Example

Prove by induction that $3^n > n^2$ for all $n > 1$, $n \in \mathbb{N}$.

Solution

$\quad\quad\quad P(n):\quad 3^n > n^2$ for all $n \in \mathbb{N}$

Step 1: $P(2)$: $\quad$ LHS $= 3^n = 3^2 = 9$

$\quad\quad\quad\quad\quad\quad\quad$ RHS $= n^2 = 2^2 = 4$

$\quad\quad\quad\quad\quad \therefore\quad$ LHS $>$ RHS

$\quad\quad\quad\quad\quad \therefore\quad P(2)$ is true.

> Given $n > 1$, the smallest value for n is 2.

Step 2: Assume $P(k)$ is true, i.e. $3^k > k^2$.

Step 3: Test $P(k + 1)$: $\quad 3^{k+1} > (k + 1)^2$

$$3^k > k^2$$

$$3(3^k) > 3k^2$$

$$3^{k+1} > 3k^2$$

Is $\quad 3k^2 > (k + 1)^2$?

$\quad\quad 3k^2 > k^2 + 2k + 1$

$\quad\quad 2k^2 > 2k + 1$

$\quad 2k^2 - 2k > 1$

$\quad 2k(k - 1) > 1 \quad$ (true for $k > 1$)

$\quad \therefore \quad 3k^2 > (k + 1)^2$

$$\therefore \quad 3^{k+1} > (k + 1)^2$$

Step 4: $\therefore \quad P(k + 1)$ is true if $P(k)$ is true.

Hence, by the principle of mathematical induction, $P(n)$ is true.

Graphical

This method of proof involves drawing diagrams or graphs in order to complete the proof.

Use the unit circle to prove $\sin^2 A + \cos^2 A = 1$.

Solution

Draw the unit circle and mark in angle A. The radius of the unit circle is 1.

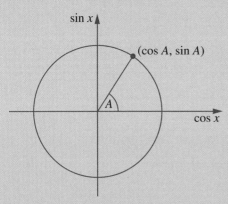

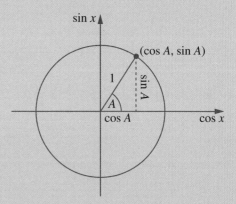

Draw out the triangle, with angle A.

The hypotenuse of the triangle is the radius of the circle, which is 1.

Right-angled triangle, so apply Pythagoras's theorem:

$$(\sin A)^2 + (\cos A)^2 = 1^2$$

$$\therefore \quad \sin^2 A + \cos^2 A = 1$$

This is a proof from the trigonometry section of this course.

Draw the line $2x + 3y + 12 = 0$ and the circle $x^2 + y^2 - 4x - 6y - 12 = 0$ accurately on graph paper. Hence, prove that the line and circle do not have any points of intersection.

Solution

Line: $2x + y + 12 = 0$

At the x-axis, $y = 0$	At the y-axis, $x = 0$
$2x + 3(0) + 12 = 0$	$2(0) + 3y + 12 = 0$
$2x + 12 = 0$	$0 + 3y + 12 = 0$
$2x = -12$	$3y = -12$
$x = -6$	$y = -4$
x-intercept: $(-6, 0)$	y-intercept: $(0, -4)$

Circle: $x^2 + y^2 - 4x - 6y - 12 = 0$

Centre $= (2, 3)$

Radius $= \sqrt{2^2 + 3^2 - (-12)}$

Radius $= \sqrt{25} = 5$

Plot both the line and the circle on the same graph paper:

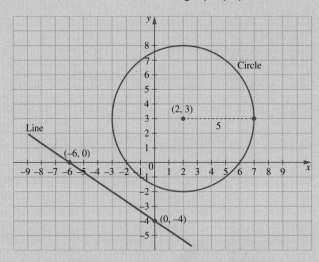

From the graph, we can see that the line and the circle do not intersect. Therefore, the line $2x + 3y + 12 = 0$ and the circle $x^2 + y^2 - 4x - 6y - 12 = 0$ do not have any points of intersection.

This method of proof may not be suitable or acceptable unless it is specifically asked for by the examiner.

15 Differential Calculus I: First Principles

aims

☐ To grasp the fundamental idea of a limit as it applies to slope of a tangent

☐ To learn and apply the mechanical operation required to differentiate from first principles

☐ To know about continuous and discontinuous graphs and the role played by limits in these situatIons

Gradient (slope) of a curve

The gradient of a curve at a point P is the gradient of the tangent to the curve at the point P.

From the diagram below, we obtain the tangent to the curve at point P by considering lines through P and neighbouring points Q_1, Q_2, Q_3, Q_4 and so on. As the points Q approach P, the lines approach the tangent line.

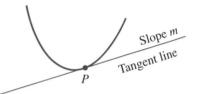

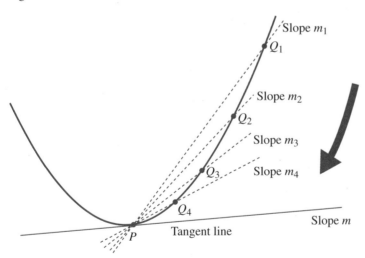

Each line has a slope. The slopes m_1, m_2, m_3, m_4 and so on approach the slope of the tangent line, m.

We define **the tangent line** as the line that contains the point P and has slope m, where m is **the limit** of the slopes of the lines as the points Q approach P.

How might we calculate the limit of the slope of the tangent, m?

Let P have coordinates $(x, f(x))$.

Then the first coordinate of Q is ($x +$ some number h) or $x + h$.

The coordinates of Q are $(x + h, f(x + h))$.

The slope of the line PQ is given by the formula $m = \dfrac{y_2 - y_1}{x_2 - x_1}$.

$$\therefore m = \frac{f(x + h) - f(x)}{x + h - x} = \frac{f(x + h) - f(x)}{h} \text{ as in the diagram below.}$$

Also as the points Q approach P, $x + h$ approaches x. That is, h approaches zero. Hence, we write:

$$\text{The slope of the tangent line } = \lim_{h \to 0} \frac{f(x + h) - f(x)}{h}$$

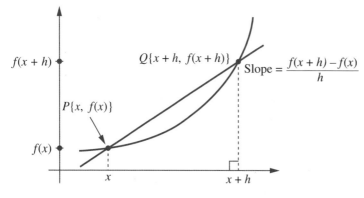

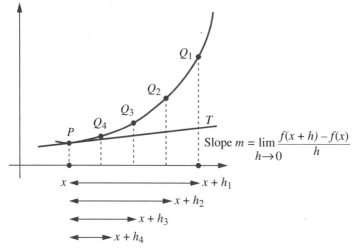

- It is important to realise that h approaches zero but **never** actually becomes zero.
- We can never divide by zero, i.e. the denominator can never equal zero.
- In general, $f(x + h) \neq f(x) + h$ or $f(x + h) \neq f(x) + f(h)$.

We can now write the formal definition of **the derivative of a function** f.

For a function $y = f(x)$, its **derivative** at x is defined by:

$$\frac{dy}{dx} = f'(x) = \lim_{h \to 0} \frac{f(x + h) - f(x)}{h}$$

In other words, the derivative at x is the slope of the tangent to the curve at x.

- $f'(x)$ is pronounced 'f dash of x' or 'f prime of x'.

  $\dfrac{dy}{dx}$ is pronounced 'dee y dee x'.

- It is important to understand that $\dfrac{dy}{dx}$ does not mean $dy \div dx$.
  It means the derivative of y with respect to x.

  The $\dfrac{d}{dx}$ is an operator. $\dfrac{d}{dx}$ means the derivative with respect to x of.

  The $\dfrac{dy}{dx}$ is often written $\dfrac{d}{dx}(y)$.

Procedure for first principles

Differentiation from first principles involves four steps:

1. $f(x + h)$

2. $f(x + h) - f(x)$

3. $\dfrac{f(x + h) - f(x)}{h}$

4. $\lim\limits_{h \to 0} \dfrac{f(x + h) - f(x)}{h}$

(2017 Q.3 (a))

Differentiate $\dfrac{1}{3}x^2 - x + 3$ from first principles with respect to x.

Solution

$$f(x) = \frac{1}{3}x^2 - x + 3$$

$$f(x + h) = \frac{1}{3}(x + h)^2 - (x + h) + 3$$

Subtract: $f(x + h) - f(x) = \frac{1}{3}(x + h)^2 - (x + h) + 3 - \left[\frac{1}{3}x^2 - x + 3\right]$

$$f(x + h) - f(x) = \frac{1}{3}(x^2 + 2hx + h^2) - x - h + 3 - \frac{1}{3}x^2 + x - 3$$

$$f(x + h) - f(x) = \frac{1}{3}x^2 + \frac{2}{3}hx + \frac{1}{3}h^2 - h - \frac{1}{3}x^2$$

$$f(x + h) - f(x) = \frac{2}{3}xh + \frac{1}{3}h^2 - h$$

$$\frac{f(x + h) - f(x)}{h} = \frac{2}{3}x + \frac{1}{3}h - 1 \qquad \text{(dividing both sides by } h)$$

$$\lim_{h \to 0}\left(\frac{f(x + h) - f(x)}{h}\right) = \lim_{h \to 0}\left(\frac{2}{3}x + \frac{1}{3}h - 1\right)$$

$$f(x) = \frac{2}{3}x - 1$$

Candidates are expected to be able to differentiate linear and quadratic functions from first principles.

This question was awarded 20 marks $\left(6\frac{2}{3}\%\right.$ of paper). Overall, it was not well answered. While first principles is not asked every year, it is a must-learn technique.

(i) Prove, using first principles, that the differentiation of a constant is always zero.

(ii) Sketch the line $y = -3$.

(iii) What does your answer to part (i) tell you about the line in part (ii)?

Solution

(i) Let $f(x) = C$ where C constant $\in \mathbb{R}$.

$$f(x + h) = C$$
$$f(x + h) - f(x) = 0$$
$$\frac{f(x + h) - f(x)}{h} = \frac{0}{h}$$
$$\lim_{h \to 0}\frac{f(x + h) - f(x)}{h} = \lim_{h \to 0}(0)$$
$$\therefore f'(x) = 0$$

This concept is significant when dealing with curve sketching.

(ii)

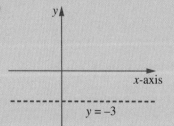

(iii) $f(x) = y = -3$

$$\Rightarrow f'(x) = \frac{dy}{dx} = 0 \text{ from (i)}$$

That is, the slope of the line is zero, i.e. the line is horizontal.

Continuous and discontinuous functions

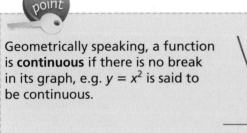

Geometrically speaking, a function is **continuous** if there is no break in its graph, e.g. $y = x^2$ is said to be continuous.

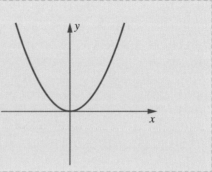

A **discontinuous** function is not continuous everywhere, e.g. $y = \tan x$ is said to have an infinite number of discontinuities.

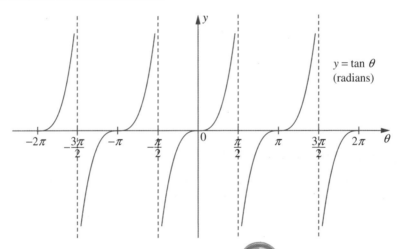

$y = \tan \theta$ (radians)

In addition, a function is **differentiable** (i.e. a derivative exists) at any points where it is 'smooth'.

You can think of continuous as meaning the graph of the function can be fully drawn without lifting the point of your pen off the page.

Example

Examine each graph below and determine whether the function it represents is continuous. If not, state why the function is discontinuous.

(i) $y = \begin{cases} 1 - x, & \text{if } x \leq -5 \\ 2x + 11, & \text{if } x > -5 \end{cases}$

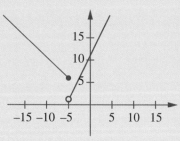

Solution

This graph is discontinuous as there is a 'break' at $x = -5$

(ii) $f(x) = x^3 - 9x$

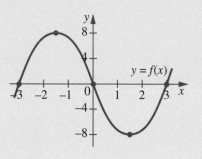

Solution

This graph is continuous.

An informal introduction to limits and continuity of functions

Here we examine the concept of a limit. It is often useful to investigate the trends in the values of different functions as x approaches a particular value, say, x_0. In the following two examples we examine the trends as x approaches a particular value. The two examples give us very different conclusions.

Example

(i) Investigate the trends in the value of $f(x) = \dfrac{x - 2}{x^2 - 4}$ as x approaches 2 by completing the following table:

x	1·9	1·99	1·999	2	2·001	2·01	2·1
$f(x)$							

(ii) When x approaches 2 (but $x \neq 2$), does the value of $f(x)$ approach a fixed value? If so, write down that value.

Solution

(i)

x	1·9		1·99		1·999	
f(x)	$\dfrac{1\cdot9 - 2}{(1\cdot9)^2 - 4} =$	$\dfrac{10}{39}$	$\dfrac{1\cdot99 - 2}{(1\cdot99)^2 - 4} =$	$\dfrac{100}{399}$	$\dfrac{1\cdot999 - 2}{(1\cdot999)^2 - 4} =$	$\dfrac{1{,}000}{3{,}999}$

x	2	2·001		2·01		2·1
f(x)	$\dfrac{2 - 2}{4 - 4} = \dfrac{0}{0}$ Not defined	$\dfrac{2\cdot001 - 2}{(2\cdot001)^2 - 4} =$	$\dfrac{1{,}000}{4{,}001}$	$\dfrac{2\cdot01 - 2}{(2\cdot01)^2 - 4} =$	$\dfrac{100}{401}$	$\dfrac{10}{41}$

(ii) From the table in (i), $f(x)$ seems to approach a fixed value of $\dfrac{1}{4}$ from both directions. This indicates that $f(x)$ is continuous at $x = 2$.

Example

(i) Investigate the trends in the value of $g(x) = \dfrac{5}{x - 1}$ as x approaches 1 by completing the following table:

x	0·9	0·99	0·999	1	1·001	1·01	1·1
g(x)							

(ii) When x approaches 1 (but $x \neq 1$), does the value of $g(x)$ approach a fixed value? If not, comment on what you think is happening.

Solution

(i)

x	0·9		0·99		0·999
$g(x) = \dfrac{5}{x - 1}$	$\dfrac{5}{0\cdot9 - 1} =$	-50	$\dfrac{5}{0\cdot99 - 1} =$	-500	$-5{,}000$

x	1		1·001		1·01		1·1
$g(x) = \dfrac{5}{x - 1}$	$\dfrac{5}{1 - 1} =$	not defined	$\dfrac{5}{1\cdot001 - 1} =$	$5{,}000$	$\dfrac{5}{1\cdot01 - 1} =$	500	50

(ii) From the table in (i), $g(x)$ does not approach the same fixed value from both sides $\Rightarrow g(x)$ is not continuous at $x = 1$.

Example

Examine each of the following graphs of functions $f(x)$.

(i) Determine whether $f(x)$ is continuous at $x = a$.

(ii) Find $\lim\limits_{x \to a} f(x)$.

(a)

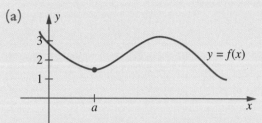

Solution

(i) Yes, continuous at $x = a$.

(ii) As x gets closer to a, the function gets closer to 1·5 from both sides. So, the limit is 1·5.

(b)

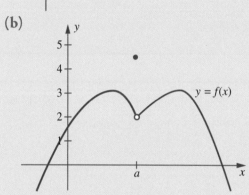

Solution

(i) No, not continuous at $x = a$.

(ii) As x gets closer to a, the function gets closer to 2 from both sides. So, the limit is 2.

(c)

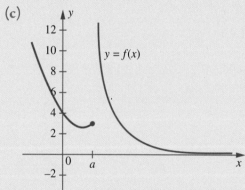

Solution

(i) No, not continuous at $x = a$.

(ii) As x gets closer to a, the function does not gets closer to the same value, from both sides. So, no limit exists when $x = a$.

(d)

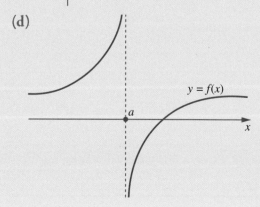

Solution

(i) No, not continuous at $x = a$.

(ii) As x gets closer to a, the function does not gets closer to the same value, from both sides. So, no limit exists when $x = a$.

16 Differential Calculus II: Differentiation by Rules

- [ ] To learn how to differentiate by rule
- [ ] To apply differentiation by rule to situations involving
    - The product rule
    - The quotient rule
    - The chain rule (composite functions)
- [ ] To become familiar with the rules for differentiating the functions found in the booklet of formulae and tables, page 25
- [ ] To learn how to evaluate derivatives for specific values
- [ ] To be aware of the skills required from algebra, trigonometry and elsewhere for success in exam questions on calculus
- [ ] To know the basic rules of logs and how to apply them
- [ ] To understand the importance of e^x and how it behaves

Differentiation by rule

It would be very tedious and time consuming if we had to use the limit definition every time we wanted to find the rate of change/slope of a tangent to a curve. To speed up the process we learn a number of standard derivatives and rules of differentiation, most of which are in the *booklet of formulae and tables* on page 25.

key point

$$f(x) = x^n \Rightarrow f'(x) = nx^{n-1}$$

Example

Differentiate the following with respect to x: (i) $2x^5 + x^3$ (ii) $\dfrac{1}{x^4}$

Solution

(i) Let $y = 2x^5 + x^3$.

$$\Rightarrow \frac{dy}{dx} = 10x^4 + 3x^2$$

(ii) Let $y = \dfrac{1}{x^4} = x^{-4}$.

$$\Rightarrow \frac{dy}{dx} = -4x^{-5} = \frac{-4}{x^5}$$

Example

Let $f(x) = 8 + x^2 - \dfrac{1}{x}$. Find $f'(x)$, the derivative of $f(x)$.

Solution

$$f(x) = 8 + x^2 - \frac{1}{x} = 8 + x^2 - x^{-1}$$

$$\Rightarrow f'(x) = 2x - (-1)x^{-2} = 2x + \frac{1}{x^2}$$

Differentiate $\sqrt{x}\,(x + 2)$ with respect to x.

key point

$\sqrt{x} = x^{\frac{1}{2}}$

Solution

Method 1: Let $y = \sqrt{x}\,(x + 2)$, which becomes

$$y = x^{\frac{1}{2}}(x + 2)$$

$$\Rightarrow \quad y = x^{\frac{3}{2}} + 2x^{\frac{1}{2}} \qquad \text{(multiply out)}$$

Now $\dfrac{dy}{dx} = \dfrac{3}{2}x^{\frac{1}{2}} + \dfrac{1}{2}(2)x^{-\frac{1}{2}}$

$$= \frac{3}{2}\sqrt{x} + \frac{1}{\sqrt{x}}$$

Method 2: Use the product rule from the *booklet of formulae and tables*, page 25.

Let $y = \sqrt{x}(x + 2)$.

Then $u = \sqrt{x} = x^{\frac{1}{2}}$ and $v = x + 2$.

$$\frac{du}{dx} = \frac{1}{2}x^{-\frac{1}{2}} \qquad \text{and} \quad \frac{dv}{dx} = 1$$

$$\frac{dy}{dx} = u\frac{dv}{dx} + v\frac{du}{dx} = (x^{\frac{1}{2}})(1) + (x + 2)\left(\frac{1}{2}x^{-\frac{1}{2}}\right)$$

$$= x^{\frac{1}{2}} + \frac{1}{2}x^{\frac{1}{2}} + x^{-\frac{1}{2}}$$

$$= \frac{3}{2}x^{\frac{1}{2}} + x^{-\frac{1}{2}}$$

$$= \frac{3}{2}\sqrt{x} + \frac{1}{\sqrt{x}}$$

key point

The given function is a product because two functions of x are being multiplied to give y.

Differentiate $\dfrac{1}{2 + 5x}$ with respect to x.

Method 1: Use the quotient rule from the *booklet of formulae and tables*, page 25

> The given function is a quotient because two functions of x are being divided to give y.
>
> v always equals the denominator (bottom)

Let $y = \dfrac{1}{2 + 5x}$.

Then $v = 2 + 5x$ and $u = 1$.

$$\frac{dv}{dx} = 5 \quad \text{and} \quad \frac{du}{dx} = 0$$

$$\frac{dy}{dx} = \frac{v\dfrac{du}{dx} - u\dfrac{dv}{dx}}{v^2} = \frac{(2 + 5x)(0) - (1)(5)}{(2 + 5x)^2}$$

$$= \frac{-5}{(2 + 5x)^2}$$

Method 2:

Let $y = \dfrac{1}{2 + 5x} = (2 + 5x)^{-1}$.

The chain rule is required to differentiate any composite function.

Let $u = 2 + 5x$.

$$\frac{du}{dx} = 5 \qquad\qquad y = (2 + 5x)^{-1} = u^{-1}$$

$$\frac{dy}{du} = -1u^{-2}$$

Thus, using the chain rule:

$$\frac{dy}{dx} = \frac{dy}{du}\frac{du}{dx} = (-1u^{-2})(5)$$

$$= \frac{-1}{u^2}(5)$$

$$= \frac{-5}{(2 + 5x)^2}$$

Differentiate each of the following with respect to x:

(i) $\cos^4 x$

(ii) $\sin^{-1}\dfrac{x}{5}$

$$\cos^4 x = (\cos x)^4$$

Solution

(i) This is a composite function, which means we require the chain rule.

Let $\quad y = (\cos x)^4 \quad$ and $\quad u = \cos x$.

Then $y = u^4 \quad$ and $\quad u = \cos x$.

$$\frac{dy}{du} = 4u^3 \qquad \text{and} \qquad \frac{du}{dx} = -\sin x \qquad \text{(see } booklet\ of\ formulae\ and\ tables,\ \text{page 25)}$$

Thus, using the chain rule:

$$\frac{dy}{dx} = \frac{dy}{du}\ \frac{du}{dx} = 4u^3(-\sin x) = 4\cos^3 x(-\sin x) = -4\cos^3 x\ \sin x$$

(ii) $y = \sin^{-1}\dfrac{x}{5}$

(see $booklet\ of\ formulae\ and\ tables$, page 25)

$$y = \sin^{-1}\frac{x}{a} \quad \Rightarrow \quad \frac{dy}{dx} = \frac{1}{\sqrt{a^2 - x^2}}$$

$$\therefore \quad \frac{dy}{dx} = \frac{1}{\sqrt{5^2 - x^2}} = \frac{1}{\sqrt{25 - x^2}}$$

It is vital to understand that $\sqrt{25 - x^2} \neq 5 - x$. This is a very common error for many candidates.

Given $y = 2x - \sin 2x$, find $\dfrac{dy}{dx}$.

Give your answer in the form $k\sin^2 x$, where $k \in \mathbb{Z}$.

Solution

$$y = 2x - \sin 2x$$

$$\frac{dy}{dx} = 2 - 2\cos 2x \qquad \text{(notice 2 from the chain rule)}$$

This is a typical exam tactic used by the examiner: asking a question where the solution requires knowledge from two (in this case) or more different topics. Here we are required to work on a trigonometric identity after performing the $\dfrac{dy}{dx}$ operation.

We continue with:

$$\frac{dy}{dx} = 2 - 2[\cos^2x - \sin^2x] \qquad \text{(see \textit{booklet of formulae and tables}, page 14)}$$

$$\frac{dy}{dx} = 2 - 2[(1 - \sin^2x) - \sin^2x] \quad \text{(see \textit{booklet of formulae and tables}, page 13)}$$

$$\frac{dy}{dx} = 2 - 2 + 2\sin^2x + 2\sin^2x$$

$$\frac{dy}{dx} = 4\sin^2x \qquad \text{(as required)}$$

Example

If $y = \ln(x^2 + 1)$, find $\dfrac{dy}{dx}$.

Solution

$$y = \ln(x^2 + 1)$$

$$\frac{dy}{dx} = \left(\frac{1}{x^2 + 1}\right)(2x) \qquad \text{(using the rule for differentiating } \ln x \text{ on page 25}$$
$$\qquad\qquad\qquad\qquad \text{of the \textit{booklet of formulae and tables} and the chain rule)}$$

$$\therefore \frac{dy}{dx} = \frac{2x}{x^2 + 1}$$

Laws of logs

$\ln AB = \ln A + \ln B$	$\ln \dfrac{A}{B} = \ln A - \ln B$	$\ln A^p = p\ln A$

In general, the above three rules of logs are very poorly known or understood by candidates. The following exam question was a disaster for candidates.

Given $y = \ln\left(\dfrac{3 + x}{\sqrt{9 - x^2}}\right)$, find $\dfrac{dy}{dx}$ and express it in the form $\dfrac{a}{b - x^n}$.

Solution

$$y = \ln\left(\frac{3 + x}{\sqrt{9 - x^2}}\right)$$

$$= \ln(3 + x) - \ln\sqrt{9 - x^2}$$

$$= \ln(3 + x) - \frac{1}{2}\ln(9 - x^2)$$

$$\frac{dy}{dx} = \frac{1}{3 + x} - \frac{1}{2}\left[\frac{1}{9 - x^2}(-2x)\right]$$

$$= \frac{1}{3 + x} + \frac{x}{9 - x^2}$$

$$= \frac{1}{3 + x} + \frac{x}{(3 - x)(3 + x)}$$

$$= \frac{(3 - x) + x}{(3 - x)(3 + x)} = \frac{3}{9 - x^2}$$

Notice that $9 - x^2 = (3 - x)(3 + x)$ factorising, from algebra, can be very important in the final stage of a successful solution.

Let $y = \sin^{-1}\left(\dfrac{x}{\sqrt{1 + x^2}}\right)$.

Find $\dfrac{dy}{dx}$ and express it in the form $\dfrac{a}{a + x^b}$ where $a, b \in \mathbb{N}$.

Solution

$$y = \sin^{-1}\left(\frac{x}{\sqrt{1 + x^2}}\right)$$

$$\sin y = \frac{x}{\sqrt{1 + x^2}}$$

This technique was used by less than 1% of candidates in a recent exam.

$$\sin y = \frac{\text{opp}}{\text{hyp}} \quad \text{means}$$

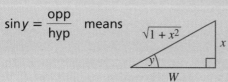

Pythagoras's theorem $\Rightarrow (\sqrt{1 + x^2})^2 = x^2 + W^2$

$$1 + x^2 = x^2 + W^2$$

$$\Rightarrow \qquad 1 = W^2 \qquad \therefore 1 = W$$

$$\tan y = \frac{\text{opp}}{\text{adj}} = \frac{x}{1} = x$$

$$\Rightarrow y = \tan^{-1}x$$

It is vital to read the question. It asks for $\dfrac{dy}{dx}$.

$y = \tan^{-1}x$ means $\dfrac{dy}{dx} = \dfrac{1}{1 + x^2}$ (see *booklet of formulae and tables*, page 25)

exam focus

$\frac{7}{20}$ was the most common mark achieved by candidates on the above question.

Examiners are very fond of inverse functions. Inverse functions are not well known or understood by candidates. To cope, remember:

Opp and $\sin(\sin^{-1}k) = k$ and information in the *booklet of formulae and tables*, page 25

Evaluating derivatives

exam Q

(i) If $y = \sin x \cos x$, evaluate $\dfrac{dy}{dx}$ at $x = \dfrac{\pi}{4}$.

(ii) If $f(x) = \dfrac{x^2}{\ln x}$, evaluate $f'(e)$.

Solution

(i) Using the product rule

$$\frac{dy}{dx} = (\sin x)(-\sin x) + (\cos x)(\cos x)$$

$$\frac{dy}{dx} = -\sin^2 x + \cos^2 x$$

$$\frac{dy}{dx}\bigg|_{x=\frac{\pi}{4}} = -\sin^2\frac{\pi}{4} + \cos^2\frac{\pi}{4} = -\frac{1}{2} + \frac{1}{2} = 0$$

(ii) Using the quotient rule

$$f'(x) = \frac{(\ln x)(2x) - (x^2)\left(\frac{1}{x}\right)}{(\ln x)^2}$$

$$f'(e) = \frac{(\ln e)(2e) - e^2\left(\frac{1}{e}\right)}{(\ln e)^2}$$

$$f'(e) = \frac{(1)(2e) - e}{(1)^2} = \frac{2e - e}{1} = e$$

(2016 Q.6 (b))

(i) If $y = x \sin\left(\frac{1}{x}\right)$, find $\frac{dy}{dx}$.

(ii) Find the slope of the tangent to the curve $y = x \sin\left(\frac{1}{x}\right)$, when $x = \frac{4}{\pi}$. Give your answer correct to two decimal places.

Solution

(i) Using the product rule

$$u = x \qquad V = \sin\left(\frac{1}{x}\right)$$

$$\frac{du}{dx} = 1 \qquad \frac{dV}{dx} = \left(\cos\frac{1}{x}\right)\left(-\frac{1}{x^2}\right)$$

$$y = x\sin\frac{1}{x}$$

$$\frac{dy}{dx} = \sin\frac{1}{x} + x\left(\cos\frac{1}{x}\right)\left(-\frac{1}{x^2}\right)$$

$$\frac{dy}{dx} = \sin\frac{1}{x} - \frac{1}{x}\cos\frac{1}{x}$$

(ii) Let $x = \frac{4}{\pi}$, so $\frac{1}{x} = \frac{\pi}{4}$

$$\frac{dy}{dx} = \sin\frac{\pi}{4} - \frac{\pi}{4}\cos\frac{\pi}{4} = 0.15$$

The majority of candidates could not handle $\frac{1}{x}$. It is vital to know $\frac{1}{x} = x^{-1}$ and then differentiate x^{-1} to get $-1x^{-2} = \frac{-1}{x^2}$.

A penalty of -4 marks out of a total of 15 marks for using the incorrect mode on calculator.

Application of the chain rule

A function involving x and y can be differentiated with respect to x as it stands using the chain rule.

It is useful to remember that by the chain rule:

$$\frac{d}{dx}(y^2) = 2y\frac{dy}{dx} \quad \text{and} \quad \frac{d}{dx}(y^3) = 3y^2\frac{dy}{dx}$$

as y is considered as a function of x.

Method:

1. Differentiate, term by term, on both sides with respect to x.
2. Bring all terms with $\frac{dy}{dx}$ to the left and bring all other terms to the right.
3. Make $\frac{dy}{dx}$ the subject of the equation.

Find the slope of the tangent to the curve $9x^2 + 4y^2 = 40$ at the point $(2, 1)$.

Solution

Differentiate $9x^2 + 4y^2 = 40$ with respect to x.

$$\Rightarrow 18x + 8y\frac{dy}{dx} = 0 \quad \text{(using a chain rule)}$$

$$8y\frac{dy}{dx} = -18x$$

$$\frac{dy}{dx} = \frac{-18x}{8y} = \frac{-9x}{4y}$$

It is vital to know that the slope of the tangent $= m = \dfrac{dy}{dx}$.

Substitute $x = 2$ and $y = 1$ to get

$$\frac{dy}{dx} = \frac{-9(2)}{4(1)} = \frac{-18}{4} = \frac{-9}{2} = \text{slope of the tangent}$$

(2017 Q.3 (b))

$f(x) = \ln(3x^2 + 2)$ and $g(x) = x + 5$, where $x \in R$. Find the value of the derivative of $f(g(x))$ at $x = \dfrac{1}{4}$.

Give your answer correct to 3 decimal places.

Solution

key point

$$fg(x) = f(x + 5) = \ln[3(x + 5)^2 + 2]$$

$$= \ln[3(x^2 + 10x + 25) + 2]$$

$$= \ln[3x^2 + 30x + 77]$$

Refer to *Chapter 6: Functions and Graphing Functions* for a straightforward example on composite functions.

$$\frac{df(g(x))}{dx} = \left[\frac{1}{3x^2 + 30x + 77}\right](6x + 30) \quad \text{(chain rule)}$$

Now substitute $x = \dfrac{1}{4} = 0.25$ to get

$$\frac{df\left(g\left(\frac{1}{4}\right)\right)}{dx} = \left[\frac{1}{3(0.25)^2 + 30(0.25) + 77}\right](6(0.25) + 30) = 0.372$$

Candidates had trouble with this question. By 2017, a question on composite functions was long overdue, but the examiner was maybe too ambitious combining functions and calculus, when candidates had little or no experience on this type of question.

The marking scheme reflected this bad question which was awarded a total of 5 marks (=$1\frac{2}{3}$ % on this paper). It is nonetheless worth remembering that 3 marks were awarded to candidates with any correct differentiation. Always make an attempt. Learn composite functions.

The exponential function

The exponential function is written
$$y = e^x \quad \text{or} \quad y = \exp x$$
where e is an irrational constant with value $\approx 2{\cdot}718$.

The graph of $y = e^x$ has no turning points.
$y = e^x \geq 0$ for all values of $x \in \mathbb{R}$ and e^x is the only basic function where $y = e^x$

$$\Rightarrow \quad \frac{dy}{dx} = e^x$$

i.e. e^x is its own derivative.
In addition, you may notice from your calculator that
$$e^{\ln x} = x \quad \text{and} \quad \ln e^x = x.$$
It's also worth noting the chain rule operating on exponential:

$$\text{If } y = e^{\sin x} \quad \text{then} \quad \frac{dy}{dx} = \cos x \; e^{\sin x}.$$

> If $y = e^{ax}$, then $\dfrac{dy}{dx} = a\, e^{ax}$
>
> e.g. if $y = e^{-2x}$, then $\dfrac{dy}{dx} = -2\, e^{-2x}$

Let $y = \dfrac{e^x - e^{-x}}{e^x + e^{-x}}$. Show that $\dfrac{dy}{dx} = \dfrac{4}{(e^x + e^{-x})^2}$.

Solution

Quotient rule required

Let $v = e^x + e^{-x}$ (denominator) $u = e^x - e^{-x}$

$$\frac{dv}{dx} = e^x - e^{-x} \qquad\qquad \frac{du}{dx} = e^x + e^{-x}$$

$$\therefore \; \frac{dy}{dx} = \frac{v\dfrac{du}{dx} - u\dfrac{dv}{dx}}{v^2} = \frac{(e^x + e^{-x})(e^x + e^{-x}) - (e^x - e^{-x})(e^x - e^{-x})}{(e^x + e^{-x})^2}$$

key point

$$(e^x + e^{-x})(e^x + e^{-x}) = e^{2x} + e^0 + e^0 + e^{-2x} = e^{2x} + 2 + e^{-2x}$$

Now $\dfrac{dy}{dx} = \dfrac{e^{2x} + 2 + e^{-2x} - (e^{2x} - 2 + e^{-2x})}{(e^x + e^{-x})^2}$

$\dfrac{dy}{dx} = \dfrac{e^{2x} + 2 + e^{-2x} - e^{2x} + 2 - e^{-2x}}{(e^x + e^{-x})^2} = \dfrac{4}{(e^x + e^{-x})^2}$

exam focus

Multiplication in algebra, $(a + b)^2 = a^2 + 2ab + b^2$, and handling indices, $(q^5)(q)^{-3} = q^2$, are required skills for success in this question on differential calculus.

Higher derivatives

Given $y = f(x)$ is a function, then its derivative, $\dfrac{dy}{dx} = f'(x)$, is another function of x.

$\dfrac{dy}{dx} = f'(x)$ can itself be differentiated to obtain what is called the second derivative.

This is written $\dfrac{d}{dx}\left(\dfrac{dy}{dx}\right) = \dfrac{d^2y}{dx^2} = f''(x)$.

For example: $\quad y = f(x) = 9x^5 + x^2 - 3$

$$\dfrac{dy}{dx} = f'(x) = 45x^4 + 2x$$

$$\dfrac{d^2y}{dx} = f''(x) = 180x^3 + 2$$

Higher derivatives, e.g. the third derivative, may be obtained by continuing the process:

$$\dfrac{d^3y}{dx^3} = f'''(x) = 540x^2$$

Example

Find the value of the constant k if $y = e^{2x}$ is a solution of the equation

$$y + \frac{dy}{dx} + \frac{d^2y}{dx^2} = ke^{2x}.$$

Solution

$$y = e^{2x} \implies \frac{dy}{dx} = 2e^{2x} \implies \frac{d^2y}{dx^2} = 4e^{2x}$$

$$\therefore \quad y + \frac{dy}{dx} + \frac{d^2y}{dx^2} = ke^{2x}$$

Becomes $\quad e^{2x} + 2e^{2x} + 4e^{2x} = ke^{2x}$

$$7e^{2x} = ke^{2x}$$

$$\therefore 7 = k$$

Example

If $f(x) = 3\cos(2x + 5)$, show that $f''(x) + 4f(x) = 0$.

Solution

$$f(x) = 3\cos(2x + 5)$$
$$f'(x) = -6\sin(2x + 5)$$
$$f''(x) = -12\cos(2x + 5)$$

Now $f''(x) + 4f(x) = 0$

Becomes $-12\cos(2x + 5) + 4(3\cos(2x + 5)) = 0$

$$-12\cos(2x + 5) + 12\cos(2x + 5) = 0$$

$$0 = 0$$

$$\therefore f''(x) + 4f(x) = 0 \text{ as required}$$

17 Differential Calculus III: Applications to Curve Sketching

☐ To learn what differentiation can tell us about curves
☐ How to find the slope and equation of a tangent to a curve
☐ Finding local maxima, minima and points of inflection (also called the critical, stationary or turning points)
☐ Sketching $f'(x)$ and $f''(x)$ from a graph of $f(x)$ and associated exam-type questions
☐ To learn what polynomials and their degrees mean
☐ To acquire the skills to cope with examination questions

What can differentiation tell us?

We may know the rules of differentiation, but what can we do with them? In this chapter we look at how it is possible to describe graphs which are changing and how to find out the rate of this change.

We begin by looking at an example that models an in-context situation. This can help us see how differential calculus is employed to clarify situations that can be described by a graph. In addition, studying this example can help gain an insight into what an examiner requires from candidates.

Sketching derived graphs

An engineer is working on a new mega rollercoaster for a theme park. The diagram shows the cross-section of the roller coaster over the first 270m from its start.

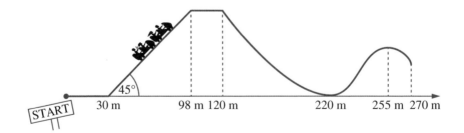

She considers the steepness experienced as the riders move along the track.

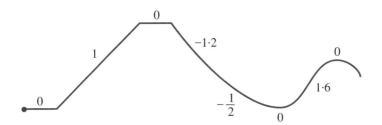

- When the track is level, the slope (gradient) is 0.
- Going upwards in a straight line at an angle of 45°, the slope is 1(=tan 45°)
- The track is then level again, with a gradient of 0.
- Going down the track is curved, so the slope varies. She estimates the slope is steep $(-1\cdot2)$, then less steep $\left(-\dfrac{1}{2}\right)$. Notice going down, negative slope.
- At the bottom of the curve, for a moment, the slope is 0.
- Going up again, the slope increases to an estimated 1·6.
- Then the steepness (slope) goes down from about 1·6 until the track is level and slope 0 for a moment.
- The track continues downward.
- This graph shows the slope (drawn in red) at each distance from the start.

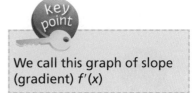

We call this graph of slope (gradient) $f'(x)$

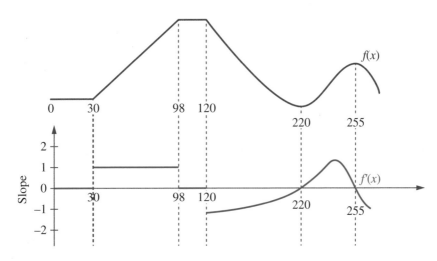

Looking at the red graph we observe:
- $f'(x)$ is 0 between 0 and 30 and between 98 and 120. This is where the track is level.
- $f'(x)$ is also 0 for two moments, at distances of 220m and 255m from the start.

- When the roller coaster is going up (height increasing), the slope function $f'(x)$ is positive.
- When the roller coaster is going down (height decreasing), the slope function $f'(x)$ is negative.

The best place to draw the slope graph or the derived function $f'(x)$, is immediately below the function graph. See the next example.

Remember

The steepness (or gradient or slope) will depend upon where we are on the curve.

The gradient (or steepness) at a point P on a curve is defined as the slope of the tangent drawn to the curve at the point P. That is, the slope of the line that just touches the curve at the point P.

A very accurate drawing would help, but this is not easy to do so we need an alternative method for finding the slope (rate of change) of the tangent at P.

Key points for sketching graphs and their derivatives

It is vital to know the following:

1. At the turning points of any graph $f(x)$, its derivative $f'(x) = 0$.
2. Similarly, at the turning points of $f'(x)$, its derivative $f''(x) = 0$ etc.
3. When a function or its derivative is of the form $y = mx + c$, the graph has no turning points and is a straight line.
4. If a function or its derivative is of the form $h(x) = k$, where $k \in \mathbb{R}$, the graph of $h(x)$ is a straight line parallel to the x-axis.

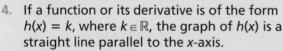

5. Around the turning points, we constantly apply the following two facts.

   (a) For an increasing section of a graph $f(x)$ we know $f'(x) > 0$, i.e. $f'(x)$ above the x-axis.

   (b) For a decreasing section of a graph $f(x)$ we know $f'(x) < 0$, i.e. $f'(x)$ below the x-axis.

Example

Sketch the graphs of the first and second derivatives of the functions
(i) $k(x)$ (ii) $g(x)$, given below.

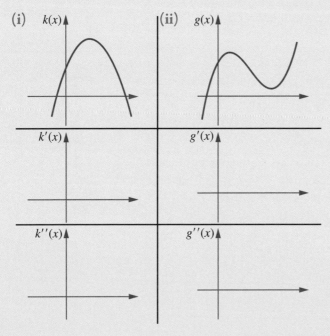

Solution

(i) $k(x) \rightarrow k'(x) \rightarrow k''(x)$

At P, the local maximum (turning) point of $k(x)$, we know that $k'(x) = 0$.

From the graph (across) we observe the point Q on $k'(x)$ associated with the point P on $k(x)$.

In addition, we note Q is on the x-axis. The graph of $k(x)$ can be considered in two sections.

(a) The section of $k(x)$ to the left of P, where $k(x)$ is increasing $\Rightarrow k'(x) > 0$, i.e. $k'(x)$ is above the x-axis to the left of Q.

(b) The section of $k(x)$ to the right of P, where $k(x)$ is decreasing $\Rightarrow k'(x) < 0$, i.e. $k'(x)$ is below the x-axis to the right of Q.

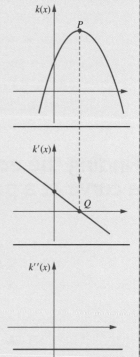

From the graph (previous), we observe $k'(x)$ is a constantly decreasing straight line of the form

$$k'(x) = mx + c \quad \text{where } m \text{ is negative}$$

$$\Rightarrow k''(x) = m \quad \text{a negative number}$$

Hence, the graph of $k''(x)$ is a straight line **below** and parallel to the x-axis.

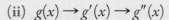

(ii) $g(x) \rightarrow g'(x) \rightarrow g''(x)$

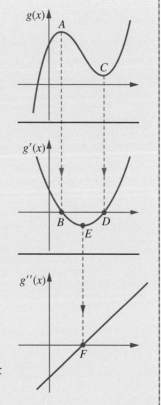

At A and C, the turning points of $g(x)$, we know that $g'(x) = 0$.

From the graph (across) we observe the points B and D on $g'(x)$ associated with the points A and C, respectively, on $g(x)$.

In addition, we note B and D are on the x-axis. The graph of $g(x)$ can be considered in three sections.

(a) The section of $g(x)$ to the left of A where $g(x)$ is increasing $\Rightarrow g'(x) > 0$, i.e. $g'(x)$ is above the x-axis to the left of B.

(b) The section of $g(x)$ between the points A and C where $g(x)$ is decreasing $\Rightarrow g'(x) < 0$, i.e. $g'(x)$ is below the x-axis between B and D.

(c) The section of $g(x)$ to the right of C, where $g(x)$ increasing $\Rightarrow g'(x) > 0$, i.e. $g'(x)$ is above the x-axis to the right of D.

From the above graph we observe $g'(x)$ is a U-shape quadratic graph with a local minimum (turning) point at E where we know $g''(x) = 0$. Again from the graph we observe the point F on $g''(x)$ is associated with the point E on $g'(x)$.

We further observe F is on the x-axis.

In a similar argument to solution (i) we conclude that $g''(x)$ is below the x-axis to the left of F and that $g''(x)$ above the x-axis to the right of F.

$\Rightarrow g''(x)$ is a straight line with a positive slope. (As the line is going upwards.)

Finding the equation of a tangent to a curve at a point on the curve

$\dfrac{dy}{dx}$ = the slope of a tangent to a curve at any point on the curve

To find the slope and equation of a tangent to a curve at a given point, (x_1, y_1), on the curve, do the following.

Step 1: Find $\dfrac{dy}{dx}$.

Step 2: Evaluate $\left.\dfrac{dy}{dx}\right|_{x=x_1}$ (this gives m, the slope of the tangent)

(If the angle the curve makes with the x-axis is required, use the calculator.)

Step 3: Use m (from step 2) and the given point (x_1, y_1) in the equation:

$$(y - y_1) = m(x - x_1)$$

key point

Sometimes only the value of x is given. When this happens, substitute the value of x into the original function to find y for step 3.

Example

Find the equation of the tangent to the curve $y = \dfrac{x - 1}{x + 2}$ at $x = -1$.

Solution

$$y = \frac{x - 1}{x + 2}$$

Using the quotient rule:

$$\frac{dy}{dx} = \frac{(x + 2)(1) - (x - 1)(1)}{(x + 2)^2}$$

$$= \frac{3}{(x + 2)^2}$$

$$\left.\frac{dy}{dx}\right|_{x=-1} = \frac{3}{(-1 + 2)^2} = 3$$

$\therefore$ Slope $= 3$

$$y = \frac{x - 1}{x + 2}$$

when $x = -1, y = \dfrac{-1 - 1}{-1 + 2} = -2$

Thus, the point $(-1, -2)$ is on the curve.

Slope $= 3$ at this point.

Then $y - y_1 = m(x - x_1)$ becomes

$$(y + 2) = 3(x + 1)$$

$$y + 2 = 3x + 3$$

$$3x - y + 1 = 0$$

(2018 Q.3 (a))

Let $h(x) = \cos(2x)$, where $x \in R$.

A tangent is drawn to the graph of $h(x)$ at the point where $x = \dfrac{\pi}{3}$. Find the angle that this tangent makes with the positive sense of the x-axis.

Solution

$$h(x) = \cos(2x)$$

$$h'(x) = -\sin(2x) \ [2] \qquad\qquad \text{(using the chain rule)}$$

$$h'\left(\frac{\pi}{3}\right) = -\sin\left(\frac{2\pi}{3}\right) [2] = -\frac{\sqrt{3}}{2} [2] = -\sqrt{3}$$

Then $\tan\theta = -\sqrt{3}$

$$\theta = \tan^{-1}(-\sqrt{3})$$

$$\theta = -60°$$

However, the question asked for the angle with the positive sense:

Slope of tangent $= h'\left(\dfrac{\pi}{3}\right) = \tan\theta$

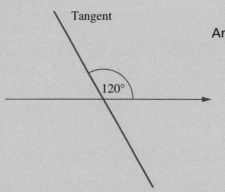

Answer $= 120°$

Maximum, minimum and points of inflection

The figure shows the sketch of $y = f(x)$ at the points P, Q and R. The tangent to the curve is parallel to the x-axis and therefore the gradient of the curve at P, Q and R is zero.

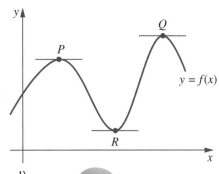

The point P is said to be a (local) **maximum** point. It is important to realise that at a maximum point such as P the value of y may not be the greatest value of y on the entire curve. The important fact is that the value of y at P is greater than at points close to P. Similarly, Q is another (local) **maximum** point. The value of y at R is less than the values of y at points on the curve close to R and so R is said to be a (local) **minimum** on the curve.

Such maximum and minimum points are said to be stationary or turning or critical points on the curve.

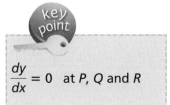

key point

$$\frac{dy}{dx} = 0 \quad \text{at } P, Q \text{ and } R$$

However, there may be some point on a curve at which $\dfrac{dy}{dx} = 0$, but the point is neither a maximum nor a minimum. The point S on the figure is such a point, but S is neither a maximum point nor a minimum point.

S is called a **point of inflection**.

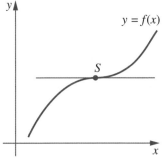

To distinguish between the three types of stationary points, we require **the second derivative**. That is, $\dfrac{d^2y}{dx^2}$ or $f''(x)$.

key point

When we find $\dfrac{dy}{dx} = 0$ then:

If $\dfrac{d^2y}{dx^2} > 0$ we have a **minimum** point

If $\dfrac{d^2y}{dx^2} = 0$ we have a point of **inflection**

If $\dfrac{d^2y}{dx^2} < 0$ we have a **maximum** point

(2017 Q.5 (b))

The function f is such that $f(x) = 2x^3 + 5x^2 - 4x - 3$

Find the coordinates of the local maximum point and the local minimum point of the function f.

Solution

$$f(x) = 2x^3 + 5x^2 - 4x - 3$$

$$f'(x) = 6x^2 + 10x - 4$$

$$f''(x) = 12x + 10$$

At the local maximum and local minimum turning points $f'(x) = 0$

Hence $6x^2 + 10x - 4 = 0$

$3x^2 + 5x - 2 = 0$ (divide each term by 2)

$(3x - 1)(x + 2) = 0$

$3x - 1 = 0$ or $x + 2 = 0$

$x = \dfrac{1}{3}$ or $x = -2$

Now consider the value of $f''(x) = 12x + 10$

When $x = \dfrac{1}{3}$ $\qquad f''\left(\dfrac{1}{3}\right) = 12\left(\dfrac{1}{3}\right) + 10 = 14 > 0$

This tells us $x = \dfrac{1}{3}$ gives a minimum turning point.

When $x = -2$ $\qquad f''(-2) = 12(-2) + 10 = -14 < 0$

This tells us $x = -2$ gives a maximum turning point.

Finally, we find the y values associated with $x = \dfrac{1}{3}$ and $x = -2$.

$$f(x) = 2x^3 + 5x^2 - 4x - 3$$

$$x = \frac{1}{3} \rightarrow f\left(\frac{1}{3}\right) = 2\left(\frac{1}{3}\right)^3 + 5\left(\frac{1}{3}\right)^2 - 4\left(\frac{1}{3}\right) - 3 = -\frac{100}{27}$$

$$x = -2 \rightarrow f(-2) = 2(-2)^3 + 5(-2)^2 - 4(-2) - 3 = 9$$

Thus, minimum point at $\left(\dfrac{1}{3}, -\dfrac{100}{27}\right)$

and maximum point at $(-2, 9)$.

The examiner made the 2017 Q5 too long, this was an error. Part (b) above was only awarded 5 marks. In addition to the question being overlong, candidates' answers were significantly below expectations. This type of question should appear regularly and should be worth at least 10 marks.

(2015 Q.5 (b)–(c))

(b) Differentiate $x - \sqrt{x + 6}$ with respect to x.

(c) Find the co-ordinates of the turning point of the function
$y = x - \sqrt{x + 6}$, $x \geq -6$.

Solution

(b) $f(x) = x - \sqrt{x + 6} = x - (x + 6)^{\frac{1}{2}}$

$f'(x) = 1 - \frac{1}{2}(x + 6)^{-\frac{1}{2}}$

$f'(x) = 1 - \frac{1}{2\sqrt{x + 6}}$

> **exam focus**
>
> Candidates were not asked to distinguish the type of turning point. It is in fact a minimum.

(c) $f'(x) = 0$ at turning points

$f'(x) = 1 - \frac{1}{2\sqrt{x + 6}}$

By comparison $1 - \frac{1}{2\sqrt{x + 6}} = 0$

$1 = \frac{1}{2\sqrt{x + 6}}$ (add $\frac{1}{2\sqrt{x + 6}}$ to both sides)

$2\sqrt{x + 6} = 1$ (multiply both sides by $2\sqrt{x + 6}$)

$\sqrt{x + 6} = \frac{1}{2}$ (divide both sides by 2)

$x + 6 = \frac{1}{4}$ (square both sides)

$x = -5\frac{3}{4}$ (subtract 6 from both sides)

Now substitute $x = -5\frac{3}{4}$ into $y = x - \sqrt{x + 6}$

To get $y = -5\frac{3}{4} - \sqrt{-5\frac{3}{4} + 6}$

$y = -5\frac{3}{4} - \frac{1}{2} = -6\frac{1}{4}$

Turning point $\left(-5\frac{3}{4}, -6\frac{1}{4}\right)$

exam Q

(2015 Q.7(a)–(c))

A plane is flying horizontally at P at a height of 150 m above level ground when it begins its descent. P is 5 km, horizontally, from the point of touchdown O. The plane lands horizontally at O.

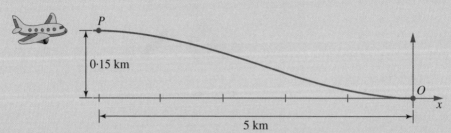

Taking O as the origin $(x, f(x))$ approximately describes the path of the plane's descent where $f(x) = 0{\cdot}0024x^3 + 0{\cdot}018x^2 + cx + d$, $-5 \leq x \leq 0$, and both x and $f(x)$ are measured in km.

(a) (i) Show that $d = 0$

(ii) Using the fact that P is the point $(-5, 0{\cdot}15)$, or otherwise, show that $c = 0$.

(b) (i) Find the value of $f'(x)$, the derivative of $f(x)$, when $x = -4$.

(ii) Use your answer to part (b)(i) above to find the angle at which the plane is descending when it is 4 km from touchdown. Give your answer correct to the nearest degree.

(c) Show that $(-2{\cdot}5, 0{\cdot}075)$ is the point of inflection of the curve $y = f(x)$.

Solution

(a) (i) Origin $= (0, 0) \in f(x) = 0{\cdot}0024x^3 + 0{\cdot}018x^2 + cx + d$

$$f(0) = 0 + 0 + 0 + d$$

$$0 = d$$

(ii) $(-5, -0{\cdot}15) \in f(x) = 0{\cdot}0024x^3 + 0{\cdot}018x^2 + cx$

$$f(-5) = 0{\cdot}0024(-5)^3 + 0{\cdot}018(-5)^2 + c(-5)$$

$$0{\cdot}15 = -0{\cdot}3 + 0{\cdot}45 - 5c$$

$$5c = 0$$

$$c = 0$$

(b) (i) $f(x) = 0{\cdot}0024x^3 + 0{\cdot}018x^2$

$$f'(x) = 0{\cdot}0072x^2 + 0{\cdot}036x$$

Substitute $x = -4$ then $f'(-4) = 0{\cdot}0072(-4)^2 + 0{\cdot}036(-4) = -0{\cdot}0288$

(ii) $\tan\theta = f'(x) = $ gradient $=$ slope

$\tan\theta = -0 \cdot 0288$

$\quad \theta = \tan^{-1}(-0 \cdot 0288)$

$\quad\quad = -1 \cdot 64966°(178 \cdot 3503°)$

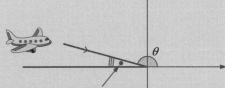

Angle of descent $= 1 \cdot 64966° = 2°$

(c) $f'(x) = 0 \cdot 0072x^2 + 0 \cdot 036x$

$f''(x) = 0 \cdot 0144x + 0 \cdot 036$

$f''(x) = 0$ at the point of inflection

By comparison $0 \cdot 0144x + 0 \cdot 036 = 0$

$$0 \cdot 0144x = -0 \cdot 036$$

$$x = -2 \cdot 5$$

Now substitute $x = -2 \cdot 5$ into $f(x) = 0 \cdot 0024x^3 + 0 \cdot 018x^2$

To get $\quad\quad\quad\quad\quad f(-2 \cdot 5) = 0 \cdot 0024(-2 \cdot 5)^3 + 0 \cdot 018(-2 \cdot 5)^2$

$$f(-2 \cdot 5) = -0 \cdot 0375 + 0 \cdot 1125$$

$$f(-2 \cdot 5) = 0 \cdot 075$$

We have shown $(-2 \cdot 5, 0 \cdot 075)$ is a point of inflection.

Parts (a) (b) and (c) of this question was awarded a total of 35 marks ($11\frac{2}{3}$% of paper). A very good, fair question.

It was a great place to gain marks. Candidates did well here.

Sketching trigonmetric graphs and their derivatives

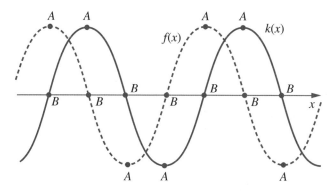

Each turning point marked A has a corresponding point B on the x-axis.

Each point B is always directly above or below the corresponding point A.

The derivative of $\sin x$ is $\cos x$

The derivative of $\cos x$ is $-\sin x$

Exam questions on derivatives and sketching curves

(2013 Q.5)

Each diagram below shows part of the graph of a function. Each of these functions is either quadratic or cubic or trigonometric or exponential (not necessarily in that order).

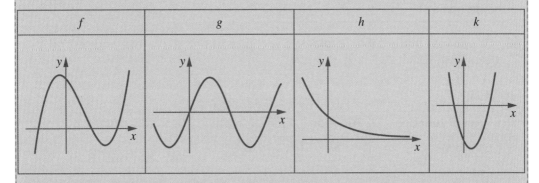

Each diagram below shows part of the graph of the first derivative of one of the above functions (not necessarily in the same order).

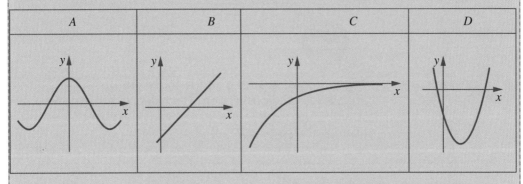

Each diagram below shows part of the graph of the second derivative of one of the original functions (not necessarily in the same order).

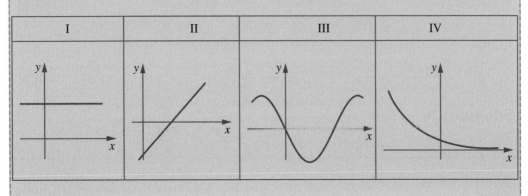

(a) Complete the table below by matching the function to its first derivative and its second derivative.

Type of function	Function	First derivative	Second derivative
Quadratic			
Cubic			
Trigonometric			
Exponential			

(b) For **one** row in the table, explain your choice of first derivative and second derivative.

Solution

(a)

Type of function	Function	First derivative	Second derivative
Quadratic	k	B	I
Cubic	f	D	II
Trigonometric	g	A	III
Exponential	h	C	IV

(b) $h = e^{-x}$

$\dfrac{dh}{dx} = -e^{-x} = C$

$\dfrac{d^2h}{dx^2} = +e^{-x} = IV$

key point

Trigonometric graphs g and A and III are clearly linked, see previous section. The cubic, quadratic and straight line f and D and II are clearly linked, see the example on page 220.

Example

Given that $h(x)$ is a polynomial of degree 5, then $h'(x)$ is a polynomial of degree 4, fill in the relevant box for each of the following statements.

(i) If $g(x)$ is a polynomial of degree 6, then $g'(x)$ is a polynomial of degree ☐.

(ii) If $f(x)$ is a polynomial of degree ☐, then $f''(x)$ is a polynomial of degree 2.

Solution

(i) 5   (ii) 3

Two linked families of curves appear throughout calculus on our course.

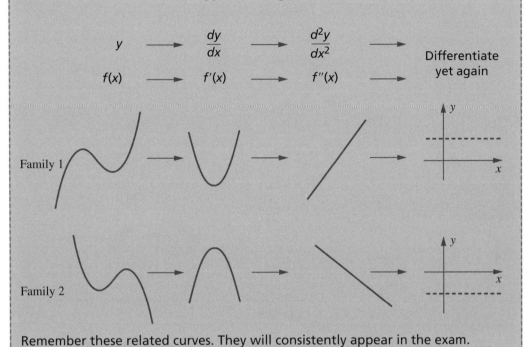

Remember these related curves. They will consistently appear in the exam.

Draw a rough sketch of $f(x)$, a polynomial of degree four, given that:

(i) $\left(1\frac{1}{2}, -3\frac{13}{16}\right) \in f(x)$

(ii) $f'(x) = 0$ at $x = -1$, $x = 0$ and $x = \frac{3}{2}$ only at these three values

(iii) $f''(x)$, the second differential of $f(x)$, is such that $f''\left(\frac{3}{2}\right) > 0$

(iv) $f(0) = 8$ and $f(-1) = 4$

(v) $f'(x) > 0$ for $-1 < x < 0$

(vi) $f'(x) < 0$ for $x < -1$

Solution

(i) And **(iv)** gives us three points on the curve $f(x)$.

They are $\left(\dfrac{3}{2}, -3\dfrac{13}{16}\right)$, $(0, 8)$ and $(-1, 4)$.

(ii) Tells us there are only three stationary points and they are the three given above.

(iii) Indicates $\left(\dfrac{3}{2}, -3\dfrac{13}{16}\right)$ is a local minimum point.

At this stage we know:

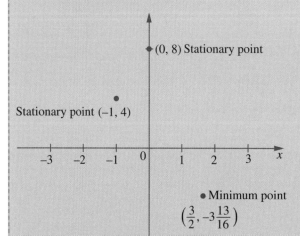

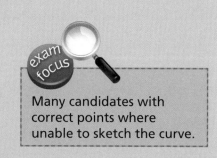

Many candidates with correct points where unable to sketch the curve.

(iv) Tells us the curve is increasing in the domain $-1 < x < 0$ while **(vi)** tells us the curve is decreasing in the domain $x < -1$.

Parts **(v)** and **(vi)** combine to indicate a local minimum at $x = -1$.

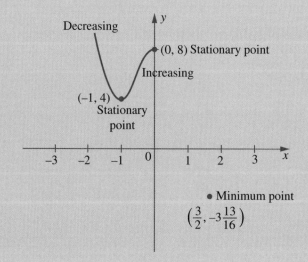

To complete the curve we analyse the data. We know $\left(\dfrac{3}{2}, -3\dfrac{13}{16}\right)$ is a local minimum point. (0, 8) is the last remaining unclassified stationary point. Because the polynomial curve is continuous, we conclude (0, 8) is a local maximum point. Since there are no other stationary points on this curve, this means $f(x)$ decreases in the domain $0 < x < \dfrac{3}{2}$. Finally, from the minimum point $\left(\dfrac{3}{2}, -3\dfrac{13}{16}\right)$, $f(x)$ increases to infinity.

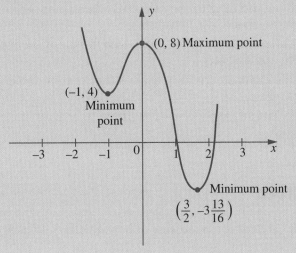

18 Differential Calculus IV: Applications to In-Context Problems

aims

□ First we attempt to gain an insight into rates of change in context

□ To understand how to use calculus in questions seeking maximums, minimums, speed, acceleration, etc.

□ To see and understand the chain rule in operation in some of its many real-life applications

□ To tackle exam-standard questions that require the chain rule application

□ To gain insight into the skills required to answer in-context questions in calculus

Rates of change

The slope (gradient) of a curve is a measure of how quickly y is changing in relation to x. We say $\dfrac{dy}{dx}$ is the rate of change of y with respect to x.

This idea can be extended to other variables. We can use calculus to find rates of change when any two variables are linked by a formula.

Example

The volume of a sphere is given by the formula $V = \dfrac{4}{3}\pi r^3$. Calculate the rate at which the volume is changing with respect to the radius when the radius of the sphere is 5 cm.

Solution

key point

The rate of change of the volume with respect to the radius is $\dfrac{dV}{dr}$. This is called the derivative of V with respect to r, or simply the derivative.

$$V = \frac{4}{3}\pi r^3 \qquad \text{(booklet of formulae and tables, p. 10)}$$

$$\frac{dV}{dr} = 3\left(\frac{4}{3}\pi r^2\right) = 4\pi r^2$$

Now substitute $r = 5$ to find $\frac{dV}{dr} = 4\pi(5)^2 = 100\pi = 314.16$

Related rates of change (chain rule)

In many situations, as one variable changes, a related variable changes as well. A good example is the radius of a circle; as the radius increases so does the area of the circle. However, if the radius increases at 1.5cm/s, the area does not necessarily increase at $1.5\text{cm}^2/\text{s}$.

Rates of change can be expressed as derivatives. The key is to use the **chain rule** to link three derivatives together.

There are three related rates of change for the area of a circle as the radius increases:

- $\dfrac{dA}{dt} =$ rate of change of area with respect to time

- $\dfrac{dr}{dt} =$ rate of change of radius with respect to time

- $\dfrac{dA}{dr} =$ rate of change of area with respect to radius

The chain rule links these three derivatives together

$$\frac{dA}{dt} = \frac{dA}{dr} \times \frac{dr}{dt}$$

These derivatives behave like fractions that the *dr* parts cancel out.
In many rate of change problems, we deal with three things:

1. What we are required to find
2. What we are given
3. What link connects the variables.

In general we write,

$$\text{Required} = \text{(Link)(Given)}$$

exam Q

(2016 Q.7 (a))

(i) Air is pumped into a spherical exercise ball at the rate of 250 cm³ per second. Find the rate at which the radius is increasing when the radius of the ball is 20 cm. Give your answer in terms of π.

(ii) Find the rate at which the surface area of the ball is increasing when the radius of the ball is 20 cm.

Solution

(i) 1. Required to find $\dfrac{dr}{dt}$

2. We are given $\dfrac{dV}{dt} = 250$

3. Link connecting V and r

Use $V = \dfrac{4}{3}\pi r^3$

$$\frac{dV}{dr} = 3\left(\frac{4}{3}\pi r^2\right) = 4\pi r^2$$

Also $\dfrac{dr}{dV} = \dfrac{1}{4\pi r^2}$ (inverting both sides)

Required = (Link)(Given)

$$\frac{dr}{dt} = \frac{dr}{dV}\frac{dV}{dt}$$

$$\frac{dr}{dt} = \left(\frac{1}{4\pi r^2}\right)(250)$$

Substitute $r = 20$ then

$$\frac{dr}{dt} = \frac{1}{4\pi(20)^2}(250) = \frac{5}{32\pi}\,\text{cm/s}$$

(ii) 1. Required to find $\dfrac{dA}{dt}$

2. We are given, from part (i)

$$\frac{dr}{dt} = \frac{5}{32\pi}$$

3. Link connecting A and r

Use $A = 4\pi r^2$

$$\frac{dA}{dr} = 8\pi r$$

Required = (Link)(Given)

$$\frac{dA}{dt} = \frac{dA}{dr}\frac{dr}{dt}$$

$$\frac{dA}{dt} = (8\pi r)\frac{5}{32\pi}$$

Substitute $r = 20$ then

$$\frac{dA}{dt} = (8\pi(20))\left(\frac{5}{32\pi}\right) = 25\,\text{cm}^2/\text{s}$$

 exam focus

Candidates can struggle with related rates of change, but a little extra effort during revision will be worthwhile.

Part a (i) was awarded 10 marks.

Part a (ii) was awarded 10 marks.

Kinematics: the study of motion

Velocity and acceleration of particles

Suppose s represents the distance an object travelled and t represents the time.

Then $\dfrac{ds}{dt}$ represents the velocity at any time (rate of change of distance with respect to time) and $\dfrac{d^2s}{dt^2}$ represents the acceleration at any time (rate of change of speed with respect to time).

Example

A particle is moving in a straight line. Its distance, s metres, from a fixed point o after t seconds is given by $s = t^3 - 9t^2 + 15t + 2$.

Calculate:

- **(i)** Its velocity at any time t
- **(ii)** Its velocity after 6 seconds
- **(iii)** The distances of the particle from o when it is instantly at rest
- **(iv)** Its acceleration after 4 seconds

Solution

(i) $s = t^3 - 9t^2 + 15t + 2$

Velocity $= \dfrac{ds}{dt} = 3t^2 - 18t + 15$

(velocity at any time t)

(ii) Velocity after 6 seconds

$\left.\dfrac{ds}{dt}\right|_{t=6} = 3(6)^2 - 18(6) + 15 = 15 \text{ m/s}$

(iii) The particle is at rest when its velocity $\dfrac{ds}{dt}$ is zero.

$\dfrac{ds}{dt} = 3t^2 - 18t + 15 = 0$

$t^2 - 6t + 5 = 0$

$(t - 5)(t - 1) = 0$

$t = 1 \ \text{ or } \ t = 5$

Thus, the particle is stopped after 1 second and again after 5 seconds.

Distance $= s = t^3 - 9t^2 + 15t + 2$

$t = 1; \ s = (1)^3 - 9(1)^2 + 15(1) + 2 = 9 \text{ m}$

$t = 5; s = (5)^3 - 9(5)^2 + 15(5) + 2 = -23 \text{ m}$

Thus, after 1 second the particle is 9 m from 0 and after 5 seconds the particle is 23 m from 0 (distance cannot be negative).

(iv)

$$\frac{ds}{dt} = 3t^2 - 18t + 15$$

$$\text{Acceleration} = \frac{d^2s}{dt^2} = 6t - 18$$

$$\left.\frac{d^2s}{dt^2}\right|_{t=4} = 6(4) - 18 = 6 \text{ m/s}^2$$

Maxima and minima

Introduction

For a maximum: $\dfrac{dy}{dx} = 0$ and $\dfrac{d^2y}{dx^2} < 0$

For a minimum: $\dfrac{dy}{dx} = 0$ and $\dfrac{d^2y}{dx^2} > 0$

Example

George and Brendan are investigating whether they should start a business taking tourists around Dublin in their minibus. Their projected annual profit in euros (y) will depend on the number of tours (x) they run.

The rule is $y = -x^3 + 120x^2 - 1728x - 16000$

(i) Calculate the value of y when $x = 0$. Explain what this represents.

(ii) Write expressions for $\dfrac{dy}{dx}$ and $\dfrac{d^2y}{dx^2}$.

Hence calculate the number of tours George and Brendan will run in order to maximise their profit.

(iii) Find the maximum profit.

Solution

(i) Substitute $x = 0$ into $y = -x^3 + 120x^2 - 1728x - 16000$

$$\text{To get } y = 0 + 0 - 0 - 0 - 16000 = -16000$$

Their fixed costs if they run no tours at all are €16000.

(ii) $y = -x^3 + 120x^2 - 1728x - 16000$

$$\frac{dy}{dx} = -3x^2 + 240x - 1728$$

$$\frac{d^2y}{dx^2} = -6x + 240$$

Now $\dfrac{dy}{dx} = 0$ for maximum or minimum

$$\text{By comparison } -3x^2 + 240x - 1728 = 0$$

$$x^2 - 80x + 576 = 0$$

$$x = \frac{+80 \pm \sqrt{6400 - 2304}}{2} = \frac{80 \pm 64}{2}$$

$$x = \frac{80 + 64}{2} \text{ or } x = \frac{80 - 64}{2}$$

$$x = 72 \text{ or } x = 8$$

Now to determine the maximum we require $\dfrac{d^2y}{dx^2} = -6x + 240$

Substitute $x = 72$ then $\dfrac{d^2y}{dx^2} = -6(72) + 240 = -192 < 0$

Hence $x = 72$ tours give a maximum profit.

Substitute $x = 8$ then $\dfrac{d^2y}{dx^2} = -6(8) + 240 = 192 > 0$

Hence $x = 8$ tours indicates a minimum profit.

(iii) Substitute $x = 72$ into $y = -x^3 + 120x^2 - 1728x - 16000$

$$y = -(72)^3 + 120(72)^2 - 1728(72) - 16000$$

$$y = \text{€108,416 maximum profit}$$

Applications of maxima and minima to exam questions

Calculus can be used to find the maximum or minimum values of quantities, such as area, volume, cost etc. The method involves expressing the quantity, for example surface area, as a function of one variable, and then differentiating to find when the quantity is a maximum or minimum.

Example

A company that grows beans wishes to pack their product in closed catering pack cylindrical tins. Each tin must have a volume of $332{\cdot}75\pi$ cm^3 and the minimum possible surface area. Find the dimensions of each tin.

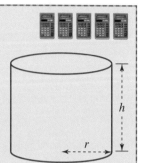

Solution

Let each tin have a base radius r and perpendicular height h, we write the total surface area of the tin as top + curved surface + bottom $= \pi r^2 + 2\pi rh + \pi r^2$.

Hence, the total surface area $S = 2\pi r^2 + 2\pi rh$.

Since S is an expression in two variables, r and h, we use the given information to write h in terms of r.

The volume of the tin $V = \pi r^2 h$ and this volume is $332{\cdot}75\pi$.

$$\therefore \quad \pi r^2 h = 332{\cdot}75\,\pi$$

$$h = \frac{332{\cdot}75}{r^2}$$

Now $\quad S = 2\pi r^2 + 2\pi rh$ becomes

$$S = 2\pi r^2 + 2\pi r\left(\frac{332{\cdot}75}{r^2}\right)$$

$$S = 2\pi r^2 + 665{\cdot}5\pi r^{-1}$$

$$\frac{dS}{dr} = 4\pi r - 665{\cdot}5\pi r^{-2} = 0 \qquad \text{(for maximum or minimum)}$$

$$4\pi r^3 - 665{\cdot}5\pi = 0 \qquad \text{(multiply each term by } r^2\text{)}$$

$$r^3 = 166{\cdot}375$$

$$r = 5{\cdot}5 \text{ cm.}$$

Since $h = \dfrac{332{\cdot}75}{r^2}$ we find $h = \dfrac{332{\cdot}75}{(5{\cdot}5)^2} = 11$ cm

To confirm the surface area is a minimum we require $\dfrac{d^2S}{dr^2}$

$$\frac{dS}{dr} = 4\pi r - 665{\cdot}5\pi r^{-2}$$

$$\Rightarrow \frac{d^2S}{dr^2} = 4\pi + 1{,}331\pi r^{-3}$$

Substitute $r = 5.5$ into $\dfrac{d^2S}{dr^2}$ to get a positive answer.

Hence, $\dfrac{d^2S}{dr^2} > 0 \Rightarrow$ minimum surface area.

∴ Each catering pack cylindrical tin should have a perpendicular height of 11 cm and a base radius of 5·5 cm.

The question may ask you to comment on the suitability or otherwise of the size of the tin and/or its suitability as a catering tin given that its volume is one litre.

A company wishes to market a new phone. It consults a market research company to conduct surveys and to evaluate the response of the consumer.
(Here the examiner may embark on a question on samples – from the topic of statistics, e.g. describe two ways of selecting a sample. However, this is not our focus in this question.)

Based on its surveys the research company presents the phone company with the following price demand equation:

$$x = 15000 - 100Q$$

where x is the demand (the number of phones the consumer will buy) and Q is the price per phone in euros.

(i) If $Q \geq 0$, write down an inequality for x.

Solution

$$x = 15000 - 100Q$$

As the **smallest** possible value for Q is 0, then a maximum value for x is $15000 - 100(0) = 15000$

Hence $x \leq 15000$

In this question the solution is done part by part.

(ii) The overall revenue R is given by $R = xQ$ for making and selling x phones at €Q each.

    (a) Express R in terms of x.

    (b) If $R \geq 0$, find an inequality satisfied by x.

Solution

(ii) (a) Revenue $= R = xQ$

$$x = 15000 - 100Q$$
$$100Q = 15000 - x$$
$$Q = 150 - \frac{x}{100}$$

$$\therefore \quad R = x\left(150 - \frac{x}{100}\right)$$

$$R = 150x - \frac{x^2}{100}$$

(b)

$$R \geq 0 \implies 150x - \frac{x^2}{100} \geq 0$$

$$x\left(150 - \frac{x}{100}\right) = 0$$

$$x = 0 \quad \boxed{or} \quad 150 - \frac{x}{100} = 0$$

$$x = 0 \quad \boxed{or} \quad 15000 = x$$

Hence, we write $0 \leq x \leq 15000$.

exam focus

Again, this question can continue to examine material from the inequality/graph/algebra topics. However, our focus here is on calculus applications.

(iii) Find the maximum revenue.

Solution

(iii)

$$R = 150x - \frac{x^2}{100}$$

$$\frac{dR}{dx} = 150 - \frac{2x}{100} = 0 \qquad \text{(for maximum or minimum)}$$

$$15000 - 2x = 0 \qquad \text{(multiply each term by 100)}$$

$$15000 = 2x$$

$$7500 = x$$

$$\therefore \quad R = 150x - \frac{x^2}{100} = 150(7500) - \frac{(7500)^2}{100} = 562500$$

$$\frac{dR}{dx} = 150 - \frac{2x}{100}$$

$$\implies \quad \frac{d^2R}{dx^2} = -\frac{2}{100} < 0 \quad \therefore \quad \text{maximum } R = 562500$$

(iv) Using calculus, show the maximum profit $P = €240,000$, where the net profit is given by $P = R - C$.

where R = revenue function and $C = 120000 + 30x$

Solution

(iv)
$$P = R - C = 150x - \frac{x^2}{100} - (120000 + 30x)$$

$$P = 120x - \frac{x^2}{100} - 120000$$

$$\frac{dP}{dx} = 120 - \frac{2x}{100} = 0 \qquad \text{(for maximum/minimum profit)}$$

$$12000 = 2x$$

$$6000 = x \qquad \text{(the number of phones)}$$

$$\therefore \quad \text{Profit } P = 120(6000) - \frac{(6000)^2}{100} - 120000 = €240000$$

$$\frac{dP}{dx} = 120 - \frac{2x}{100}$$

$$\frac{d^2P}{dx^2} = -\frac{2}{100} < 0 \quad \Rightarrow \quad \text{maximum profit} = €240,000$$

(v) For maximum profit, what should the phone retail (sell) at?

Solution

(v)
$$x = 15000 - 100Q$$

Substitute $x = 6000$ for maximum to get

$$6000 = 15000 - 100Q$$

$$100Q = 9000$$

$$Q = €90$$

(2017 Q.7 (g))

Sometimes it is possible to predict the future population in a city using a function. The population in Avalon, over time, can be predicted using the following function:

$$q(t) = 3.9e^{-0.05t} \times 10^6$$

In the function above, t is time, in years; $t = 0$ is the beginning of 2010.

Use the function $q(t)$ to find the predicted rate of change of the population in Avalon at the beginning of 2018.

Solution

Remember: If $f(x) = e^{ax}$ then $f'(x) = ae^{ax}$

$$q(t) = 3 \cdot 9e^{-0 \cdot 05t} \times 10^6$$

$$q(t) = 3900000e^{-0 \cdot 05t}$$

$$q'(t) = 3900000[-0 \cdot 05e^{-0 \cdot 05t}]$$

$$q'(t) = -195000e^{-0 \cdot 05t}$$

And $t = 2018 - 2010 = 8$

Then $q'(8) =$ rate of change of population in Avalon at the beginning of 2018.

$$q'(8) = -195000e^{-0 \cdot 05(8)} = -130712$$

The predicted rate of change of the population of Avalon at the beginning of 2018 is a decrease of 130,712 people per year.

(2012 Q.7)

An open cylindrical tank of water has a hole near the bottom. The radius of the tank is 52 cm. The hole is a circle of radius 1 cm. The water level gradually drops as water escapes through the hole.

Over a certain 20-minute period, the height of the surface of the water is given by the formula

$$h = \left(10 - \frac{t}{200}\right)^2$$

where h is the height of the surface of the water, in cm, as measured from the centre of the hole and t is the time in seconds from a particular instant $t = 0$.

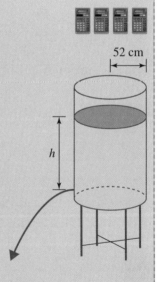

52 cm

h

(i) What is the height of the surface at time $t = 0$?

Solution

Substitute $t = 0$　into　$h = \left(10 - \dfrac{t}{200}\right)^2$ to get

$$h = (10 - 0)^2 = 100 \text{ cm}$$

(ii) After how many seconds will the height of the surface be 64 cm?

Solution

Substitute $h = 64$ into $h = \left(10 - \dfrac{t}{200}\right)^2$ to get

$$64 = \left(10 - \frac{t}{200}\right)^2$$

Take the positive square root of both sides

$$8 = 10 - \frac{t}{200}$$

$$\frac{t}{200} = 10 - 8$$

$$t = 400 \text{ secs}$$

(iii) Find the rate at which the **volume** of water in the tank is decreasing at the instant when the height is 64 cm.

Give your answer correct to the nearest cm³ per second.

Solution

To find $\dfrac{dv}{dt} = \dfrac{dv}{dh}\dfrac{dh}{dt}$

where given $h = \left(10 - \dfrac{t}{200}\right)^2$

$$\frac{dh}{dt} = 2\left(10 - \frac{t}{200}\right)^1\left(-\frac{1}{200}\right)$$

Volume of cylinder $= \pi r^2 h$

$$v = \pi(52)^2 h$$

$$\frac{dv}{dh} = 2704\pi$$

Now $\dfrac{dv}{dt} = (2704\pi)\, 2\left(10 - \dfrac{t}{200}\right)\left(-\dfrac{1}{200}\right)$

In part **(ii)** we found $h = 64 \Rightarrow t = 400$, now substitute $t = 400$ into $\dfrac{dv}{dt}$ above to get

$$\frac{dv}{dt} = (2704\pi)\left(-\frac{1}{100}\right)\left(10 - \frac{400}{200}\right) = -680 \text{ cm}^3/\text{sec}$$

$\dfrac{dv}{dt}$ has a negative value because the volume is decreasing.

(iv) The rate at which the volume of water in the tank is decreasing is equal to the speed of the water coming out of the hole, multiplied by the area of the hole. Find the speed at which the water is coming out of the hole at the instant when the height is 64 cm.

Solution

$$\frac{dv}{dt} = (\text{speed of water})(\text{area of hole})$$

$$680 = (\text{speed of water})(\pi(1)^2)$$

$$216 \text{ cm/sec} = \text{speed of water}$$

This question was extremely badly answered. The term 'front loading' i.e giving high marks for the easy parts, was vigorously applied here as follows

(i) Awarded 15 marks (= 5% of paper), this comes out in one short line!

(ii) Awarded 15 marks

(iii) Awarded 5 marks, candidates found this almost impossible!

(iv) Awarded 10 marks, with 7 marks awarded for any reasonable first step. Make an attempt at each question, as you never know what marks you could be awarded for a very basic attempt.

19 Integration

aims

- [ ] To know that the process of finding a function from its derivative is called antidifferentiation, and that this is more often referred to as integration
- [ ] To know about the constant of integration
- [ ] To be familiar with the rules for integrals as on page 26 of the *booklet of formulae and tables*
- [ ] To know how to carry out the process of finding an antiderivative (integral)
- [ ] To be able to find the constant term when given (initial) conditions
- [ ] To know how to handle antiderivatives for second order differentials
- [ ] To learn how to evaluate definite integrals
- [ ] To link antiderivatives with real-life concepts such as distance, speed and acceleration
- [ ] To learn and understand the fundamental link between area under a curve and integration
- [ ] To know how to manage questions linking integration with, for example, trigonometry, the trapezoidal rule and rates of change
- [ ] To know how to find the mean (average) value of a function
- [ ] To gain the skills necessary to successfully cope with examination questions involving antiderivatives

Introduction

In this chapter we look at the reverse process to differentiation.

When we differentiate y with respect to x in each of the following:

$$\textbf{(a) } y = x^2 + 10 \qquad \textbf{(b) } y = x^2 - \frac{7}{2} \qquad \textbf{(c) } y = x^2 - \pi$$

We get

$$\textbf{(a) } \frac{dy}{dx} = 2x \qquad \textbf{(b) } \frac{dy}{dx} = 2x \qquad \textbf{(c) } \frac{dy}{dx} = 2x$$

What might these indicate if we are asked to work backwards from $\dfrac{dy}{dx} = 2x$?

All the answers can be described as $y = x^2 + C$ where C is a constant.

When you differentiate $y = x^2 + C$, the C disappears because $\dfrac{d(\text{constant})}{dx} = 0$.

The results of these forwards and backwards processes have special names.

$\dfrac{dy}{dx}$ is called the derivative of y with respect to x.

Any y that we get by working backwards from $\dfrac{dy}{dx}$ is called the antiderivative of y.

Alternatively, when we know the equation of a curve, say $y = f(x)$, then, by differentiation, we can find the

gradient function $\dfrac{dy}{dx} = f'(x)$. If instead we are given the gradient function and asked to find

the equation of the curve, this reverse process is called integration.

key point

There is only one derivative but an infinite number of antiderivatives.

key point

There is only one gradient (slope) function but an infinite number of integral functions.

Integration and differentiation are the reverse processes of each other.

This is called the **fundamental theorem of calculus** and is crucially important to all mathematicians, scientists and engineers.

Fundamental integration skills

Example

(a) Find an expression for y if $\dfrac{dy}{dx} = e^x + 3x^2 - 2$

(b) Find an expression for $f(x)$ if $f'(x) = \sqrt{x} + \cos x$

Solution:

(a) $\dfrac{dy}{dx} = e^x + 3x^2 - 2$

$y = e^x + \dfrac{3x^3}{3} - 2x + C$

key point

We know a function can be differentiated term by term. In a similar way it can be integrated term by term.

(b) $f'(x) = x^{\frac{1}{2}} + \cos x$ (write the square root as the power of $\frac{1}{2}$)

$$f(x) = \frac{x^{\frac{3}{2}}}{\frac{3}{2}} + \sin x + C$$

key point

+C included in each solution.

exam focus

In (a) and (b) we make use of the rules on page 26 of the *booklet of formulae and tables.*

Notation: $\int f(x)dx = F(x) + C$ where C is an arbitrary constant means that $F(x) + C$ is an antiderivative of $f(x)$.

Example

Find: (i) $\displaystyle\int \frac{1}{p}\,dp$ (ii) $\displaystyle\int \left(\mu^2 + \frac{1}{\mu}\right)^2 d\mu$ (iii) $\displaystyle\int \frac{v^3 - 8}{v - 2}\,dv$

key point

In **(i)** p is the variable and so the integral is with respect to p.
In **(ii)** μ is the variable and so the integral is with respect to μ.
In **(iii)** v is the variable and so the integral is with respect to v.

Solution

(i) $\displaystyle\int \frac{1}{p}dp = \ln|p| + C$ (see *booklet of formulae and tables*, page 26)

(ii) We must multiply $\left(\mu^2 + \dfrac{1}{\mu}\right)^2$ before finding the integral.

$$\left(\mu^2 + \frac{1}{\mu}\right)\left(\mu^2 + \frac{1}{\mu}\right) = \mu^4 + \mu + \mu + \frac{1}{\mu^2} = \mu^4 + 2\mu + \mu^{-2}$$

key point

$$\int\left(\mu^4 + 2\mu + \mu^{-2}\right)d\mu = \frac{\mu^5}{5} + \frac{2\mu^2}{2} + \frac{\mu^{-1}}{-1} + C$$

$$= \frac{1}{5}\mu^5 + \mu^2 - \frac{1}{\mu} + C$$

Increase the power by one and divide by the new power

(iii) We must divide $v^3 - 8$ by $v - 2$ before finding the antiderivative (integral).

 key point

Knowing that $v^3 - 8$ can be factorised using the difference of two cubes is very useful here.

$$\Rightarrow v^3 - 8 = (v - 2)(v^2 + 2v + 4)$$

Now $$\int \frac{v^3 - 8}{v - 2} dv = \int \frac{(v - 2)(v^2 + 2v + 4)}{(v - 2)} dv = \int (v^2 + 2v + 4)\, dv$$

$$= \frac{v^3}{3} + v^2 + 4v + C$$

 exam focus

It is vital to include the constant of integration, C, in these types of questions.

 exam Q

(i) Differentiate $p = \sin^3 x$, with respect to x.

(ii) Hence, write down the antiderivative y of $\dfrac{dy}{dx} = \cos x \sin^2 x$.

Solution

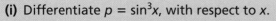

(i) $p = \sin^3 x = (\sin x)^3$

$\dfrac{dp}{dx} = 3(\sin x)^2(\cos x)$ (using the chain rule in differentiation)

$\dfrac{dp}{dx} = 3\sin^2 x \cos x$

(ii) $\dfrac{dy}{dx} = \cos x \sin^2 x$

$y = \dfrac{1}{3}\sin^3 x + \text{constant}$ (from differentiation in part **(i)**)

$y = \dfrac{1}{3}\sin^3 x + C$

The constant of integration

To develop an understanding of the constant of integration, C, we consider the following:

We can find an expression for y given $\dfrac{dy}{dx} = 4$.

We write $y = 4x + C$ where C is a constant.

The resulting expression forms an infinite set of parallel lines, as shown. Unless more information is given (a point on the line) then the value of C remains unknown.

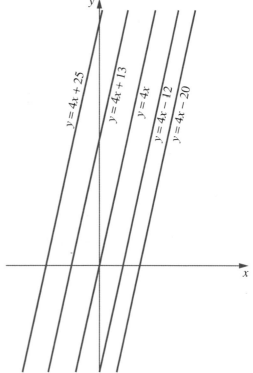

Given $(-4, 9)$ is an element of the required line we can find the value of C

$$x = -4 \quad \text{and} \quad y = 9 \quad \text{in} \quad y = 4x + C$$

$$\text{gives us} \quad 9 = 4(-4) + C$$
$$9 = -16 + C$$
$$25 = C$$

Hence we write the equation of the lines as

$$y = 4x + 25$$

key point

A **general solution** indicates C is unknown, while a **particular solution** indicates C has a definite value.

Example

Find the constant of integration given that $\int (6t^2 + 12t + 5)\,dt = 9$ when $t = -2$.

Solution

$$\int (6t^2 + 12t + 5)\,dt = 2t^3 + 6t^2 + 5t + C$$

Substitute $t = -2 \implies 2(-2)^3 + 6(-2)^2 + 5(-2) + C = 9$ (given in question)

$$-16 + 24 - 10 + C = 9$$
$$-2 + C = 9$$
$$C = 11$$

Second order differentials

Remembering that the differential of $\dfrac{dy}{dx}$ with respect to x is $\dfrac{d^2y}{dx^2}$, it follows

that $\int \dfrac{d^2y}{dx^2}\,dx = \dfrac{dy}{dx} + C$.

Example

Find y as a function of x, given that $\dfrac{d^2y}{dx^2} = 15x - 2$ and that when $x = 2$, $\dfrac{dy}{dx} = 23$ and $y = 19$.

Solution

Given $\dfrac{d^2y}{dx^2} = 15x - 2$.

Finding the antiderivative of both sides of the equation with respect to x:

$$\frac{dy}{dx} = \int 15x - 2\,dx$$

$$\frac{dy}{dx} = \frac{15x^2}{2} - 2x + C$$

But $\dfrac{dy}{dx} = 23$ when $x = 2$.

$$\therefore \quad 23 = \frac{15(2)^2}{2} - 2(2) + C$$

$$23 = 30 - 4 + C$$

$$-3 = C$$

$$\therefore \quad \frac{dy}{dx} = \frac{15x^2}{2} - 2x - 3$$

Again finding the antiderivative of both sides of this equation with respect to x:

$$y = \frac{5x^3}{2} - x^2 - 3x + K, \text{where } K \text{ is a constant}$$

But $y = 19$ when $x = 2$.

$$\therefore \quad 19 = \frac{5(2)^3}{2} - (2)^2 - 3(2) + K$$

$$19 = 20 - 4 - 6 + K$$

$$9 = K$$

The required equation is:

$$y = \frac{5x^3}{2} - x^2 - 3x + 9$$

Definite integration

Definite integration is where the integration is performed between limits and this produces a numerical answer.

A definite integral is of the form $\displaystyle\int_a^b f(x)\,dx$

Upper limit $(x = b)$

Lower limit $(x = a)$

Example

Show that $\displaystyle\int_0^{\frac{\pi}{6}} \cos 3x\,dx = \frac{1}{3}$

key point

When working with a definite integral, the values for angles are always given in radians.

Solution:

$$\int_0^{\frac{\pi}{6}} \cos 3x\,dx = \left[\frac{1}{3}\sin 3x + C\right]_0^{\frac{\pi}{6}}$$

$$= \frac{1}{3}\sin 3\left(\frac{\pi}{6}\right) + C - \left(\frac{1}{3}\sin 3(0) + C\right)$$

$$= \frac{1}{3}\sin\frac{\pi}{2} + C - \frac{1}{3}\sin 0 - C$$

key point

In every definite integral the constant term C always cancels itself. Hence, in definite integrals we can ignore the constant term.

$$= \frac{1}{3}(1) - \frac{1}{3}(0)$$

$$= \frac{1}{3}$$

exam focus

The following integrals can be written down directly although they are not included in formulae and tables. They are worth remembering.

1. $\displaystyle\int \cos(ax + b)\,dx = \frac{1}{a}\sin(ax + b) + C$ 3. $\displaystyle\int e^{ax+b}\,dx = \frac{1}{a}e^{ax+b} + C$

2. $\displaystyle\int \sin(ax + b)\,dx = -\frac{1}{a}\cos(ax + b) + C$ 4. $\displaystyle\int \frac{1}{x + a}\,dx = \ln(x + a) + C$

Where a, b and C are constants.

(i) Express $\cos 3\theta \sin 5\theta$ as a sum of two trigonometrical functions.

(ii) Hence, evaluate $\displaystyle\int_0^{\frac{\pi}{6}} \cos 3\theta \sin 5\theta \, d\theta$.

key point

Always swap the terms so that the bigger angle is first.

Solution

(i) $\cos 3\theta \sin 5\theta = \sin 5\theta \cos 3\theta$

$$= \frac{1}{2}[\sin(5\theta + 3\theta) + \sin(5\theta - 3\theta)]$$

(see *booklet of formulae and tables*, page 15)

$$= \frac{1}{2}(\sin 8\theta + \sin 2\theta)$$

(ii) $\displaystyle\int_0^{\frac{\pi}{6}} \cos 3\theta \sin 5\theta \, d\theta = \frac{1}{2}\int_0^{\frac{\pi}{6}} (\sin 8\theta + \sin 2\theta) \, d\theta$

$$= \frac{1}{2}\left[-\frac{\cos 8\theta}{8} - \frac{\cos 2\theta}{2} \right]_0^{\frac{\pi}{6}}$$

(check by differentiating back)

$$= \left[-\frac{\cos 8\theta}{16} - \frac{\cos 2\theta}{4} \right]_0^{\frac{\pi}{6}}$$

$$= \frac{-\cos\frac{8\pi}{6}}{16} - \frac{\cos\frac{2\pi}{6}}{4} + \frac{\cos 0}{16} + \frac{\cos 0}{4}$$

$$= \frac{1}{32} - \frac{1}{8} + \frac{1}{16} + \frac{1}{4}$$

$$= \frac{7}{32}$$

exam focus

Again we see topics combined in a question: here it is trigonometry with integration. Without the hint in part **(i)** many candidates perform very badly in this type of question.

Kinematics: the study of motion

Suppose a sprint runner is training for a race on a straight track. (Here we take velocity to be the same as speed, since velocity is speed with its direction given. Here the velocity is forward!)

Velocity is the rate of change of distance with respect to time, so for travel in a straight line, we can say that $v = \dfrac{dx}{dt}$.

key point

- v stands for velocity after a time t.
- x stands for the distance travelled from the starting line.
- It may help to remember the rule Speed $= \dfrac{\text{Distance}}{\text{Time}}$.

At the beginning of the sprint, the runner starts running with a constant acceleration of 2 ms^{-2} (that is, 2 metres per second per second).

Since acceleration, a, is the rate of change of velocity with respect to time, we can write

$a = \dfrac{dv}{dt} = 2 \text{ ms}^{-2}$.

We take $t = 0$ when the starting signal (pistol fires) is given.

The sprinter then starts running.

Since $\dfrac{dv}{dt} = 2$ is given, the antiderivative tells us $v = 2t + C$.

However, the sprinter has zero speed ($v = 0$) when $t = 0$. This physical knowledge is the equivalent of the given point in the two previous exam-type questions.

$$v = 2t + C \quad \text{when} \quad v = 0 \quad \text{and} \quad t = 0 \Rightarrow 0 = 0 + C \Rightarrow 0 = C$$

so we have $v = 2t$ for this case.

Now, what will be the distance travelled from the starting line after t seconds?

Again, we do the reverse process to differentiation, this time on $v = 2t$ where $v = \dfrac{dx}{dt}$.

$$\therefore \quad \dfrac{dx}{dt} = 2t \quad \Rightarrow \quad x = t^2 + K$$

Once again, the physical situation decides the value of K. Again, the sprinter has travelled no distance ($x = 0$) when $t = 0$.

$$x = t^2 + K \quad \text{when} \quad x = 0 \quad \text{and} \quad t = 0 \quad \Rightarrow \quad 0 = 0 + K \quad \Rightarrow \quad 0 = K$$

Then we have $x = t^2$ for this case.

Exam focus on acceleration, velocity and distance

An exam question might be: given the curve or the graph for a or v or x, could you find the other two curves or sketch the other two graphs?

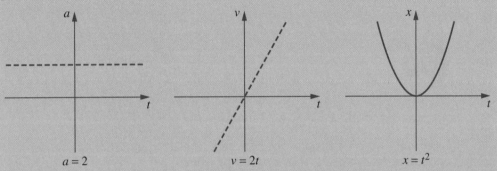

In such a question the candidate should recognise

- The acceleration curve is the derivative of the velocity curve.
- The velocity curve is the derivative of the distance curve.

Example

If a particle is moving in a straight line so that the acceleration $a = 2 + 6e^{3t}$, find:

(i) The speed v after a time t given that $v = 5$ when $t = 0$

(ii) The distance x travelled after a time t given that $x = 0$ when $t = 0$

Solution

(i) Since $a = \dfrac{dv}{dt} = 2 + 6e^{3t}$ (the antiderivative tells us)

$$v = 2t + 2e^{3t} + C$$ (check this by differentiating back)

Given that $v = 5$ when $t = 0$

$$\Rightarrow 5 = 0 + 2e^0 + C$$ $(e^0 = 1)$

$$5 = 2 + C$$

$$3 = C$$

Answer $v = 2t + 2e^{3t} + 3$

(ii) Since $v = \dfrac{dx}{dt} = 2t + 2e^{3t} + 3$

We find $x = t^2 + \dfrac{2}{3}e^{3t} + 3t + K$ (again check by differentiating back)

LESS STRESS MORE SUCCESS

Given that $x = 0$ when $t = 0$

$$0 = 0 + \frac{2}{3}e^0 + 0 + K$$

$$-\frac{2}{3} = K$$

$$x = t^2 + \frac{2}{3}e^{3t} + 3t - \frac{2}{3}$$

Since $a = \dfrac{dv}{dt}$ and $v = \dfrac{dx}{dt}$, we can also write a as $\dfrac{d}{dt}\left(\dfrac{dx}{dt}\right) = \dfrac{d^2x}{dt^2}$.

Remember, the little superscript numbers refer to the number of times x has been differentiated. They are not powers.

An in-context application of integration

The total revenue obtained (in €000) from selling x hundred items in a particular day is given by R, which is a function of variable x.

Given that $\dfrac{dR}{dx} = 20 - 4x$:

(i) Determine the total revenue function R

(ii) Find the number of items sold in one day that will maximise the total revenue and evaluate this total revenue

Solution

(i) We are given $\dfrac{dR}{dx} = 20 - 4x$. Integrating this must therefore give R.

That is:

$$\int \frac{dR}{dx}dx = \int (20 - 4x)\, dx$$

$$R = 20x - 2x^2 + C$$

But when *no* items are sold (i.e. $x = 0$), there will be *no* revenue (i.e. $R = 0$). Thus, substituting $x = 0$ into R above gives $C = 0$, so that total revenue, $R = 20x - 2x^2$.

(ii) The value of x that maximises R is found by solving the equation $\dfrac{dR}{dx} = 0$.

That is, where $20 - 4x = 0$

this gives $x = 5$

In other words, total revenue is maximised if 500 items are sold in a day.
The value of this total revenue is found by substituting $x = 5$ into R.
This gives $20(5) - 2(5)^2 = 100 - 50 = 50$.
Thus, the maximum total revenue (obtained by selling 500 items) is €50,000.

Area under a curve

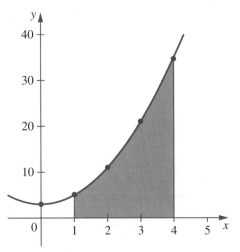

Consider $y = 2x^2 + 3$.

How to find the shaded area under the curve
is of major importance in mathematics.

How to do this is not immediately obvious.

This area could be approximated by splitting
it into rectangles.

Below are diagrams showing three cases
for 3, 6 and 12 rectangles, respectively.

In order to sketch these three graphs, we require the following table:

x	1	$1\frac{1}{4}$	$1\frac{1}{2}$	$1\frac{3}{4}$	2	$2\frac{1}{4}$	$2\frac{1}{2}$	$2\frac{3}{4}$	3	$3\frac{1}{4}$	$3\frac{1}{2}$	$3\frac{3}{4}$	4
y	5		$7\frac{1}{2}$		11		$15\frac{1}{2}$		21		$27\frac{1}{2}$		35

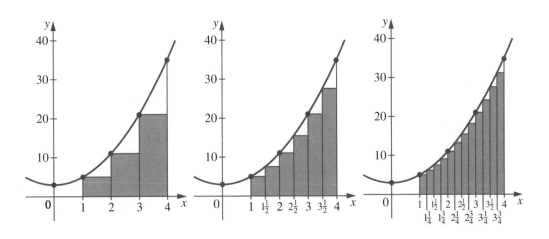

As the rectangles become thinner, the approximation becomes more accurate.

The approximate area using three rectangles is given by:

$$1 \times 5 + 1 \times 11 + 1 \times 21$$
$$= \quad 5 \quad + \quad 11 \quad + \quad 21$$
$$= 37 \text{ square units, which is clearly not very accurate}$$

The approximate area using six rectangles is given by:

$$\frac{1}{2} \times 5 + \frac{1}{2} \times 7\frac{1}{2} + \frac{1}{2} \times 11$$
$$+ \frac{1}{2} \times 15\frac{1}{2} + \frac{1}{2} \times 21 + \frac{1}{2} \times 27\frac{1}{2}$$
$$= \frac{1}{2}\left[5 + 7\frac{1}{2} + 11 + 15\frac{1}{2}\right.$$
$$\left. + 21 + 27\frac{1}{2}\right]$$
$$= \frac{1}{2}\left[87\frac{1}{2}\right]$$
$$= 43\frac{3}{4} \text{ square units}$$

The approximate area using 12 rectangles is given by:

$$\frac{1}{4}\left[\sum y\right]$$
$$= 47 \cdot 3125 \text{ square units}$$

You may wish to verify this yourself!

Each answer is progressively more accurate but is always on the low side.

If we continue to make the strips thinner we get an increasingly more accurate area.

The area under the curve can therefore be found by the summation $\left(\sum \text{ of infinitesimally narrow strips}\right)$.

Area under the curve $= \displaystyle\int_{1}^{4} y\, dx$, where $y = f(x)$.

The $\int$ sign actually means 'sum of' (it is an elongated S).

$A = \displaystyle\int_{a}^{b} y\, dx$ is the basic formula for finding the area between the curve and the x-axis in the range $a \le x \le b$, $a, b \in \mathbb{R}$.

Finally:

$$\int_1^4 y\,dx = \int_1^4 (2x^2 + 3)\,dx$$

$$= \left[\frac{2x^3}{3} + 3x\right]_1^4$$

$$= \frac{2(4)^3}{3} + 3(4) - \left(\frac{2(1)^3}{3} + 3(1)\right)$$

$$= \frac{128}{3} + 12 - \frac{2}{3} - 3$$

$$- 51 \text{ square units. This is the exact answer for the area in this case.}$$

NOTES ON AREA

Area between a curve and the x-axis

The area, A, bounded by the curve $y = f(x)$, the x-axis, and the lines $x = P$ and $x = Q$ is given by:

$$A = \int_P^Q y\,dx$$

This is positive if the area is above the x-axis.

This is negative if the area is below the x-axis.

If the curve cuts the x-axis between the limits, then:

(i) Find the areas above and below the x-axis separately

(ii) Add these two values together

Area between a curve and the y-axis

The area, A, bounded by the curve $y = f(x)$, the y-axis, and the lines $y = P$ and $y = Q$ is given by:

$$A = \int_P^Q x\,dy$$

This is positive if the area is to the right of the y-axis.

This is negative if the area is to the left of the y-axis.

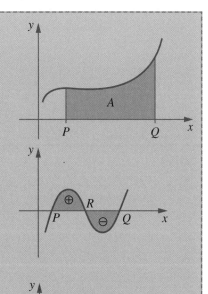

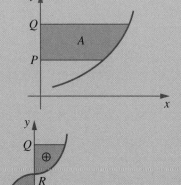

Area between two curves

1. We need to find where the curves intersect.
2. Subtract the areas under the curves between the points of intersection.

This can be done by the evaluation of one integral using the x-coordinates of the point of intersection as the limits.

(2018 Q.6 (b)(i))

Parts of the graphs of the functions $h(x) = x$ and $k(x) = x^3, x \in R$ are shown in the diagram below.

Find the total area enclosed between the graphs of the two functions.

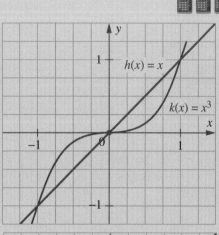

Solution

$$\text{Area } Q = \int_0^1 h(x)\, dx - \int_0^1 k(x)\, dx$$

$$\text{Area } Q = \int_0^1 h(x) - k(x)\, dx$$

$$= \int_0^1 x - x^3 dx$$

$$= \left[\frac{x^2}{2} - \frac{x^4}{4}\right]_0^1$$

$$= \frac{(1)^2}{2} - \frac{(1)^4}{4} - \left(\frac{0^2}{2} - \frac{0^4}{4}\right)$$

$$= \frac{1}{2} - \frac{1}{4} - 0$$

$$\text{Area } Q = \frac{1}{4}$$

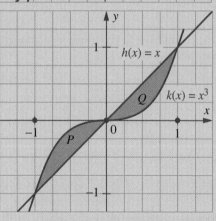

Hence, the total area between the

graphs $= \text{Area } P + \text{Area } Q = \dfrac{1}{4} + \dfrac{1}{4} = \dfrac{1}{2}$

Area P = Area Q because the drawing is symmetrical.

(2017 Q.6)

The graph of the function $g(x) = e^x$, $x \in R, 0 \leq x \leq 1$, is shown on the diagram below.

(a) On the same diagram, draw the graph of $h(x) = e^{-x}$, $x \in R$, in the domain $0 \leq x \leq 1$.

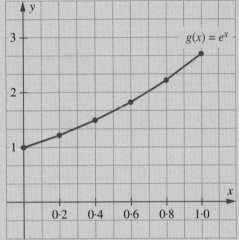

(b) Find the area enclosed by $g(x) = e^x$, $h(x) = e^{-x}$, and the line $x = 0.75$. Give your answer correct to 4 decimal places.

Solution

(a)

x	0	0·2	0·4	0·6	0·8	1
$y = e^{-x}$	1	0·82	0·67	0·55	0·45	0·37

Plot the points (0, 1) (0·2, 0·82) (0·4, 0·67) (0·6, 0·55) (0·8, 0·45) (1, 0·37)

To get $h(x)$ on graph.

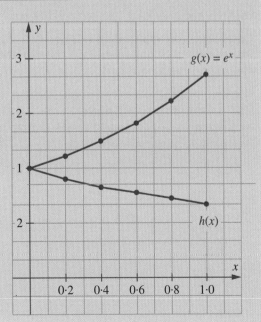

(b)

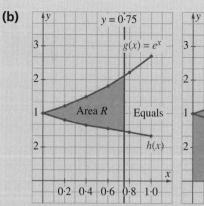
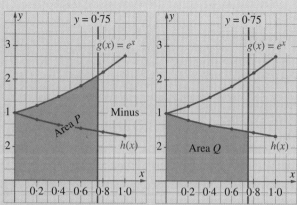

Area R = Area P − Area Q

$$Area\ R = \int_0^{0.75} e^x dx - \int_0^{0.75} e^{-x} dx$$

$$= [e^x]_0^{0.75} - [-e^{-x}]_0^{0.75}$$

$$= e^{0.75} - e^0 - [-e^{-.075} - (-e^0)]$$

$$= 2.117 - 1 + 0.472366 - 1 = 0.589366$$

Answer = 0.5894

Part (a) was awarded 15 marks, it was well answered.

Part (b) was awarded 10 marks, it was not well answered.

Note: Some candidates found the required area by using the trapezoidal rule. Trapezoidal rule must have at least five divisions and fully correct work was awarded 5 marks out of 10, otherwise zero marks awarded.

The trapezoidal rule is very well covered in a chapter of *Less Stress More Success Maths Revision Paper 2* book. In many exam questions, area under a curve is used to link the trapezoidal rule with integration. The link is significant. Learn how to apply the trapezoidal rule.

The diagram on the right shows a sketch of the function $f: x \rightarrow x^2 - 16$.

If shaded area OPQ = shaded area PRS, find the value of S.

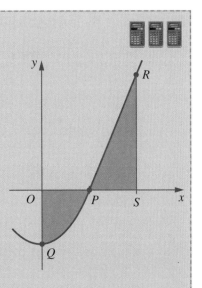

Solution

Given: shaded area OPQ = shaded area PRS.

Thus $\int_0^S (x^2 - 16)\,dx = 0$ (as area below x-axis cancels area above)

$\left[\dfrac{1}{3}x^3 - 16x\right]_0^S = 0$ (finding the antiderivative)

$\dfrac{1}{3}S^3 - 16S = 0$

$S^3 - 48S = 0$

$S(S^2 - 48) = 0$

$S = 0$ or $S^2 = 48$

$S = 0$ or $S = \pm\sqrt{48} = \pm 4\sqrt{3}$

As $S > 0$, $S = 4\sqrt{3}$.

Mean (average) value of a function

We define the mean value of a function $y = f(x)$ in

the range $a \le x \le b$ as

$$\frac{1}{(b - a)}\int_a^b f(x)\,dx.$$

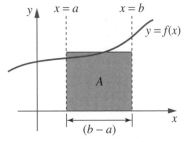

(2018 Q.3 (b))

Let $h(x) = \cos(2x)$, where $x \in R$.

Find the average value of $h(x)$ over the interval $0 \le x \le \dfrac{\pi}{4}$, $x \in R$.

Give your answer in terms of π.

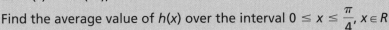

Solution

By definition, the average value

$$= \frac{1}{\frac{\pi}{4} - 0} \int_0^{\frac{\pi}{4}} \cos(2x)dx$$

$$= \frac{1}{\frac{\pi}{4}} \left[\frac{1}{2} \sin 2x \right]_0^{\frac{\pi}{4}}$$

$$= \frac{4}{\pi} \left[\frac{1}{2} \sin 2\left(\frac{\pi}{4}\right) - \frac{1}{2} \sin 2(0) \right]$$

$$= \frac{4}{\pi} \left[\frac{1}{2}(1) - \frac{1}{2}(0) \right]$$

$$= \frac{4}{\pi} \left[\frac{1}{2} \right] = \frac{2}{\pi}$$

The average (mean) value is a very popular question in recent exams. Be sure to know this.

Thus the average value of $\cos(2x)$ over the range $0 \le x \le \frac{\pi}{4}$ is $\frac{2}{\pi}$

Plutonium has a decay rate of 0.004% per year. The amount of energy released from a radioactive sample is measured in rem units and is given by

$150 \int_0^b e^{-kt}dt$ where k is the decay rate and b is the number of years. Find

correct to the nearest integer, the mean number of rems per year released in the first 100 years.

Solution

$$\text{Mean value} = \frac{1}{100 - 0} \left[150 \int_0^{100} e^{-0.004t}dt \right]$$

$$= 1.5 \int_0^{100} e^{-0.004t}dt$$

$$= 1.5 \frac{1}{-0.004} \left[e^{-0.004t} \right]_0^{100}$$

$$= -375 \left[e^{-0.004(100)} - e^{-0.004(0)} \right]$$

$$= -375 \left[e^{-0.4} - e^0 \right]$$

$$= -375 [0.67 - 1]$$

$$= 124 \text{ rems per year}$$